FREAKS AND MARVELS
OF INSECT LIFE

HAROLD BASTIN

has also written

Insects, Their Life-Histories and Habits
British Insects and How To Know Them
Introducing British Butterflies
Etc.

Ants attacking a slug which has unfortunately wandered into their territory.

Hutchinson's Nature Library

Freaks and Marvels of
INSECT LIFE

HAROLD BASTIN

Drawings by Jane Burton

Foreword by Frederick Laing
M.A., B.Sc.

HUTCHINSON
Stratford Place
London

Hutchinson & Co. (Publishers) Ltd.

London   Melbourne   Sydney   Auckland

Bombay   Cape Town   New York   Toronto

First published 1954

Set in ten point Monotype Times Roman
two point leaded

Printed in Great Britain
by The Anchor Press, Ltd.,
Tiptree, Essex

CONTENTS

LIST OF PHOTOGRAPHS

(Between pages 64 and 65)

7

LIST OF DRAWINGS IN TEXT

FOREWORD

by

FREDERICK LAING

Formerly Principal Scientific Officer in Entomology
British Museum (Nat. Hist.)

In this interesting book Mr. Harold Bastin has selected for presentation to his readers certain aspects of insect life. The scope is wide, but even so, each chapter could without the least difficulty be expanded into a large book, such is the material and information available. Intended primarily for those anxious to obtain some knowledge of what is a fascinating study the book should serve also to refresh the memory of older and more advanced students of forgotten facts.

Insects are everywhere except in the depths of the ocean; we accept them as part of our lives and would miss them if they disappeared from the earth. They are dominant in the world both in numbers and in kinds; their fecundity may be astonishing. More than two hundred years ago Réaumur, who had a taste for mathematics as well as for natural history, pointed out that the tiny whitefly found on our cabbages could by beginning to lay its eggs in March be the progenitor of some 200,000 descendants by September and infinitely more in mild winters when it could continue to feed and propagate. When statisticians estimate that one greenfly could be within a season the ancestress of 5,904,900,000 individuals the human mind boggles at the figure and it was T. H. Huxley, a master in the use of a telling phrase to illustrate a striking fact, who put the position slightly differently. "I will assume that an *Aphis* weighs one-thousandth of a grain, which is certainly vastly under the mark. A quintillion of Aphides will, on this estimate, weigh a quatrillion of grains. He is a very stout man who weighs two million grains; consequently, the tenth brood alone, if all its members survive the perils to which they are exposed, contains more substance than 500,000,000 stout men—to say the least, more than the whole population of China!" Fortunately other factors affect this prodigality, as the reader will find, but he will also find further examples of excessive reproductivity in groups other than the greenfly.

Mr. Bastin implies that there are already over half a million described insects in the world, but quite recent estimates give figures as widely apart as 640,000 (1951) to 1,500,000 (1940). The figures apply, however, rather to the *names* that have been given to the insects than to the actual number of different kinds, or *species*, for it should be borne in mind that for one reason or another the same insect

11

may receive more than one name, that agreement as to the standing of such names may not be stable but vary with individual opinion. The disparity in the estimates quoted may, within limits, be explained by applying the former and lower figure to the number of valid species, the latter and higher to the number of names used and to be found in the catalogues. A suitable example of the difficulty may be seen in a recent "stocktaking" of our islands; in the "list" of the British insect-fauna 33,000 names have been applied to what the compilers regard as some 20,000 valid species, but the position provides plenty of room for wrangling amongst students.

All these thousands of different forms of insect life remain but a chaotic heap until they have been brought into some sort of classificatory system; the characters used for this systematization are based on similarities of structure and the ultimate aim is to divide and subdivide until the unit, or species, is reached, as it is the possession of this that serves as the key that unlocks the door of all that is known about it. In his introductory chapter the author has given an outline of the primary divisions of this classification which should be sufficient to enable the reader, who desires only the broader generalizations on biology, the adaptation of structure and physiology to environment and so on, to understand what follows, but a much finer division is implied. To avoid being too technical Mr. Bastin has refrained from using scientific names in the text, but has banished them instead to the end—perhaps wisely.

To the reader no doubt the subject-matter of some of the chapters will appeal more strongly than others. Those, for instance, dealing with the relation between plants and insects are of great historical interest, have provided a favourite field of investigation to successive generations of students, and the subject is far from being exhausted. The evolution of the botanical families could be linked up with that of the insects. There is also a close relationship between the insect and what it feeds on; if tiny holes appear in the buttons of a coat it is fairly safe to assume that a minute Scolytid beetle is, or has been, at work and that the buttons are made of vegetable ivory and not of bone or plastic. If the biology of one or more members of a small group differs markedly from the normal, suspicion as to the classification may be aroused. An instance—not the best, perhaps—may be given. Most of us know about the clothes moths and what they do, but there is at least one, perhaps two, classed with the Case-bearing Clothes Moth whose caterpillar burrows in the horns of antelopes, some big-game hunters would say while the animal was alive. This difference in habit of *Tinea vastella* suggests that it should be removed from *Tinea*, as some students have done.

Readers of this book with receptive minds, eyes in their heads and capable hands will find plenty of fields where valuable research work may be done.

Putney,

January, 1954.

Chapter·One

INTRODUCTORY

IN THE past, the name "insect" was used indiscriminately, even by naturalists, to describe all such creepy-crawly creatures as spiders, centipedes, slaters and mites; but nowadays it is usually reserved for those whose legs are limited to six. More than half a million of these have already been named and preserved as specimens in the various natural history museums of the world; while it has been estimated that this number, vast as it is, will probably be at least doubled when all the species that have so far eluded the vigilance of collectors can be brought to book.

The segments of an insect's body are sometimes fairly uniform in shape and size from head to tail—as is the case with most caterpillars. More frequently, however, those behind the head form two well-marked groups, known respectively as the "thorax" and the "abdomen". Moreover, these two groups are often deeply constricted at the junctures of the head with the thorax and the thorax with the abdomen: in other words, the creature has a "neck" and a "waist"—as we see if we look critically at a wasp or a fly. This explains the time-honoured term "insect"—derived, as it is, from the Latin verb *insecare*, to cut into. Similarly the term "entomology", signifying the study of insects, has its root in the Greek verb *temno*, meaning "to cut". The class-name Hexapoda, which replaces Insecta in some modern textbooks, is also derived from the Greek, and signifies "six-legged".

At first sight a caterpillar appears to contradict the assertion that insects have six legs. It seems to have a great many more! But the anomaly is explained when we realize that most of these so-called legs are temporary structures—mere muscular warts, so to speak, termed by naturalists "claspers", "pro-legs" or "false legs". They are usually furnished with numerous minute hooks or claws, and serve admirably to grasp firmly the twigs and leaves of their owner's food-plant; but when the caterpillar moults for the last time and changes to a pupa or chrysalis they are cast off with the old skin and disappear. Its six "true legs", on the contrary, which spring from the thoracic segments, undergo further development and are passed

13

on as a heritage to the butterfly or moth into which the caterpillar is eventually transformed.

This reference to the caterpillar as a sort of anticlimax in its own life-story, and not a final end in itself, reminds us that most insects undergo a remarkable series of form-changes as they grow from extreme youth to maturity. There are exceptions to this rule; but usually an insect's egg gives rise at the time of hatching to an organism which is very different in appearance from its adult guise. The most familiar instance of this "metamorphosis", as it is called, has already been mentioned: an unattractive "worm" (the caterpillar) is changed in the course of a few weeks or months into a being (the butterfly) whose elegance and beauty are proverbial. But the transformation is not abrupt: for the caterpillar, after a succession of moults, enters an intermediate stage of inaction, when we call it a "pupa" or "chrysalis". Outwardly it evinces little sign of life, but inwardly a marvellous reconstruction of its substance is taking place. So that when in due course the husk of the pupa splits asunder, the butterfly appears as if by magic.

In the life-histories of many other insects only two contrasted stages occur, the pupal stage being omitted. This is the case with most of the insects whose early life is passed in streams and ponds— dragon-flies, stone-flies, shad-flies and so forth; as also with the harvest-flies (or cicadas), plant-lice (or aphides) and the great family of bugs, as distinct from beetles. In all these instances the immature insect, having reached the final stage of its adolescence, becomes adult through one change of skin. It is noteworthy, however, that its wings do not attain their full proportions, nor are they capable of use, until the last moult of all has been effected. The only exception to this is provided by the may-flies, which for some unexplained reason undergo their final moult after having acquired the use of their wings. When the aquatic prelude to its short aerial life ends, the nymph or larva creeps out of the water, and soon afterwards its skin splits down the back, allowing the winged insect to escape and flutter sluggishly to a neighbouring twig or grass-stem. But its transformation is not yet quite complete. At this stage the may-fly (known to science as the "sub-imago") is dull in hue and seems, so to speak, lacking in polish. It is, in fact, completely enveloped in a delicate, loosely fitting cuticle, from which it extricates itself almost immediately, or in the course of several hours; and not until this has occurred can it properly be called an imago or perfect insect. It is worth noting that the latter is termed a "spinner" by fly-fishers, whose corresponding "dun" is the sub-imago.

The majority of adult insects are equipped with wings—usually with two pairs, though in some instances with only one pair. In this respect they differ from all other invertebrate animals. If, therefore, we come across a six-legged creature equipped with wings we need have no hesitation in calling it an "insect".

We shall avoid redundancy in subsequent chapters if we devote this paragraph to defining certain terms which are constantly used when insects and their habits are under discussion. An immature

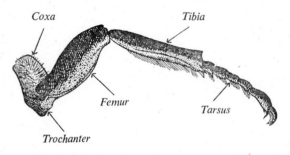

The leg of a beetle, naming the principal parts

insect is technically a "larva"—a word which is applicable to any young animal that differs conspicuously in appearance from its parents. But several distinct varieties of larvae have special names of their own. Thus, the "caterpillar" is a larva characterized by its worm-like form and the presence of pro-legs or clasper on certain of its abdominal segments. The alternative term "grub" is used rather vaguely for such larvae as those of the cockchafer and the mealworm beetle. Grubs have no pro-legs, and usually burrow in or among the substances on which they feed—or in the soil, when they attack the roots of plants. Then we have the "maggot"—e.g. the larva of the house-fly—in which all traces of legs and pro-legs have disappeared, while the head reminds us of the ideal geometrical point, since it may almost be said to have position without magnitude. Again, the larvae of insects whose metamorphosis includes no pupal stage are often spoken of as "nymphs"—especially during the later period of their development. The word "chrysalis" is often used to describe an insect's pupa as if the two terms were synonymous. Since, however, it is derived from the Greek word signifying "gold", it is really applicable only to pupae—like those of the "tortoiseshells" and "fritillaries" among butterflies—that have brilliant, metal-like areas on their surfaces.

An insect has no internal skeleton, its soft tissues being held together and supported by a superficial layer of non-living matter called "chitin". In young insects this layer is usually thin and flexible, but in many adults it takes the form of thick, hard plates—like armour, or the bark of a tree. Such insects as beetles, for example, are clad in veritable coats of mail; and this outer crust not only affords protection but also provides stable areas for the attachment of the muscles, which are thus rendered capable of considerable contractile force.

The head and face of an insect call for special remark. Masked by the unyielding chitinous layer, the features preserve always a sphinx-like immobility. Yet the emotions may be estimated in some degree by watching the movements of the feelers or antennae. That these are important sense-organs is certain, although it is often far from easy to determine precisely what offices they serve. In many instances they are unquestionably "feelers" in function no less than in name, being used to explore the surface of objects, and to examine food. Evidence is not lacking to support the view that some insects exchange information through the medium of a kind of touch-language; and when one sees, for example, two ants or bees caressing or tapping each other's antennae, little imagination is needed to foster the belief that they are chatting amicably or even debating some knotty problem. We may be quite sure, however, that the antennae are often—perhaps always—more than mere organs of touch. Observation and experiment tend to show that the beautiful frond-like outgrowths from the heads of certain male moths serve the sense of smell, while the feathery antennae of male midges and mosquitoes, being delicately responsive to sound-waves, may well be auditory in function. Indeed, we shall probably not be far wrong if we think of these marvellous and variously formed organs as cunningly contrived receiving-sets capable of selecting and passing inward to the nerve-centres "messages" of many kinds which evoke in the insect an awareness of, and an adequate response to, its surroundings.

Most adult insects have two sorts of visual organs, namely a pair of large, many-faceted eyes, one on each side of the head, and several small ones, termed "ocelli", upon the brow. Each of the latter is a tiny polished lens, set above a cup-shaped mass of pigment cells forming a retina, or visual area ; but the focus is so short that they seem to be chiefly serviceable as a means of estimating light-intensity. Relying on their aid an insect might find its way from a dark corner of a room to the window—and thus, if the latter were open, escape into the outer air ; but we can hardly suppose them capable of "vision" in the full and complete sense of the word, save perhaps at the closest possible range. A caterpillar, which has six of these simple eyes on each side of its head, low down near the mouth, can probably see a part of the leaf that it is eating, or the twig upon which it is crawling; but the scope of its vision can scarcely extend beyond these narrow limits. All else must appear as a blurred and misty background of lights and shades.

The large and conspicuous eyes of adult insects are of the many-faceted or compound kind. They are very remarkable organs, and fall little, if at all, short of the human eye in delicacy of structure, although planned on totally different lines. Every facet of the cornea or surface layer is a separate lens capable of projecting an image ; so that it is possible by the aid of the microscope to photograph an object through the detached cornea and obtain a multiplex picture— one image for every facet. Each facet—or lens—is mounted upon the broad end of a cone-shaped group of sensitive visual cells ; and each of these "crystaline cones", as they are called, is optically separated or "blacked out" from its neighbour by means of opaque pigment, and conterminous at its inner, tapering end with a nerve-rod connecting with the brain.

The compound eye of some moths have as many as 27,000 lenses, each with its crystaline cone and nerve-rod ; and all the elements in such an eye are theoretically capable of independent vision—a fact which led certain of the early naturalists to conclude that a multitude of distinct pictures must be perceived by the eye's owner. But this notion was long ago discarded in favour of one which credits the insect with what is called "mosaic vision". According to this theory each element of the eye is sensitive only to light reflected from that portion of the object in view which is exactly opposite the one lens—all oblique rays being absorbed by the dark pigment which surrounds its crystaline cone. These fragmentary images are believed to combine in the retinal area to form a complete picture. A mosaic pavement helps us to grasp the idea ; or we may think of the countless isolated dots (distinguishable under a magnifying-glass) which make up the picture printed on paper from an ordinary process-

block. But we must not carry the analogy too far, or we may easily
lose sight of the never-to-be-forgotten fact that every kind of eye is
merely part of a mechanism for converting light-waves, which are
a form of energy, into something very different, namely a sensation.
How this conversion is accomplished is one of Nature's closely
guarded secrets.

The primitive ancestors of insects seem to have been equipped
with three pairs of biting jaws which opened and closed transversely,
like pairs of pincers held vertically. Jaws of this type are still favoured
by such insects as grasshoppers and beetles, whose food requires
much breaking or crushing before it can be passed into the gullet.
But many modern insects consume liquid food, such as nectar, sap
or blood, and in these instances the appendages of the mouth have
been so greatly altered that to speak of them as "jaws" would be
pedantic. For this reason they are usually referred to as "mouth-
parts", while the three pairs are distinguished as "mandibles", "first
maxillae" and "second maxillae"—this being the order of their
arrangement from front to back. The second maxillae are often
called the "labium", because they are usually more or less closely
united along the middle line, thus forming a kind of plate, or "lower
lip"—the corresponding "labrum" or "upper lip" occupying a
position in front of the mandibles.

The reader's patience need not be taxed here by a detailed description of the mouth-parts in their various modified forms. Suffice
it to say that they include all manner of appliances for cutting,
piercing, pumping, sucking and licking, and that every insect is
furnished with a set of instruments which accord exactly with its
method of feeding and the kind of food which is eaten. It must not
be supposed, however, that all the three pairs of mouth-parts are
invariably present, even in modified guise. Some of them may be
reduced to mere vestiges, or entirely suppressed; while a few adult
insects—e.g. may-flies—have no mouth-parts at all, and in consequence are unable to feed. Sustained in their unbroken fast by the
nourishment stored in their tissues during the larval period of their
existence, they are free to devote their entire energy to the business
of reproduction and parentage.

Each of an insect's six legs consists normally of five joints, the
names and positions of which are worth memorizing for future
reference. First comes the haunch or "coxa", which fits into a socket
in the thorax; then the "trochanter"; then the thigh or "femur";
then the shin or "tibia"; and finally the "tarsus"—often referred to

as the "foot". This last usually consists of four or five articulated
pieces, and carries a pair of claws at its extremity. All these names,
with the exception of "trochanter", were originally used to distinguish bones in the legs of vertebrate animals; but there is little if
any justification for the implied analogy in their use for the parts
of an insect's leg. The latter, both in its structure and mode of use,
is very far removed from that of a horse or a man. When walking
or running, most insects lift their legs in alternate groups of three—
which means that in motion the weight of the body is always upheld
by a tripod, the best mechanical basis of support.

Little need be said here of the insect's internal organs; but
several points are of sufficient interest to warrant brief mention. The
central nervous system consists of a brain—which encircles the
gullet like a collar, and twin nerve-cords extending along the ventral
or lower body wall on its inner side to the hinder extremity. These
twin cords connect up a number of nerve-knots, or ganglia, which
function as minor brains, directing the activities of the parts by
which they are immediately surrounded. This arrangement makes it
possible for an insect which has been deprived of its head to walk
or fly without difficulty, although its movements will be aimless and
erratic. The explanation is that the motor nerves connected with the
muscles of the wings and legs communicate with ganglia in the
thorax, but the brain in the head exercises supreme control, and in
its absence purposive locomotion becomes impossible.

The insect's heart or "dorsal vessel" is a lengthy series of muscular chambers through which the blood-stream is driven in the
direction of the head, where it is discharged above the brain. There
are no arteries and veins; so that afterwards the blood circulates
sluggishly in the spaces between the internal organs, and is eventually re-absorbed into the heart through valvular slits in the walls of
its chambers. The relative simplicity of this circulatory system is
accounted for by the fact that the insect's blood is less vitally important than that of a vertebrate animal. It nourishes and cleanses
the tissues, but does not oxygenize them. In other words, insects
have no lungs. They breath through small holes, called "spiracles",
which may be found at intervals along the sides of the body. The
air so admitted enters an extensive system of minute tubes
("tracheae") which ramify in the tissues, thus supplying them with
the oxygen necessary for the performance of their several functions.
There is no part of the insect's body which is not permeated by these
tracheal tubes, the smaller branches of which are more delicate than

the finest hairs. Yet all are lined with a supporting thread of chitin spirally coiled, like the metal wire in certain kinds of rubber tubing made by man. By this means the risk of short-circuiting is obviated. The elastic, chitinous coil keeps the trachea open even when it is subjected to pressure—as, for example, by the bending of a joint through which it passes. It should be added that amphibious and aquatic insects are equipped with various devices for keeping water out of their breathing-tubes; while in the case of those which are continually submerged, the spiracles are usually connected with gills, which extract dissolved air from the water.

If we examine a miscellaneous collection of insects from any part of the world, we often find that while some of the species are obviously near relatives, others seem to have little in common at first sight; which leads us to conclude that although insects have evolved from one and the same original stock, they have developed along many different lines of descent. The aim of the systematic entomologist is to indicate this natural branching of the insects' family tree in his scheme of classification, those species which exhibit close affinity being placed together in groups called "Orders".

The early naturalists regarded the wings—the structure and veining of which are always similar in nearly related insects—as the surest guide to correct classification. More recently, attention has been paid to the modification of the mouth-parts, as also to the degree of metamorphosis which takes place in the life-cycle. Some wingless insects—the bristle-tails, spring-tails and so forth—undergo no real metamorphosis, but simply "grow up", with no marked change except in size. More highly specialized insects undergo a "direct" or "incomplete" metamorphosis, as it is called. They often resemble their parents in a general way when they leave the egg, but lack wings—these organs developing *outside* the body as flaps or "pads" which become larger with each moult. Among the most highly specialized insects of all metamorphosis is "indirect" or "complete": that is to say, the newly hatched young is always extremely different in guise from its parents, while the wings develop *inside* the body, and hence are hidden from view until the full-grown larva moults and becomes a pupa.

By a careful comparison of all these points, namely the structure of the wings, the modification of the mouth-parts and the character of the life-history, entomologists have been able to sort out the vast majority of insects, and to group them according to their relationships in the following eight Orders.

APTERA. "Wingless" insects which undergo no metamorphosis. Being small or tiny they seldom attract the notice of the general public. The best-known example is the "silver lady" or "silver fish", common in many houses, where it feeds on a variety of substances, and sometimes does mischief to old prints, books, etc., by gnawing away the surface of the paper.

ORTHOPTERA. "Straight-winged" insects, including cockroaches, mantids or "praying insects", "leaf" and "stick" insects, grasshoppers, locusts and crickets. All these have biting mouth-parts and undergo a direct metamorphosis. The wings have numerous veins, predominantly rectilinear, while the fore-wings are usually thickened or "leathery", and serve as protective covers under which the more delicate hind-wings are folded fan-wise when not in use.

HEMIPTERA. "Half-winged" insects, including bugs of all kinds, cicadas or harvest-flies, lantern-flies, aphides or "green-fly", scale insects and their allies. The mouth-parts are modified for piercing and sucking. Arranged as a series, the life-histories of these insects show an interesting transition from direct to indirect metamorphosis : e.g. the full-grown larva of a bug is active right up to the moment of its last moult, but many scale insects pass through a quiescent, pupal stage before they become adult. Two sub-orders are recognized. *Heteroptera*, which includes the true bugs, is distinguished by having the basal portion of the fore-wing much thicker than the rest ; whereas in the sub-order *Homoptera* the fore-wings, although sometimes firmer in texture than the hind-wings, never have this hard, basal area.

NEUROPTERA. "Nerve-winged" insects, such as the alder-flies, snake-flies, ant-lion flies and lacewings. These have all the wings similar in texture with the membrane supported by a complicated network of veins or nervures. The mouth-parts are formed for biting, and metamorphisis is indirect, a quiescent pupal stage always preceding the final moult.

COLEOPTERA. "Sheath-winged" insects, comprising the beetles, which have biting mouth-parts, while the fore-wings are thickened and hardened to form protective sheaths or cases beneath which the hind-wings can be folded safely when not in use. Metamorphosis is indirect, with a definite pupal stage ; while the larva is either a more or less active, six-legged creature, or a legless grub, according to its mode of life.

LEPIDOPTERA. "Scaly-winged" insects : i.e. butterflies and moths, whose wings and bodies are clothed with minute, overlapping scales, as may be seen under the microscope. With very few exceptions the mouth-parts are modified to form a sucking tube, or proboscis, by means of which nectar or other juices can be imbibed. Metamorphosis is indirect, the larva being a caterpillar with not more than five pairs of abdominal pro-legs or claspers, and changing when full-grown to a pupa or chrysalis.

DIPTERA. "Two-winged" insects. These are the gnats or mosquitoes, midges of many sorts, crane-flies or "daddy-longlegs", house-flies—in short, all the true flies whose hind-wings are reduced to mere stalked knobs termed "balancers" or "halteres". The functional fore-wings are membranous, usually transparent, and have few supporting nervures. The mouth-parts are extremely various in structure, but are always adapted for sucking, or for piercing and sucking—never for biting. Metamorphosis is indirect, the larva being a grub or maggot. Among the more highly specialized forms the last larval skin is not cast off but retained as a protective case—the "puparium"—under cover of which the pupa is formed. The perfect insect eventually escapes through an opening which it makes by pushing up a little cap or lid.

HYMENOPTERA. "Membranous-winged" insects, including saw-flies, gall-wasps, ichneumons, ants, wasps and bees. These have four wings, which are usually transparent, with comparatively few nervures. Except in a few minute species the wings on either side of the body are united during flight by a series of tiny hooks on the front margin of the hind-wing which engage with a corresponding fold in the fore-wing. Metamorphosis is indirect. The larvae are usually legless grubs; but those of some saw-flies resemble the caterpillars of butterflies and moths, except that they have more numerous pro-legs. The higher Hymenoptera—e.g. wasps and hive-bees—form co-operative associations which comprise large numbers of individuals known as "neuters" or "workers" in addition to the ordinary males and females of the species, which in these instances are known as "drones" and "queens" respectively.

Besides these eight major Orders modern systematists recognize about a dozen smaller ones which need not be dealt with in detail here. Something must be added, however, with respect to the scientific naming of insects. In accordance with the method introduced by the Swedish naturalist Linnaeus, every distinct species is given two Latin or latinized names. The first of these—usually written or printed with a capital initial letter—is generic: that is to say, it is a kind of surname, frequently shared by several—perhaps by a considerable number of—closely allied species. The second name belongs to one species only, and in this respect bears some analogy to our baptismal or christian names—although we must not forget that it stands for a succession of similar individuals, not for any one individual exclusively. Individuality in nature is of so little importance from the scientific standpoint that so long as we know to what *species* a given insect or other animal belongs its own particular status in space and time need not concern us, because one member of a species usually looks and behaves like all the rest.

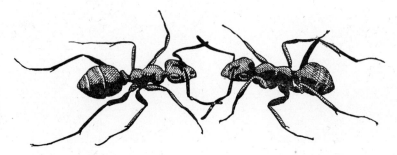

Ants communicate with one another by means of a "touch" language

For example, the well-known painted lady butterfly is called *Vanessa cardui*—meaning that it is the particular member of its genus whose caterpillars feed by preference on the leaves of thistles. The reason why Latin names are used is that they convey a clear and precise meaning to students in all parts of the world where insects are a subject of scientific investigation. The painted lady, being a great traveller, is met with almost everywhere—except South Africa and the Arctic regions. A gay and attractive creature, not easily overlooked, its colloquial names are probably as numerous as the countries in which it makes itself at home. But these will not serve the purpose of science, which requires that the same species shall have the same name, no matter where it may be found.

The need for this is obvious. Science is not dealing with a few score of insects but with hundreds of thousands, while more are being discovered and described almost every day of the year. Without a universally recognized method of naming and classification

this vast and growing mass of material would be hopelessly un-
manageable. So related species are grouped together first as genera,
then as families, and these again as the orders which, taken together,
comprise all the six-legged invertebrates of which the class of insects
consists.

Chapter Two

EGGS AND EGG-LAYING

THE life-histories of all but the simplest living things are recurrent cycles, starting with the germ or "vital spark" enshrouded in the egg, and ending with the adult organism capable of reproduction. In certain respects the eggs of insects resemble the seeds of plants. Both have strong outer coats, well adapted to guard the contents from the dangers to which they would otherwise be exposed. Both, when subjected to apparently adverse conditions, exhibit an almost uncanny capacity for passing unscratched through the ordeal. Many insects' eggs may actually be frozen into a solid block of ice and kept thus for a considerable period without detriment to their vitality. Indeed, the outer husk or "shell" consists of a substance so tough and impervious that it is even capable of withstanding the corrosive action of fairly strong acids. Moreover, insects' eggs exhibit an astonishing diversity of shape while their surface texture may be glassy or opaque, smooth or exquisitely sculptured—those of many butterflies and moths being especially attractive in this last respect. Still more beautiful in their adornment are the eggs of certain minute parasites (*Mallophaga*) which live among the feathers of birds. But the appearance is always characteristic in the case of each species, so that the student soon learns to tell at a glance the particular kind of insect that may be expected to hatch from a given egg. Here again we trace a point of resemblance to seeds, which for the most part are readily distinguishable as the product of this or that species of plant.

Contrary to popular belief, insects' eggs are seldom excessively minute, most of them being within the range of our unaided vision. Judged in relation to the size of the parent, the eggs of many insects are definitely on the large side. That of the common house-fly, for instance, is about one millimetre (approximately one-twenty-fifth of an inch) in length, or roughly one-seventh of the fly's own measurement from head to tail. Yet a single fly, after pairing, is capable of laying from 800 to 1,000 of these eggs in the course of her short lifetime; and the calculation has been made that if this process were to continue unchecked through successive generations during only one summer, the progeny of one pair of flies, pressed together into a solid mass, would occupy about a quarter of a million cubic feet of space! But the egg-laying capacity of the fly is greatly exceeded by certain social insects—for example, the queen hive-bee, whose daily average at the height of the season may exceed 2,000 for weeks on end!

When an insect lays an egg it usually ejects simultaneously from its body a drop of viscid fluid—a kind of quick-drying waterproof varnish, which not only flows over the egg, thereby providing it with a sort of "finishing coat", but serves also to cement it firmly to its appointed place. The beautiful but evil-smelling insects known popularly as lacewings have developed the curious habit of drawing up this natural cement while it remains plastic into a long, flexible thread, at the summit of which the egg is poised. These quaint stalked eggs may often be found in summer dotted about on leaves and twigs, one here, another there, or in little groups of twenty or more in close proximity. The precise *raison d'être* is debatable. Perhaps the most plausible explanation so far offered is that the newly hatched lacewing's larvae, being inveterate cannibals, would attack one another if the eggs were laid side by side on a leaf in the ordinary way. As it is, each is so much preoccupied in clambering down its stalk that the brood is likely to disperse without untoward incident.

The eggs of those weird-looking insects called spectres or "walking-sticks" are often deceptively like seeds in appearance, as also in the minuter details of their structure; so that botanists, examining for the first time under the microscope a thin section cut from the husk, have believed that they were looking at a vegetable preparation. Like seeds, too, these eggs fall from the branches of trees and shrubs to the ground, being dropped unconcernedly by the parents while they feed among the foliage. In tropical countries where these insects abound the continuous pattering of their eggs upon the herbage exactly resembles the sound produced by a heavy fall of rain or hail. These eggs vary in size and form according to their kind, but each has always a little cap or lid which is pushed off by the occupant at the time of hatching. Experts tell us that this external and visible envelope, including the lid, is really a kind of pod or capsule within which the true egg-shell and its contents are hidden. In other words, what we see is a sort of packing case—a further development of the varnish-like finishing-coat mentioned above.

This plan of providing the eggs with an extra covering is carried to greater lengths by some other insects, such as the cockroaches, whose females assemble their eggs, usually sixteen together, in packages or purses which are carried about by the mother until such time as they can be hidden in some dry crevice. Gangs of cockroaches, most of them females with egg-purses, have been seen on dark days or at night in the streets of towns migrating from one building to another; which shows how easily new houses may become infested with these pests.

The mantids or "rearhorses"—also termed "praying insects" because their characteristic resting attitude falsely suggests piety and devotion—fabricate very wonderful egg-capsules and fix them to stationary objects, such as stems or twigs. Generally the eggs are laid a number together in flask-shaped receptacles, which are then arranged one against another in two overlapping rows, the whole series being enveloped in a copious glutinous secretion which quickly solidifies to form the protective outer case. Along its ridge may often be seen a double row of small slits or holes through which eventually the newly hatched young make their escape. But mantids' egg-capsules vary widely in size and shape. In many instances they are bulky objects, two or more inches in length, with from 200 to 300 eggs in each. Some are compact and hard and might easily be mistaken for nuts or seed-vessels. Others resemble masses of solidified foam—which, in fact, they are, since the female insect whisks the secretion as it comes from her body into a spongy froth that hardens rapidly in the air.

What advantage is gained by this procedure? Apparently it serves to protect the living contents of the egg from sudden chill, for it seems to be practised only by those species of mantids whose eggs remain unhatched throughout the winter months in regions where frosts are apt to occur. The late Lord Rutherford, wishing on one occasion to demonstrate the low conductivity of atmospheric air where heat other than radiant heat is concerned, surrounded a frozen cheese with a mass of well-beaten eggs. The dish so prepared was placed in an oven until a light omelette was obtained, piping hot, although the cheese in the centre remained as cold as it was at the outset of the experiment. Now it is clear that if air-bubbles serve to repel heat they will likewise keep cold at bay; and, in fact, the mantid does exactly what Lord Rutherford did, although her aim, so to say, is reversed. Her solidified froth secures the temperature

within the egg-flasks from sudden changes which might prove fatal
to their contents.

Most insects deposit their eggs either upon or near to the substance which is to serve as food for the larvae. Thus, the house-fly
visits for the purpose manure heaps and middens; the brimstone
butterfly scours the woodlands in search of buckthorn bushes; while
in autumn the lackey moth fixes her eggs as "bracelets" round the
smaller twigs of fruit and other trees, almost in contact with the fat
leaf-buds which in spring will provide her progeny with abundant
sustenance. The brown-tail moth roofs in her egg cluster, which is
usually fixed to the under-surface of a leaf, and invariably covered
with a dense thatching of hairs from the mother's tail-tuft. The
moths known popularly as "thorns" lay brick-shaped eggs which
they arrange side by side in rows, exactly like the first course in the
foundation of a wall. Blue-bottle flies and the small tortoiseshell
butterfly tend to make heaps of their eggs, the former either on or
in the immediate neighbourhood of carrion, the latter on stinging-
nettle leaves. Ladybird beetles, hover-flies and lacewings, whose
larvae prey upon aphides or green-fly, fix their eggs to the shoots
or leaves of plants infested by these pests; while bot-flies, warble-
flies and lice attach theirs—often by means of a kind of clip or clasp
—to the hairs of their victims; and these eggs are usually so firmly
secured that no amount of ordinary rubbing or scratching can
dislodge them.

The eggs of the midges whose aquatic larvae—called "blood
worms"—are common in the mud of stagnant ditches, envelop their
eggs in a jelly-like substance which is said to serve more than one
purpose: e.g. it makes them so slippery that birds and other enemies
cannot grasp them; it spaces them, so that each gets its fair share
of air and sunlight; also, possessing some antiseptic property, it
probably protects them from attack by moulds. Some gnats lay their
eggs in batches, sometimes of 300 or more, all glued together to form
a sort of raft so cannily constructed that if perchance it should be
upset it rights itself immediately. On the other hand, the eggs of the
germ-carrying gnats usually termed mosquitoes are launched singly
upon the surface of the water and buoyed up by air-containing flaps
or floats on each side.

Something may be said here concerning the ovipositors, or egg-
laying appliances of insects. Typically, the mechanism consists of
six-paired shafts or valves; but those vary greatly in size, shape and
performance. Often they are so small and compact as to be hardly

noticeable, or they may even be completely withdrawn from view when not in use. But the sword-like ovipositors of certain grass-hoppers, by means of which the eggs are thrust deeply into the soil, and the equally conspicuous boring apparatus of the wood-wasps or "horntails", used for inserting them into the trunk of a fir tree, are not easily overlooked.

Some of the ichneumons associated as parasites with wood-boring grubs and caterpillers have remarkably long, bristle-like ovipositors—very inadequate, one might imagine, to the work which they must perform. Yet the female of the large blue-black, white-marked species with orange-coloured legs that lays her eggs on the immured wood-wasp's larvae can drill a hole $1\frac{1}{4}$ in. deep through solid timber in less than twenty minutes. In this way it reaches its victims, whose hidden whereabouts is apparently detected by the sense of smell. Saw-flies—which in fact are not "flies" at all, but akin to wood-wasps—owe their familiar name to the fact that the innermost valves of their ovipositors take the form of tiny fret-saws with which cuts are made in the tissues of leaves and stems for the reception of the eggs. Egg-laying by certain other small insects of the Hymenopterous category results in the formation of the curious and often attractive growths known as vegetable galls, of which more will be said in a later chapter. In the case of stinging insects—bees, wasps and the like—the original function of the ovipositor has been superseded by its conversion into a complex poison-injecting instrument—of which also more anon.

Although the vast majority of insects lay eggs, a few are vivi-parous: i.e. fully formed and active young are produced. Yet these exceptions are more apparent than real, since the eggs may be said to hatch within the parent's body instead of being extruded after the more usual fashion. It has been found, indeed, that in the case of certain plant-lice or aphides the same individual may produce eggs and living young simultaneously in neighbouring tubes of its ovaries. Thus, there is nothing very surprising in the fact that among these insects oviparous and viviparous generations sometimes follow one another in regular alternation. The latter method is favoured while summer lasts and food is plentiful; but with the approach of winter, when the nourishing sap ebbs from the infested shoots, the last generation of the season lays eggs.

In some families of insects, notably among aphides and gall-wasps, parthenogenesis or virgin birth occurs: i.e. larvae hatch from the eggs although these have not been fertilized by sperms. In the

case of the hive-bee—probably also in that of other social species—
unfertilized eggs laid by the queen give rise only to males or drones,
whereas those which have been fertilized produce either workers or
young queens according to the way in which the grubs that hatch
from them are nurtured. During the nuptial flight, the queen mother
receives from the successful drone a sufficiency of spermatozoa for
the whole of her normal egg-laying career.

As with most other animals, the reproductive faculty of nearly
all insects remains dormant until the imago or adult stage is reached ;
but a very few begin to multiply while they are still larvae—a method
of procedure, this, termed "paedogenesis", which may be translated
"infantile procreation". The discovery that this occurs in several
species of gall-midges was made many years ago by the Russian
biologist Wagner. What actually happens is that the female midge
lays during the summer some extra large eggs. Each of these gives
rise to a larva which instead of undergoing the usual metamorphosis produces in its own body a batch of smaller larvae that
behave exactly like parasites, first consuming the vitals of their hap-
less progenitor and then escaping by way of holes bored in its empty
skin. During the winter this process continues through several successive generations. Then, in the early summer, the final batch of
larvae in the series change to pupae and eventually become male
and female midges.

Quite recently a still more astonishing state of affairs has been
found to exist among certain of the minute wasp-like parasites
(Chalcids) which lay their eggs singly in those of moths. Each of
these eggs produces a plurality of larvae ; so that, for example, one
egg laid by the particular species which infests the common silver-Y
moth suffices to inoculate the miserable caterpillar with no less than
a thousand alien grubs ! This bizarre method of reproduction is
termed "polyembryony", meaning the multiplication of embryos
within an egg.

The way in which a young insect escapes from its egg-shell and
its behaviour immediately afterwards is interesting to watch. We
have already noted that the infant stick-insect issues through a kind
of trap-door, the cover of which it pushes off. Many other juveniles
simply gnaw a hole through the egg's shell, or else split it asunder
by their lively contortions within. Not infrequently the newly
hatched larva devours the shell which it has just vacated before
turning to more inviting food. The wasp's grub, however, keeps its
tail-end in what is left of the egg-shell and turning on this pivot

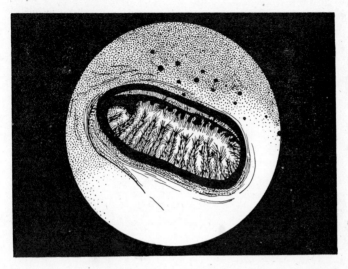

The spiracle or "breathing hole" of a
beetle, enormously magnified

thrusts its gaping jaws towards the opening of its nursery-cell to
receive the rations of pap brought to it by its adult sisters, the
"workers".

This display of instinctive resourcefulness by a raw beginner
serves to emphasize the fact that the most marvellous part of the
egg is its contents. If we open an insect's egg soon after it has
been laid we find a small quantity of semi-fluid matter; and by in-
voking the aid of the microscope we can demonstrate that this is
not without definite structure. Yet there is nothing to suggest the
surprising sequel that the future holds in store—the sudden dis-
closure of an organism fully equipped for the battle of life and
destined by fortune's favour to perpetuate all the achievements of
its parental stock—perhaps, even, to initiate some novel departure
from the ancestral type. For it must not be forgotten that the entire
potentialities of the perfect insect—its bodily form, colours, capaci-
ties, habits and instincts—are all latent in the small package that
we call the egg. In what manner this miracle is accomplished is far
from being perfectly understood. The mere mechanical difficulties
that are successfully surmounted afford no little food for thought.
For instance, a baby stick-insect appears to be many sizes too large
for the egg-case which it has just vacated, even before it has

swallowed its first mouthful. Of course it is easy, and no doubt true, to explain that its members have undergone a rapid process of unfolding and inflation—that something of the kind happens when a clever salesman at the stores takes a fine Cashmere shawl or wrap from its box and displays it for the benefit of a potential customer. But fancy doing this with a living animal!

Chapter Three

TRANSFORMATION SCENES

THE grey flesh-flies, whose habits in many respects resemble those of the more familiar blue-bottles, dispense entirely with egg-laying, scattering their tiny, new-borne maggots on the meat destined to feed them. Such adepts are they at this accomplishment that they can hit their objective from a considerable height and through the meshes of our so-called "safes" if these are large enough to admit the tip of their trunk-like ovipositor.

Flies of several other affinities—notably the African tse-tse flies, those dreaded carriers of sleeping sickness in man, and nagana disease in horses and cattle—give birth to mature larvae that turn to pupae without feeding. But this very unusual state of affairs, completely superseding the original function of the larval stage, seems to be correlated with the highly developed blood-sucking habits of the maternal parents. The rich and easily digested diet so obtained is sufficiently nourishing to enable these vampires to assume responsibility for their offspring in all the stages of their development; so the larva, instead of pursuing its time-honoured vocation of foraging for food, is adequately fed by its mother in her own body.

The same almost complete suppression of the larval stage is a feature in the life-cycle of another family of blood-suckers represented in Britain by several eccentric-looking flies which are parasitic on various beasts and birds, each species usually restricting itself to a particular "host"—as the miserable victim is euphemistically styled. The New Forest fly—also called the "spider fly" on account of its furtive, sidelong gait—is especially common in the wooded districts of Hampshire, where it may sometimes be seen clustered in hundreds on the flanks of horses and ponies. Although normally sluggish, it is capable of sustained and fairly rapid flight. Apparently the stab or "bite" which it inflicts is not very painful, for forest-bred animals pay little heed to its attacks. But a single fly, merely by crawling on the skin of a horse unaccustomed to the sensation, will drive the creature almost frantic; and in pre-mechanized days this insect caused serious stampeding on more than one occasion when cavalry manœuvres were in progress.

An allied species of fly, which is found on horses or deer—especially red deer—begins adult life with serviceable wings, but casts these off as soon as it has found its quarry. Both this and the forest-fly drop their larvae to the ground, where pupation takes place at once, and whence eventually the newly emerged adults wing their way back to a deer or a horse, whither they seem to be guided by their sense of smell. This routine, simple by contrast with the life-cycles of many other insects, appears nevertheless to be perfectly effective; for although the birth-rate is phenominally low—each female probably producing not more than four or five larvae in the course of her life—the adult population does not decline, but remains steady from year to year; which means that the incidence of mortality is amply compensated by the rate of reproduction.

The nearly related bird-flies spend most of their lives among the feathers of birds, whose blood they suck. Birds large and small are liable to attack, and if the "host" should die, the lodgers immediately leave the body to seek residence elsewhere. Indeed, they resemble in habits gigantic fleas, capable in virtue of their wings of making vastly extended "hops" from one sufferer to another. One species, incapable of flight owing to the greatly reduced size of its wings, somehow manages to establish itself, often in considerable numbers, in nests of the swallow tribe, where it must prove a perfect plague to parents and fledglings alike; while the grotesque bat-flies. which have no wings at all, frequent the haunts and persons of bats,

Strangely enough, bees are victimized by a tiny wingless parasite, which may—like the foregoing—be a retrograde Dipteron, though its status is still debated by the experts. It lives and breeds in the hive, and is most commonly found clinging to the body of the queen —in one instance fourteen individuals were counted; and by thus attaching itself to the "leading lady" it makes sure of free transport to new quarters when swarming takes place. Recent investigations, however, suggest that it is not a blood-sucker as was formerly supposed; for when hungry it has been seen to creep close to the mouth of its carrier, whose food it apparently shares. Its eggs are laid on the comb, and its larvae burrow into and feed on the wax used by the bees to cap their cells.

This bee-haunter is a midget compared with the insect known to shepherds as the "ked" (but sometimes incorrectly referred to as a "tick" or "louse"), which lives among the wool of sheep and sucks their blood. As it never develops wings and is a poor pedestrian its sole chance of migrating from one animal to another is furnished by the close contact in which sheep are accustomed to pass much of their time. A badly infested sheep rubs and bites itself, which not only harms the fleece, but is apt also to cause abrasions of the skin that tempt the pestilential green-bottle flies to lay their eggs, with disastrous results; for when the maggots hatch they burrow into and devour the living flesh of their victims, which have no means of protecting themselves.

From what has been said it is clear that the life-cycles of these viviparous blood-sucking flies are anomalous. There is a metamorphosis, but one of a very abbreviated kind. As a rule an insect's larva is left by the parent to fend for itself, and casts its inelastic skin several times in succession before its growth is complete. In the case of the least specialized insects, such as the wingless bristle-tails and spring-tails, this skin-changing does not constitute a metamorphosis in the strict sense of the word, although the youngster is refashioned during the process into an adult organism capable of reproduction. But when the perfect insect is winged a notable transformation necessarily takes place.

That the metamorphosis of a dragon-fly is more spectacular and so has attracted more attention than that of a cockroach or a grasshopper arises in the main from the fact that its sluggish, dull-coloured and rather repulsive larva or nymph—which lives for at least a year in some pool or lake—is transformed literally overnight into a resplendent being capable of exceptionally rapid and perfectly controlled flight. As the time for the final moult draws near, the nymph—now full grown and mysteriously apprised of the approaching ordeal—quits the water by climbing up some stem or reed to a point of vantage, where it remains passive for a brief period, this usually happening in the late afternoon or early evening. Then, suddenly, the skin splits above the thorax, and through this opening the dragon-fly begins to extricate itself, first freeing its head and thorax. This done it throws itself backward and rests motionless in a curved position for about half an hour, supported by the hinder segments of the abdomen which remain in the nymphal skin. The significance of this pause is that the legs are as yet too soft and feeble for use. As soon as they become dry and firm the creature jerks itself upward and grasps the nymphal skin, thus gaining the purchase needed to drag its abdomen free. This completes the actual process of emergence; but some hours must still elapse before the wings— at first mere crumpled flaps—will have filled out and stiffened. Probably the first flight will not be essayed before tomorrow's sun is high in the heavens; while the bright colours and metallic sheen of the body need a day or two more for their perfecting.

The quiescent or pupal stage which marks the life-cycles of insects that undergo a complete metamorphosis is fraught with many dangers, especially when its duration extends over a period of weeks, or it may be through the entire winter. Not only has the risk of hostile attack to be guarded against, but the vagaries of the weather must also be taken into account. We shall see later how important a part is played by camouflage, or protective disguise, as a means of outwitting enemies, while provision against adverse weather conditions is usually made by the larva before the momentous change takes place. In many instances it buries itself in the earth, forming a cell or chamber by repeated contortions of its body. Very often, however, it constructs a cocoon, either of pure silk or of sundry odds and ends bound or cemented together with the same adaptable material. The caterpillar of the puss-moth, for example, combines camouflage with architecture by gnawing off fragments of bark and roofing itself in under a stout dome, smooth within, but with a rough exterior perfectly matching the surface of the tree-trunk to which it is attached.

Not less remarkable is the cocoon of the emperor moth which the caterpillar spins in the later autumn, usually among twigs of its favourite food-plant, ling or heather. These cocoons are not at all conspicuous because their colour varies from very pale to very dark brown in accordance with the particular situation in which they are constructed. This is due to the photopathy or light-sensitiveness of nerve-endings in the skin of the caterpillar, which—having chosen a suitable site—exposes itself, so to say, for some hours before commencing to spin. But this camouflage is only the first line of the cocoon's defence. If we cut one open—using a pair of sharp-pointed scissors held obliquely, so as not to injure the pupa within—we find that it is formed of (1) an outer layer of coarse silk, and (2) an inner layer so fine in texture as to resemble a coat of varnish. This inner layer, however, does not extend to the extreme upper part of the broadly pear-shaped cocoon, where it tapers to a neck-like opening. Here, through which the moth eventually makes its escape, the caterpillar has contrived a sort of conical valve that opens easily when pressed from within, but presents a disconcerting tuft of bristles to a would-be intruder attempting to force an entry from without. Some enthusiasts have claimed that the human inventor of the lobster-pot must first have studied one of these cocoons, since the principle involved is precisely that of this contrivance in reverse: an easy way of egress is provided, whereas nothing can enter.

When the time comes for the puss-moth to leave its closely sealed cocoon, it emits from its mouth a powerful liquid solvent by the action of which the hard-set cement used by the larva is dissolved and a breach made in the prison wall. But this solvent is highly caustic, and contact with it would certainly damage the moth's delicate plumage. Yet a way through the sodden débris must be forced, and the dilemma is solved very cleverly: a fragment of the stout pupal skin remains temporarily lodged in the insect's thorax, and under cover of this shield freedom is safely gained.

As soon as a moth has escaped from its cocoon, or its subterranean pupal chamber, it climbs hastily up a tree-trunk, a fence, or some convenient stem and hangs by the claws of its feet in a position which will allow a clear drop for its wings. If, at this juncture, it should chance to fall to the ground it would inevitably be crippled for the rest of its life. On quitting the cocoon it is in every way perfect, with the form and size of maturity, save for the wings and the abdomen. The former are as yet small, pad-like organs, while the latter is swollen with the fluid destined to inflate them. This influx is exceedingly rapid when once the moth has found a suitable foothold, so that the wings grow steadily moment by moment before the observer's eyes. But even when they have attained their full size the moth must still rest suspended for several hours ere they have hardened sufficiently for use. Then, after some preliminary opening and closing, they are vibrated rapidly and as dusk falls the moth makes its first flight.

As we have seen, the inflation of the wings is due to inflowing fluid—blood, in fact—forced by muscular contraction from the abdomen. Each wing of the newly emerged insect is virtually a bag which would expand into a balloon if it were not for innumerable tiny ligaments which hold the upper and lower membranes together —closely, but not quite in contact. We may demonstrate what happens fairly accurately by blowing out a crumpled kid glove— though this, of course, has no internal ligaments to prevent it from assuming the balloon-like form.

With few and unimportant exceptions the caterpillars of butter-flies make no cocoons, but prior to their last moult weave a silken pad or cushion on a leaf or stem to which subsequently the newly formed pupa or chrysalis attaches its tail-end by means of the "cremaster"—a specially evolved organ beset with numerous micro-

scopic hooks. In the families of the "swallow-tails" and "whites"
the pupa is also supported by a belt or girdle spun by the caterpillar, so that it is held in an erect or inclined position; but in the
family of the "tortoiseshells" and "admirals" it hangs head downward. To achieve this topsy-turvy posture no little adroitness is
demanded. Gripping its silken cushion firmly with its hindermost
pro-legs the caterpillar lowers itself until it is vertically suspended;
after which nothing more happens for several hours. Then, suddenly, it is seized with convulsions, and its skin—first splitting apart
just behind the head—works in folds upwards towards the tail. From
now on events move so rapidly that close watching is necessary if
we are to detect what is happening. The object of the caterpillar—
or, as we should now call it, the incipient pupa—is twofold: it must
fix its brand-new cremaster to the silken cushion, and rid itself finally
of the obsolete skin. This is accomplished by first gripping the latter
between two of its abdominal segments, and then withdrawing its
tail and thrusting it upward so that the hooks of the cremaster
become entangled with the strands of the woven silk. A vigorous
twisting of the body follows, whereby the hold gained is made
secure, and incidentally the useless skin is dislodged and falls to
the ground. The newly formed pupa is elongate, soft and almost
white; but it rapidly contracts, hardens and in a few hours' time
assumes the colouring characteristic of its species. The pupal stage
of most British butterflies does not exceed several weeks, but in
a few instances it continues throughout the winter.

What is the biological explanation of metamorphosis in the life-
cycles of insects? This question was formerly answered by assuming
that the eggs of insects, like those of many marine invertebrates—
such as starfishes, oysters and crabs—are only meagrely provisioned
with yolk, so that hatching takes place of necessity at a very early
stage of development, with the result that the young are cast adrift
in an unfinished state, so to speak, and have perforce to do their
subsequent "growing up" by stages which recapitulate, as it were,
their past evolutionary history.

It is now recognized, however, that insects' eggs, in common
with those of almost all other terrestrial animals, are for the most
part plentifully supplied with nourishment, which obviates the need
for premature hatching; and experts are agreed that metamorphosis as undergone by insects is correlated with changes in their
modes of feeding. The feeding habits of such an insect as the cockroach are nearly the same throughout its life-cycle. But as we follow

the scale upwards we find that the adult tends to become increasingly unlike its immature forerunner as it makes use of its wings to roam more widely and to avail itself of fresh sources of food-supply. Changes in diet inevitably involve changes in the structure of the mouth-parts and of the digestive organs. In other words, a transformation so complete as when a biting caterpillar becomes a butterfly sucking sweet juices from the flowers cannot be effected without deep-seated physical modifications; and these (to quote Lord Avebury, who first gave clear expression to this view) "could hardly take place while the insect was growing fast and consequently feed-

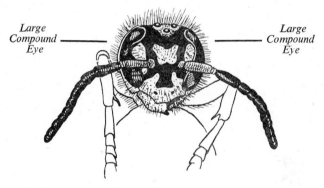

The face of a wasp. Note the large compound eyes, the three simple eyes (on forehead) and the feelers or antennae

ing voraciously; nor, if the change could be thus effected, would the mouth, in its intermediate stages, be in any way fitted for biting and chewing leaves. The same reasoning applies also to the digestive organs. Hence the caterpillar undergoes little, if any, change, except in size, and the metamorphosis is concentrated, so to say, into the last two moults. The change then becomes so rapid and extensive that the intermediate period is necessarily one of quiescence."

Much force is lent to this argument when we consider the consecutive adaptations, alike in bodily form and instinctive behaviour, which enable certain insects in the course of their larval career to overcome difficulties which at first sight might seem insuperable. As an example of this so-called "hypermetamorphosis" take the case of the common oil-beetle, whose progeny, if they are to survive, must somehow gain access to the nest of a flower-bee. Early in April, the rather repulsive-looking parent lays her very numerous, minute eggs in shallow burrows made in the soil. Some three to six weeks later, according to the state of the temperature, these hatch out as yellowish larvae, six-legged and extremely active when the weather is sunny and warm. From the ground they make their way up the stems of various herbaceous plants to the flower-heads, there to await the coming of visiting bees and other insects, to whose hairs they immediately attach themselves. In this way a few get carried to the nests of appropriate bees; the rest, which have boarded flies or bees of the wrong sort, perish by hunger. What happens to the lucky ones has been observed in detail by Fabre, of whose account the following is a digest. The bee, arriving at the cell which she has previously stored with honey, launches an egg on the viscid surface. At the same instant the beetle's larva drops down upon the egg, and shortly afterwards commences to devour its contents—a meal which occupies it for about eight days. Thereafter, using the egg-shell as a raft, since contact with the honey at this juncture would prove fatal, it changes its skin and becomes an inert, soft-skinned grub of a not uncommon type, but with the spiracles or breathing-holes so situated that it can float and feed on the honey without risk of suffocation. After other skin-changings, the larva is eventually transformed into a pupa, and the perfect insect appears in August or September, but does not quit the bee's nest until the following spring, when it feeds voraciously on the leaves of various plants, especially those of buttercups. Points of special interest in this astonishing life-cycle are (1) the prodigious fecundity of the beetle—whose egg-output is said to total 10,000—which compensates for the inevitably high rate of infant mortality, and (2) the instinctive ingenuity of the successful larvae in appropriating the food and shelter prepared by the bees for their own offspring.

Very similar is the course of action followed by a British beetle associated as a parasite with wasps. The perfect insects frequent flowers, but the females, with instinctive cunning, resort for egg-laying to wooden fences and the like, where wasps come to gather fibres for their building operations. When the tiny beetle larva hatches it lies in wait for one of these insects, springs upon it, and is thus carried to the nest, where it makes its way into a cell, and fixing upon the grub which is the rightful owner begins deliberately to suck its juices. So carefully, however, does the parasite regulate its appetite that the wasp's grub as it approaches maturity still preserves sufficient vitality to spin the customary silken cap over the cell's entrance; and this is the signal for the intruder to consummate its dark deed. The skin of the victim is sucked dry and the now fully nourished beetle larva completes its metamorphosis in the stolen cell.

Although the wasp nurses constantly investigate the cells when they come to feed their charges they seem never to discover the intruders, else they would certainly destroy them. Yet when the perfect beetles emerge they have to run the gauntlet of the whole community in order to escape from the nest, for they are now recognized and treated as enemy aliens.

Chapter Four

NESTS AND NURSERIES

To SPEAK of nests and nurseries inevitably suggests those familiar structures of grass, moss, wool and the like in which birds lay their eggs and rear their young. But just as birds share with insects the capacity for flight, so the art of nest-building is common to both these great divisions of the animal kingdom. The majority of insects are orphans at birth and large numbers of them depend for protection during their infancy upon some hiding-place or retreat formed either by their own instinctive activities or as the result of innate prescience on the part of the parents.

An outstanding instance of precocity is furnished by the tiny caterpillar of the white admiral butterfly, which when barely a month old prepares its "hibernaculum" or winter snuggery by drawing together with silken threads the edges of the honeysuckle leaf on which it has been feeding, having first secured the leaf-stalk to the stem as a precaution against falling. Here the baby slumbers in security until the advent of spring.

The caterpillars of many small moths, the grubs of certain two-winged flies, and those of a few beetles, are known popularly as "leaf-miners" because they live and feed between the upper and lower cuticles of leaves, thereby giving rise to blister-like blotches or tortuous galleries which are often very conspicuous. Among the latter the commonest are those made by the bramble leaf-miner, while the former are exemplified by the work of the hazel-blotch moth in its larval state. Of the blister-like mines made by the grubs of flies those of the celery leaf-miner may be cited—a well-known garden pest this, which attacks also parsnips and various wild *Umbelliferae*, and since the larvae are gregarious, large areas of the leaves are often destroyed so that growth is checked and the plants stunted. Another blister-like mine not easily overlooked is that of the holly leaf-miner, which in some seasons is so abundant that on the lower branches of many holly trees it is difficult to find an un-blemished leaf. The culprit in this instance is likewise the grub of a small fly; but the equally common lilac leaf-miner is the caterpillar of a diminutive moth, several of which work together in the same blotch—which, however, they vacate when half grown; and then each rolls up for itself a fresh leaf to form a funnel-shaped shelter wherein to finish its feeding.

The grub of yet another small fly is responsible for the serpentine galleries which disfigure the leaves of chrysanthemums, Michaelmas daisies and other cultivated *Compositæ*, as well as nearly one hundred wild plants of this and other Orders. Then there are the small "hopper" beetles, whose grubs mine the leaves of various forest trees, and in some seasons, when specially numerous, impart a yellowish or brownish tint to the body of the foliage.

The larvae of many other insects ensconce themselves in the fastness of a fruit or nut—examples being the codlin moth, whose newly hatched caterpillar, scarcely discernible by the naked eye, burrows into the heart of an apple, where it consumes the pips, and the filbert weevil, whose grub works havoc in cobs and hazel nuts, as well as those whose name it bears. Still others find harbourage in the soil, or by tunnelling in wood, both living and in process of decay. Among the former, wireworms and leatherjackets—the ante- cedents of skip-jack beetles and daddy-longlegs respectively—if present in vast numbers, as is often the case when waste or grass- land has been broken up for arable cultivation, are capable of immense damage to crops, ranking, indeed, among the worst foes with which the farmer has to deal. In some seasons the fat, sickle- shaped grubs of certain chafer beetles—the largest being the cock- chafer or may-bug—are also sufficiently numerous to make them- selves a nuisance. The caterpillars of a few moths are also sub- terranean in their habits and feed largely on roots. Those of the common swift moth occur all too frequently when the digging of herbaceous borders is in progress; while the so-called "surface caterpillars" or "cut-worms" pass most of their time underground during the winter and early spring.

Of the wood-tunnellers outdoor examples are the stag beetle, the goat moth and the wood-wasps, while the "wood-worms"—the larvae of the death-watch and furniture beetles—tunnel in the beams and floor-boards of buildings, as well as in furniture. All these in the larval state are wood-feeders, passing through their alimentary canals the fragments which they rasp away with their powerful jaws. Many of them appear to subsist on the starch and sugar contained in what they swallow, but some secrete cellulose-reducing enzymes or ferments, while still others have in their intestines resident colonies of bacteria or other "microbes" which act chemically on the woody tissue and render it capable of digestion. But dry wood, at best, affords scanty nourishment, and this fact doubtless accounts for the unusually long life—not infrequently extending to several years—characteristic of these larvae.

As their name suggests, the special group of wood-tunnellers known as "bark beetles" generally work either in or immediately beneath the bark of the trees which they attack, leaving curious and intricate patterns to mark their passage. Some, however, go deeper, making their way into the sap-wood, but rarely into the heart-wood. A few very interesting kinds termed "ambrosia beetles" feed exclusively on a peculiar dark-coloured mould which grows on the walls of the tunnels which they excavate; and quite apart from these special cases a considerable weight of evidence has come to light during recent years to suggest that a good many other insects, formerly supposed to be wood-feeders, are in fact dependent either directly or indirectly on fungi of one sort of another for their nutriment. In this connexion mention should be made of the fungus-feeders as a group, mostly beetles and two-winged flies, whose larvae find board and lodging in toadstools and the like. Cultivated mushrooms, for instance, are often infested with the grubs of fungus-gnats, of which there are more than one hundred British species.

The grubs of many long-horn beetles feed on dead or decaying timber, and thus play an important part in the economy of Nature by promoting the rapid circulation of matter. This is especially the case in the tropics, where the family is exceedingly numerous, and represented by many large species, the larvae of which are capable of reducing fallen trees to pulp in a surprisingly short time. Indeed, it has been claimed by more than one observer that in certain regions, such as the Amazon basin, the forests would soon be stifled by their own decay, and ultimately disappear altogether, were it not for the intervention of the Longicorns. These giants of the tropics are represented in Britain by upwards of fifty species, mostly small, the two largest being one which, in the absence of an English name, we may dub "the sawyer", and the perfumed musk beetle. The former is a heavily built insect with broadly serrated antennae; the latter is notable for its elegant form and attractive blue-green colour, frequently glossed with copper or bronze.

Typical "tent caterpillars" are those of the brown-tail moth, whose numerous brood—perhaps 250 strong—co-operate after hatching to weave a nest, or tent, sufficiently capacious to shelter the whole family. Some such retreat is eminently desirable, if not actually essential, for gregarious caterpillars such as these that leave the shelter of their egg-shells in late summer and pass through the winter—as yet only half fed—among the branches of a shrub or tree where they are exposed to the full rigours of our fickle climate. So leaves are drawn together and covered with a sheeting of tough, closely woven silk, which, being non-conductive, serves at once to keep out the cold and keep in the heat generated by the living bodies of the inmates that in the depth of winter never leave their snuggery, although on mild, sunny days both in the autumn and very early spring they may issue forth for an hour or two about noon to bask in the genial warmth.

When the winter is past the brown-tail moth's caterpillars still preserve their tent-dwelling habit; but as they continue to feed and grow the original brood splits up into two, or it may be three, parties, each of which sets to work to weave a tent of its own. These summer tents, however, are far less densely woven than those whose main object is to resist the inclemencies of the weather. They resemble those of the lackey moth's caterpillars, which do not form hibernacular or winter shelters, since this species weathers the season of frost and snow in the egg state.

Social caterpillars, besides engaging in co-operative nest-making, often display a remarkable unity of action in their other pursuits. They have set times for feeding, for basking in the sun outside their tent, and for resting within its shelter; and when one individual moves the rest follow suit like a flock of wheeling birds. The caterpillars of the European processionary moth leave their nest at sundown, after a day spent in retirement, and march to their feeding-grounds on the branches of the oak trees in wedge-shaped formation, returning just before daybreak in the same order. It is said that the pioneer emits a silken thread to which the leaders of succeeding files attach threads of their own spinning, thus linking the whole column in unison. The caterpillars of an allied moth make their nests in fir trees on the needle-like foliage of which they feed. Processionary caterpillars, and those of certain other social species, spin their cocoons in contact under cover of their tents.

Some of the smaller gregarious caterpillars—e.g. those of the little ermine moths—weave wonderful labyrinthine nests of the finest gauze among and around the leaves of their food-plant and therein dwell securely, for although they can be seen their enemies cannot pick them out of the silken tangle, that serves also to keep at bay the minute ichneumons by which they would otherwise be harried.

So far we have seen only how immature insects, often mere infants, provide nests and nurseries for themselves. But often both food and a safe retreat are furnished by the parents for their offspring at the time when the eggs are laid. Rather surprisingly, the common earwig—quite low down in the evolutionary scale—prepares a subterranean chamber in which to lay her eggs and remains with them to foster the young when they hatch. Still more noteworthy are the habits of the numerous species of "burying beetles", some of which deal with carrion, others with stercoraceous matter. In the course of a country ramble one may often come across a dead bird, mouse, hedgehog or some such carcass lying in a slight concavity of the surface soil. On turning it over with a stick several of our native sexton beetles are very likely to be found at work. Their method of procedure is as follows. The dead body being tracked down by scent, the female deposits her eggs upon it ; and she appears to know instinctively exactly how many grubs it will suffice to feed. If it chances to be that of a largish animal, such as a young rabbit, many pairs of beetles will unite their labours, both males and females taking part in the enterprise. They laboriously excavate the soil from beneath the find, and when the latter has been sunk to a sufficient depth, smooth down the surface with their rake-like forefeet. If the ground beneath is reasonably soft and a large number of beetles co-operate the interment is often completed in a surprisingly short space of time. In this way the larvae, when they hatch from the eggs, find themselves surrounded by an abundant supply of food and are secure from the attacks of birds and other insectivorous enemies to which they would be exposed above ground.

The beneficial scavengering operations of these, the true sexton beetles, are aided by various other insects which, although they do no actual burying, are ready enough to participate in the ghoulish feast. Besides a variety of lesser carrion-feeding beetles there are the numerous two-winged flies—blue-bottles, green-bottles, and so forth —that search eagerly for putrefying flesh of all kinds in which to deposit their eggs ; nor must those other beetles be overlooked which breed on skins and dried carcasses, and so complete the work begun by the burying beetles. Insects with habits of this kind do yeoman service in the economy of nature by rapidly breaking down effete and decaying matter so that it can be built up again as the vehicle of life ; but where human affairs are concerned some of them rank as serious pests. One is the notorious "bacon beetle", while several others work havoc in fur stores and museums, if perchance they gain entry.

Of the stercoraceous or dung-feeding beetles the sacred scarab of the ancient Egyptians is the typical example; but hundreds of allied species, large and small, in all but the coldest regions of the earth, have virtually identical habits. They collect and make balls of the refuse, an egg being laid in each, then roll them about in the sun to harden. Sooner or later they are buried in holes scooped in the ground, where the grubs can feed in safety, and where pupation eventually takes place.

Using the term in its widest sense, our best-known British scarab is the insect variously known to countryfolk as the dumble-dor, watchman and clock. This is the "shard-borne" beetle of Gray's *Elegy*, the so-called shards being the elytra or wing-cases—held rigidly extended and probably serving as gliders—when the insect is in flight. The much rarer lunar dung-beetle is sometimes referred to as the British sacred beetle on account of its general similarity to the famous prototype, which, by the way, is by no means confined to North Africa but has a wide range in the countries of the Mediterranean littoral. Our most spectacular native, however, is the "trident-bearer" of Edward Step, whose male has three forward-directed prongs or horns springing from the thorax. It is reminiscent

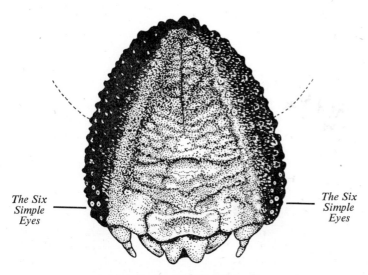

The Six Simple Eyes ———   ——— The Six Simple Eyes

The face of a caterpillar. Note the
six simple eyes on each side low down near
the three-jointed antennae

on a small scale of a Mesozoic Dinosaur, such as the horrific Triceratops! It frequents sandy commons, especially in the southern counties, and has a preference for rabbit-droppings, both sexes collaborating in collecting these for storage in the nest-burrows, which are sunk to a depth of six inches or more below the surface. In addition to the above, mention should be made of fifty or more smaller dung-beetles, some dingy, others attractively coloured, the chief of whose business is conducted in meadows or on downlands where grazing beasts provide an abundance of material for the discharge of their parental labours.

Of all invertebrate parents first place must be accorded to the bees and wasps. A mere catalogue of the nest-making and nest-provisioning of these insects would form a bulky volume. Both groups may be roughly subdivided into social and solitary species. The latter, as the name implies, know nothing of joint labour, nor as a rule do the males take part in the preparations made by the females for the benefit of posterity. But in all cases the instinct of nest-building is highly developed, while the material employed varies as much as the manner in which it is shaped into the required form.

Most of the so-called mining-bees and their near relatives are inveterate burrowers. They drive shafts in the soil, sometimes on banks, but often vertically, the openings of which are mistaken for worm-holes by the uninitiated. One of the most noticeable species, the reddish-brown "lawn-bee", is very partial to lawns, where it throws up little mounds of earth which, in the opinion of some gardeners, are "worse than worm-casts". The shafts at a certain depth communicate with several small cells or chambers, each containing an egg and provisioned with a mixture of pollen and honey, destined to feed the grub when it hatches. The cells of these mining-bees are mere scooped-out cavities, serviceable, but not very durable. Other more sophisticated burrowing bees are at pains to strengthen the walls by plastering them with a kind of cement composed of their saliva mixed with sand or clay. The bees known popularly as "masons" are especially interesting on account of their diverse habits. Most of them seem to be burrowers by inherited custom, but they are apt to shun hard material and to avoid all unnecessary exertion. One makes use of bramble stems, usually gaining entrance at a cut or broken end, and does not scoop away the whole of the pith, but excavates in it a series of small cells connected by narrow passages. Other species avail themselves of existing crevices in brickwork, empty snail-shells, the spindle-holes of cotton-reels and suchlike cavities, filling them with concrete cells and finally smoothing all down in a most workmanlike manner. A common mason bee not infrequently packs its cells into the lock of an outhouse or garden shed ; and there is a record of this insect having built between a book and the back of a book-case against which it was pressed, leaving just room for the bees to gain access. This book, with the bees' cells attached to it, may be seen in the Insect Gallery of the British Museum (Natural History). The Southern European mason bee, whose habits were studied by Fabre, does not occur in Britain. Using a particularly hard concrete of its own mixing, it first constructs a group of eight or nine cells, usually on a large stone, and finally coats the whole over with a thick layer of masonry so that a dome-shaped structure about the size of half an orange results. As the building and provisioning of each cell before the egg can be laid in it represents the labour of two days the pertinacity and endurance of this insect speak for themselves.

Our native wool-carder bee—a rather large, stoutly built species, black with conspicuous yellow spots—makes use of the deserted burrows of other insects, door-locks, empty snail-shells, and so forth, for locating its nest, which is like a ball of wool with a cluster of waxy cells as its core. The "wool" consists of downy hairs scraped from the stems of plants ; and—as Gilbert White points out in his *Natural History of Selborne*—it is very pleasant to watch the adroitness and dispatch with which this material is collected.

Equally diverting is the behaviour of the leaf-cutter bees, numbering some eight British species, several of them large and conspicuous insects, not unlike the common drone-fly in appearance. Their habits and methods of work vary in detail, but the following account, based on personal observation of Willughby's leaf-cutter, may be regarded as typical. The nest-burrow is usually made in some rotten post, beam or tree-trunk, the bee rasping away the soft wood with her strong jaws and sweeping the débris out of the entrance-hole with her hind-legs. She then repairs to some plant (in this instance nearly always a rose-bush) and cuts an oblong or lozenge-shaped portion from a leaf. This she does as quickly as an experienced tailor cuts cloth, and with equal accuracy, then conveys the fragment to her tunnel—one or more pauses being made on the way if the distance to be traversed is considerable, or if the chosen site of the nest is an elevated one, such as a beam in the roof of a building. Arrived at her destination, she drags the piece of leaf to the extremity of the tunnel, treads it into place, and immediately

D

flies back to the bush for a second, and so on until the requisite number (normally seven) have been cut and placed in position to form a substantial, thimble-shaped cell. This is then stored with a mixture of pollen and nectar gathered from the flowers, on the surface of which an egg is floated. Four or five circular pieces of rose-leaf are now cut, carried and pressed down to serve as a cover for the cell; and as soon as one cell is complete, the bee sets about making others until her tunnel is filled. Thus, each grub or "bee-baby" when it hatches finds itself in a snug little nursery, reasonably secure from enemies, and supplied with the exact amount of food requisite for its needs. When it has licked the last sweet drop from the sides of its cell it will be ready to change to the pupa, and will need no more nourishment until it creeps into the open air and sunlight as a mature winged replica of its parent.

This, surely, is a marvellous display of instinctive ingenuity and resource; but in the opinion of O. H. Latter the aforesaid masons "are undoubtedly among the most intelligent of all the solitary bees". Yet it is probably also true that their very cuteness has militated against the incipient impulses that make for co-opera-tion which have found expression among the less highly specialized miners of the genus *Halictus*. These, although solitary in the tech-nical sense of the word, behave as good companions, or—as Fabre observed—are not above the practice of "the golden rule". A number of females combine to excavate a common burrow which gives access to the groups of cells made and stored by individual members of the colony. There is also a vestibule or widening of the burrow near its entrance enabling the bees to pass one another easily as they come and go, while a sentinel is often posted to keep out would-be intruders. In short, the conditions obtaining have been likened to those of several families occupying a block of flats, each with its own separate apartments, but all using the same street-door kept by a porter; and it seems certain that through such inter-dependence and good neighbourliness we may trace the evolution of the highly organized communities of the humble- and hive-bees and the social wasps.

Although the nesting habits of solitary wasps are in general similar to those of solitary bees, the food-contents of the cells is strongly contrasted; for all bees are strict vegetarians, whereas wasps —though keen enough about sweet substances when adult—provide a meat diet—caterpillars, flies, beetles, spiders and what-not—for their progeny. Thus, for example, when we find cells in a bramble stem stored with the carcasses of flies we may conclude with certainty that they are the nurseries of a "digger-wasp", not of a bee.

Nearly all our British fossors or "digger-wasps" are comprised in the two families *Pompilidae* and *Sphegidae*, upwards of ninety different species of the latter occurring in this country. An interesting distinction, easily verified by the casual observer, is that whereas the Pompilids use their feet and the coxal joints of the legs as tools, Sphegids employ only their powerful jaws in their mining operations.

The habits of our larger diggers, the sand-wasps, have been closely studied by Fabre, Latter and other observers. The female first sinks a vertical shaft into the ground and excavates a single cell about two inches below the surface. When this has been done she carefully closes the entrance with a small stone, and hurries off on a hunting expedition, to return sooner or later dragging a caterpillar which has been paralysed by stinging, so that it can neither struggle nor attempt to escape. After storing the prey the wasp lays an egg on its body and fills in the entrance to the burrow.

Digger-wasps, like most other insects, are extremely conservative in their choice of food. Some must have caterpillars of a particular kind, others two-winged flies, others again hard beetles. Certain of the smaller species prey exclusively on aphides—and are thus beneficial from the standpoint of the farmer and gardener, while at least one is known to extract cuckoo-spit insects from their frothy shelters. The little "black-borer" wasp, not very common in Great Britain, but abundant in many districts across the Channel, often constructs its cells in hollow reeds, using a concrete of its own making for partitions and provisioning them with tiny spiders. Members of the family *Pompilidae*, of which we have about thirty native species, are also spider-killers almost without exception.

Most digger-wasps simply close up their cells after the egg has been laid and never return to them again. The mother instinctively stores a sufficiency of food for the needs of the grub and thereafter loses interest in its welfare. But members of the genus *Bembex* and their allies return again and again to their burrows after their off-spring have hatched, bringing them food day by day in the shape of two-winged flies until their appetite is satisfied. In the case of a common European species Fabre found that from fifty to eighty flies may be required before the grub shows signs of repletion—the majority of them large, blood-sucking gad-flies.

The potter-wasps are more nearly related than any of the foregoing to the social wasps, and like them fold their fore-wings longitudinally when at rest. Their cells are built in all manner of crevices, in hollow stems, or in burrows in the earth; or you may find them plastered in the angles of walls, under window-ledges, or in the gaps between bricks left by the crumbling away of mortar. One of our fifteen British species, which has been called the "heath-potter", fixes its globular nests to the branches of heather or some other low-growing shrub, and stores them with tiny caterpillars industriously collected from near-by vegetation. These potter-wasps are sometimes styled "mud-daubers"—a name which properly belongs to a group of fossors or "diggers" that do, in fact, employ clay or mud for the construction of their nests, which—with unexplained freakishness—are frequently built inside human habitations, often attached to articles of furniture. So far as the present writer has observed the British potters do not use mud, but scrape together particles of dry soil and moisten them with saliva to form a hard-setting and durable concrete.

The so-called "nests" of social insects—bees, wasps, ants and termites or white ants—would be more fittingly described as civic centres, since they not only serve for the protection and rearing of the rising generation but also house adult populations which in some instances total many thousands, consisting of one or a few egg-laying females or "queens", a small number of males or "drones", and a host of sexually neuter individuals usually spoken of as "workers"—these last playing the parts of architects, engineers, nurses, foragers, soldiers or common labourers as circumstances may dictate. But the subject of insect communities and their co-operative activities, though fascinatingly interesting, is too extensive to be dealt with in the present volume and must, therefore, be treated as a sequel.

Chapter Five

LEAF FOLDERS AND ROLLERS

LEAF-FOLDING and rolling, as practised by a number of caterpillars as well as by certain adult insects, is a kind of nest-making, but so many curious and highly specialized instincts are involved that it merits treatment in a separate chapter. Towards the end of his life, the versatile French scientist Réaumur devoted much of his leisure to studying the methods employed by caterpillars—especially those of the green tortrix moth—when constructing these shelters. This particular species, alias "the green twister", is in some seasons so numerous that during the early summer oak trees over wide areas are almost defoliated and their bare twigs left festooned with silken threads. If one of these caterpillars is watched it will be seen to draw down a part of the leaf-blade, either at the tip or the side, so as to form eventually a tightly rolled cylinder. To overcome the elasticity of the leaf it spins many silken threads, attaching one end of each to the roll, the other end to the flat surface of the leaf. These threads, though individually scarcely perceptible by the naked eye, are nevertheless strong enough to maintain the tension exerted on the cylinder, so that by continually attaching more threads and by tightening the slack of those which have become loose, the work is slowly brought to a successful conclusion. The interior of the rolled-up leaf serves as food for the little artificer, which, however, frequently issues forth to browse on neighbouring foliage, but eventually changes to a black pupa within its shelter. When alarmed, it drops towards the ground, paying out as it falls a silken thread by means of which it hauls itself up again as soon as all signs of danger have passed. Caterpillars of other kinds cut and fold leaves, thus forming a retreat to which they may resort during their periods of repose; others, again, bind together a number of terminal leaves, with a cavity in the centre in which the owner lies surrounded by a good supply of food.

All this is truly wonderful: but the accomplishments of these caterpillars seem quite amateurish when compared with those of the leaf-rolling weevils, whose activities do not benefit themselves but the succeeding generation. These insects owe their popular name to the fact that at the period of egg-laying the females cut and roll leaves after an elaborate fashion to provide food and a nidus for their offspring. They are represented in North America, but the European species are much more numerous, and one of these has gained some notoriety as a "pest", since it has been known to mutilate vine leaves in such numbers as seriously to retard the growth of the plants. In Britain the commonest is probably the birch-leaf roller.

This insect—whose head-to-tail length rarely exceeds one-eighth of an inch—first makes two S-shaped cuts in the chosen leaf from its outer edge to the midrib, which for the time being is left intact. After an interval, during which the tissue of the leaf loses much of its turgidity and becomes flexible, it is laboriously rolled round and round itself to form a "screw" or "twist" for the reception of the eggs, several of which are usually deposited at or near the centre. After this the weevil comes into the open again, tightens the roll, and fastens the overlap with her jaws. Then a small additional twist is made of the leaf's tip and coaxed upwards and inwards to close the end of the main roll. Finally the insect creeps up to the midrib at the point where her initial cuts end and makes in it a deep incision— this climax of the procedure being apparently necessary to promote the particular state of decay in the pendent part which will render it fit food for the grubs when they hatch.

Two other leaf-rolling weevils, both sealing-wax red in colour and considerably larger than the one mentioned above, are fairly common in Britain. One operates on the foliage of young oaks, the other frequents hazel bushes. A number of years ago the present writer was able, during several successive seasons, to devote some leisure hours to observing the methods employed by the former. The adults appear in early summer, and after satisfying their own hunger, and pairing, the females set about rolling up leaves into compact, thimble-shaped bundles to provide food and a safe lodging for their progeny. These little nests are found chiefly on young shoots growing as underwood, and in some coppices in the south of England may be counted by scores, or even hundreds, within an area of two or three square yards. On the average, the time expended by the insect in making one is approximately two hours. Although the actual work is done by the female, a male may usually be seen not far off; and he sometimes makes himself a nuisance by interrupting the labours of his mate.

The chosen oak leaf is cut, almost in a straight line, from the

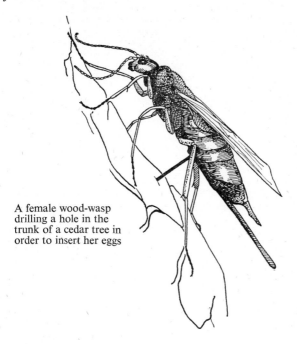

A female wood-wasp drilling a hole in the trunk of a cedar tree in order to insert her eggs

margin to the midrib at a point which is about one-third of its length from the short petiole, or stalk. The weevil then goes round to the opposite margin and makes a similar cut, with the result that the lower two-thirds of the leaf-blade is separated from the upper third, save for the midrib. A period of inaction follows—lasting, perhaps, for half or three-quarters of an hour—the object no doubt being to allow time for the severed portion of the leaf to wilt and become pliable. Afterwards this is folded inwards upon itself very methodically, and then rolled over and over from below upwards— the insect, all the while, moving deliberately from point to point, kneading and massaging the creases with her legs and snout, and in the course of these operations laying a single, bright yellow egg in such a position that it eventually lies at the centre of the finished bundle.

This complicated performance, which is not accomplished without much labour, may be witnessed by anyone who can command the necessary time and patience. The leaf-roller of the hazel, equally industrious and painstaking, has its own method of cutting, folding and rolling, which results in a neat screw not unlike that made by the weevil of the birch.

Thanks to the innate prescience of its maternal parent the leaf-roller's grub, when it hatches from the egg, finds itself in the centre of an ample store of nourishment; and when it has eaten everything except the outer crust it escapes through a small hole which it bites in the latter and allows itself to fall to the ground. Here, buried a little below the surface, it changes to the pupa. Then, in the late spring or early summer of the following year, the perfect insect emerges, climbs up an oak, hazel or birch stem as the case may be and—supposing it to be a female—begins to roll up leaves. Now the grub was blind, indolent and inept. But the adult weevil, though slow in its movement, plies her craft with the dexterity of an expert —which, indeed, she is. How are we to account for this astonishing state of things? The weevils of each succeeding generation must be complete strangers to their environment, nor can they possibly have witnessed the rolling up of leaves by individuals of the preceding generation. Therefore their proficiency must be purely instinctive, as we say, though as yet nobody has been able to tell us exactly what instinct is, or how it originates.

Most of the attempts which have been made to elucidate this mystery have been based upon one or the other of two rival theories. Orthodox Darwinians believe that the origin of instinct must be looked for in the simple reflexes which are characteristic of living protoplasm in whatever form it may occur.

The second theory, often called "the theory of lapsed intelligence", assumes that the actions which are now performed instinctively were originally the outcome of intelligent perception, this latter faculty having since fallen into obsolescence: in other words, that they are inherited habits.

When seeking an explanation of insect behaviour it is necessary to bear constantly in mind the fact that these marvellous beings are markedly deficient in what we call "common sense". True, some of the more highly organized kinds appear to recollect past happenings and to profit by experience. The Rev. Tickner Edwardes, who wrote with the authority of a life-long observer, believed that the worker hive-bee has to learn her business of foraging step by step. "Her first experiences are a succession of blunders. She appears not to know for certain where to look for the coveted sweets, and can be seen industriously searching the most unlikely places—crevices in walls, tufts of grass, or the leaves of a plant instead of its flowers. The fact that the nectar is hidden deep down in the cup of the flower, beyond its pollen-bearing mechanism, seems to dawn upon her only after much thought and many fruitless essays." Again, certain American writers of repute have seen species of digger-wasps pick up small pebbles and use them as tools to pound down the earth above the entrance of their burrows, while H. St. J. K. Donisthorpe, the eminent authority on ants and their ways, admits that he is prepared to grant these insects "something approaching reasoning power". But in general the activities of insects are governed by instinct—which, for practical purposes, we may define as an innate capacity to perform seemingly rational deeds—each succeeding generation of insects inheriting from its ancestry a kind of self-acting mechanism, comparable to an elaborate piece of clockwork wound up and ready to perform its destined movements as soon as the spring is released. This release appears to be effected by some simple stimulus, arising either from external or internal happenings, with the result that the astonishing sequence of the creature's inherent skilfulness is reeled off.

So long as everything occurs "according to plan" instinctive activity answers admirably, but its fallibility is at once evident in face of abnormal circumstances. Butterflies, guided by olfactory sense-organs situated on the antennae, unerringly seek out and lay their eggs on the particular plants indispensable as food for their caterpillars—the female of the "large white", for example, choosing those of the cruciferous tribe; but smear the leaves of any other plants—dock, dandelion, stinging-nettle or even scraps of paper— with mustard oil and she will oviposit on them without the smallest hesitation, because it is the smell of the essence, not any uncanny knowledge of botany, which serves as the stimulus evoking the impulse to her maternal activity. The result, of course, is that the baby caterpillars, after devouring their vacated egg-shells, slowly perish by starvation.

When once established an instinct having "survival value" is likely to be fostered by "natural selection", just as the form, colours and other physical attributes of an organism are maintained by this agency at the level necessary to ensure the continuity of the race. A number of caterpillars—such as those of the Cynthia moth, really an Asiatic species but naturalized in the United States—which construct their cocoons within the wrapping of a leaf first spin a tough silk covering or sheath over the leaf-stalk and make it fast to the branch. That this precaution—which prevents the cocoon from falling to the ground, where the enclosed pupa might be destroyed by damp, bacteria or moulds—is the outcome of instinct, not of

intelligent observation, is interestingly shown if one of these caterpillars is confined in a box just before it starts cocoon-making, for
in these circumstances it will spin the same long sheath over a non-
existent leaf-stalk and fix the end just as strongly to the floor or side
of its prison as if it were making fast to a branch. If one of these
caterpillars should fail to make these preparations for its future
safety it would be liable to perish before reaching maturity, since
only the fittest survive in the struggle for existence. Similarly, if a
leaf-rolling weevil should fall short in efficiency, it would fail to
provide adequately for the needs of its offspring, which would thus
be doomed to perish in infancy.

Theories apart, one easily observed fact goes to show that whatever it may have been in the remote past, the leaf-rolling activity of
these insects is now "blindly" instinctive. If we carefully open a
number of their screws or bundles we shall discover that many of
them are empty. The customary adroitness and labour have been
expended in preparation of the nest, but the egg is missing. Has the
mother forgotten this essential detail? No, for egg-laying is just one
link in the chain of reflex actions and does not depend for its performance on conscious memory. The explanation of the omission
appears to be that the parental impulse has outlasted the physical
capacity of the organism. The ovaries are exhausted: no more eggs
are forthcoming. Yet the business of leaf-rolling continues for a
time unabated, since no gleam of intelligence exists to check its
momentum.

Chapter Six

OAK-APPLES AND OTHER GALLS

AMONG the so-called "vegetable galls" of our countryside, of which well over three hundred different kinds have been identified and described, the most familiar is the rosy-cheeked oak-apple, otherwise King Charlie's apple, which in some rural districts is still sported as a buttonhole by men and lads on "Shig-shag Day" —May 29, the birthday anniversary of Charles II, who on September 4, 1651, the day following the battle of Worcester, successfully hid from Cromwell's search-parties among the branches of a large Shropshire oak.

These pretty, fruit-like objects are the nurseries of certain small four-winged insects related, though somewhat distantly, to bees and wasps—a fact which may be verified by keeping an oak-apple which had become brown and "ripe" under an inverted tumbler for some weeks, when the gall-wasps will make their appearance, tunnelling through the substance of the gall and leaving small apertures, or "flight-holes", to mark their points of exit.

To trace the complete life-cycle of the oak-apple gall-wasp we must go back to the days of mid-winter, for the insect responsible is abroad and active about Christmastide. By patient search at this usually inclement season she may be found creeping up the trunks or along the branches of oak trees. Not unlike an ant in appearance, she has no wings, and so must make all her journeys afoot. She commonly makes her way to a terminal bud, though occasionally lateral buds are visited, and inserting her ovipositor between the overlapping scales lays her eggs among the embryo leaves. These eggs are pear-shaped and translucent, the average number packed into a bud being thirty.

At the time when the oak puts forth its leaves, the buds that contain eggs develop into oak-apples, within which the grubs of the gall-wasp, each in a separate cell, are nourished on sap supplied by the tree. Later, when fully fed, each grub is transformed into a pupa, and towards the end of June the perfect insects emerge.

Now comes the really surprising part of the life-story. The gall-wasps which thus make their appearance differ in many respects from their parent, the ant-like creature whose eggs were laid in the oak bud. They are much smaller, and each has two pairs of membraneous wings. Moreover, this brood or generation comprises both males and females, whereas its precursor consisted only of so-called "agamic" females capable of parthenogenesis or "virgin reproduction". Also, the females of the winged summer brood have quite different instincts from those of their forbears, the larger wingless females. After pairing, they burrow into the soil and insert their eggs into the tender rootlets of the oak, which, after a brief interval, respond by producing brown, nut-like galls; and in these the winter generation of wingless females comes to maturity and carry on the procedure characteristic of the race.

This strange alternation of generations, a kind of seasonal interchange of personality, continues year after year as if in flat defiance of our trite dictum that like always produces like! Of course like does produce like in the long run, for the species remains the same. But the life-cycle may be said to make two successive revolutions in different gears before coming back to its starting point, instead of only one revolution, in fixed gear, as is more usual. These facts were not known to the early naturalists, who accordingly called the insects which emerge from the root-galls by one name, and those which are bred from the oak-apples by another. For the sake of convenience these obsolete titles are still used by naturalists, with the proviso that they do not stand for distinct species, but for two alternating forms of the same species.

The life-cycles of nearly all the British gall-wasps associated with the oak, of which there are more than fifty different kinds, include two generations, the one agamic, the other sexual. But one species— the originator of the well-known marble-gall—has only one generation, all the individuals of which are females. No male has ever been discovered, although entomologists have from time to time bred out and examined many thousands of specimens. Incidentally, the marble gall-wasp is first cousin to the causer of the famous Aleppo gall which has been described as the most useful and valuable of all galls because of its importance in the manufacture of writing ink. It does not occur in this country, or on the British oak elsewhere, but is common on the downy oak, a species which flourishes principally in that area of the Mediterranean littoral known as the Levant. Typical specimens may be distinguished from marble-galls by their knobbly exterior, almost stone-like hardness and greatly superior tannin content.

Besides these gall-wasps whose lives are linked with the oak, we have native species attached to rose, ground-ivy, cat's ear and certain other wild plants, the most noticeable of which is the "bedeguar" or "robin's pin-cushion" of the wild rose. This, like the oak-apple, is a sort of community, consisting of a group of separate but adherent cells, each tenanted by a larva. By contrast, the pea-gall of the rose is one-chambered and attached to the underside of the leaf, while a third species, also single-celled, is distinguished by the thorn-like projections which spring from its surface, like the spikes of a mediaeval war-club.

That virgin reproduction and alternating generations have benefited the species in whose life-cycles they are regular features may be taken for granted, otherwise they must have been suppressed by natural selection. But exactly how these conditions came to be established is less easily conjectured. The most plausible explanation is the following. Observation has shown that virgin reproduction occurs more or less frequently among all the true gall-wasps even when there is only one brood or generation in the course of the year. In the case of the single-brooded species bred from the bedeguar, for example, it is probably the rule, seeing that collectors find male specimens exceedingly difficult to come by. Moreover, it seems fair to assume that when two broods or generations succeed one another every twelve months the faculty of virgin reproduction would prove especially advantageous to the one reaching maturity during the winter, when climatic conditions render the meeting and pairing of the sexes most hazardous; and in these circumstances we may suppose that the males of this brood, being less and less in request, would eventually disappear altogether. Finally, if for some reason the summer or sexual brood should drop out of the cycle—as seems to have happened in the case of the marble gall-wasp—we should get that surprising phenomenon, a completely parthenogenetic species.

To account for the origin of vegetable galls has been a standing puzzle time out of mind. The theories advanced by the older naturalists were many and varied. Pliny the Elder believed that galls were fungi in which insects bred by chance. Later writers held that the parent insect laid its eggs in the ground, whence they were drawn up by the sap to the leaves where the galls appeared. Francisco Redi, in the seventeenth century, taught that "the plant has a vegetable soul, this vegetable soul presiding at the origin of galls, with their eggs, larvae and imagines, while it again gives issue to fruits"—whatever this may signify. Yet he himself, by a few simple experiments, had successfully exploded the doctrine of spontaneous generation current in his day.

A more modern notion was that the parent insect infects the plant tissue during egg-laying—injecting a minute drop of peculiarly poisonous fluid, and that this causes the subsequent enlargement and sub-division of the vegetable cells in such a way that a gall results. Despite its apparent plausibility, however, evidence has been adduced in disproof of this theory. In the case of the true gall-wasps it has been definitely ascertained that the growth of the gall does not commence until after the hatching of the larvae, even though this may be postponed for a considerable period. There is, therefore, every reason for thinking that with these insects, at all events, the galls originate from the irritation set up by the gnawing of the grubs, and that the drop of fluid which the parent undoubtedly injects into the wound made by its ovipositor serves either as a lubricant or kind of varnish to seal up the injury. On the other hand there are galls— e.g. the bright scarlet nodules on the leaves of the crack willow caused by the bean-gall saw-fly—whose formation is far advanced before the eggs hatch, but in these cases it is known that the egg itself undergoes changes and increases in size, thus probably supplying the stimulus—the irritation—which impels the plant to produce the gall. Probably no theory of gall-formation will be found to fit all cases; but it is safe to say that whereas the insect in one way or another furnishes the initiative—either at the time of egg-laying or later by some activity or secretion on the part of the larva or larvae—the plant, thus forced to deviate from its normal mode of growth, converts a part of its embryonic tissue into a gall subsequently nourished by sap on which the occupants feed.

To suggest reasons for the economy of Nature is unfashionable, but the theory that natural selection has favoured the production of galls because they are calculated to supply the needs of insects with a minimum of injury to the plants is attractive. It is arguable, for instance, that the immense crop of galls of various sorts carried annually by an oak is probably far less injurious to the tree than one season's attack by caterpillars of the green tortrix moth. Moreover, it is a fact that relatively few galls affect seriously the vitality of the plants upon which they occur. There are, of course, exceptions to this generalization; but usually, from the standpoint of the plant pathologist, a gall is no more than a small, non-malignant tumour which, in the majority of instances, will be got rid of when the leaves, or other deciduous organs, are shed.

A notable fact about galls is the constancy of their form, coloration, texture, etc. In other words, they have definite "specific" characters of their own no less marked than those of the insects which cause them, so that the experienced collector can nearly always identify at sight any example that may come his way. Although about

The "saws" of a saw-fly—used for cutting slits in the tissue of leaves and stems into which the insect's eggs are inserted

fifty different kinds of British plant galls are caused by mites and a few by eel-worms and fungi, by far the larger number are due to the operations of insects—gall-wasps, saw-flies, midges and other two-winged flies, several beetles, some aphides and the caterpillars of four or five moths. All the main parts of the plant—roots, stems, leaves, flowers and fruits—are liable to attack, but by far the largest number of galls originate from the leaf-buds or the leaves, and whereas some plants—such as the oak—are galled by many different insects, others are left severely alone. Some of the larger galls provide food and shelter for numerous interlopers which may be roughly divided into three categories:

1. Inquilines—i.e. uninvited guests, frequently more or less closely related to the causer of the gall in the substance of which

their parents have surreptitiously laid eggs. These intruders some-times secure most of the food-supply by killing off the rightful tenants by pressure.

2. Commensals—i.e. guests or lodgers of a less disreputable sort. They take a toll of the food-supply, but do no injury to the legitimate occupants of the gall.

3. Parasites. These prey directly upon the larvae and pupae, not only of the rightful gall-owners, but also of the interloping inquilines and commensals. They are for the most tiny "ichneumons" of the Order Hymenoptera.

From a quantity of oak-apples collected towards the end of June no less than seventy-five species of insects, representing seven different Orders, were reared, besides a few spiders and mites. In short, a large gall may and frequently does house and sustain a very mixed population.

Of galls caused by saw-flies the most conspicuous example has already been mentioned—the scarlet "bean-galls" on willow leaves. The larvae of many two-winged flies, working in the tissues of various plants, induce the formation of other galls, some easy to see, others barely noticeable unless pointed out by an expert. In the majority of instances the parents are small, frail-looking insects with long, hair-fringed antennae belonging to the immense family of midges. Among the herbaceous plants commonly affected meadow-sweet, stinging nettle, germander speedwell and bracken may be mentioned, while certain species attack shrubs and trees, some of which do mischief in withe-beds and form the subject matter of a Leaflet issued by the Board of Agriculture and Fisheries. The most harmful causes swellings, due to an excessive flow of sap into the woody tissue, on stems and branches up to four inches in diameter; and when these are numerous and coalesce they form a large, spindle-shaped gall from which the bark ultimately falls away, exposing the tiny larval chambers. Other midges of the same genus are responsible for the familiar rosette galls consisting of bunches of leaves at the apex of willow shoots; but the originator of the somewhat similar tufts on the hawthorn is a distinct species.

Two more midge gall-causers call for mention because they are attached to the blossoms of the lime and the fruits of the pear. The egg-laying of the former is followed by globular growths instead of flowers and less regular swellings of the flower-stalks and their branches. The latter is apt to be a grievous pest in orchards, where its activities arrest the growth of young pears, which are subsequently

Lamellated antennae of the male cockchafer

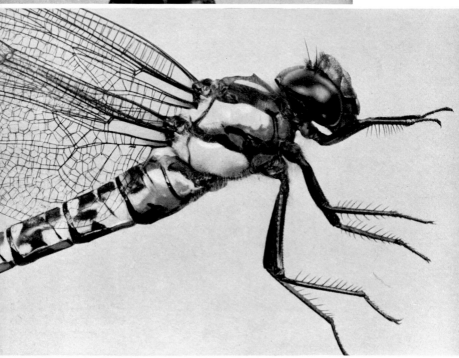

The dragon-fly's large eyes, small antennae and spiny legs

Fern-like antennae of the male emperor moth

[Plate I

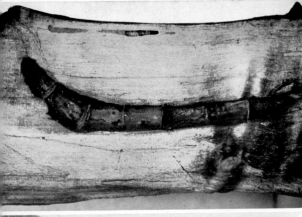

Sexton or burying-
beetles at work on
a dead greenfinch.
(*Inset*) a beetle
magnified

Leaf-cutter bee's
cells packed into
a tunnel excavated
by the insect in a
pear tree's trunk

Mine in an oak leaf
made by the larva of
a beetle (*Orchestes*)

Spangle, apple, artichoke, marble and cherry galls
found on the oak, and a bedeguar or "robin's pin-cushion" from a
wild rose bush—all caused by gall-wasps   [*Plate III*

Red bean-galls on willow leaves caused by a sawfly

(*Top*) The South American Agrippa moth, with a wing expanse of more than ten inches contrasted with the largest British moth—the death's-head

(*and below*)

The giant Indian atlas moth compared with a pygmy clothes-moth whose caterpillars feed on woollen goods and furs

Caterpillar of the English swallow-tail butterfly: green with black stripes and orange spots

Chinese lantern-fly whose curious "beak" is an unsolved puzzle

The longitudinal striping of the pine-beauty moth's caterpillar promotes its concealment

Possessing an extraordinarily long and narrow head this male Brenthus beetle is from S. America

The stalk-eyed flies of tropical Africa carry their eyes at the extremities of long horns

[Plate V

(*Left*) A Brazilian thorn-bug at rest vindicates its popular name

(*Above*) This male chafer beetle from Mexico appears over-weighted with antennae

(*Below*) Thanks to their shape and coloration the purple emperor butterfly's pupae resemble sallow leaves [*Plate*

(*Right*) South African "Basket worm" hangs to pupate

(a) The lace-like cocoon of the diamond-back moth

(b) The cocoon—with the empty pupa-skin protruding—of the webbing clothes-moth

(c) The cunning retreat of a case-making clothes-moth's caterpillar.

(d) The cocoon, resembling a drooping flower, spun by the caterpillar of a South African moth

[*Plate VII*

(a)   (b)   (c)   (d)

The praying mantis, head downwards, discusses a bluebottle

This praying mantis has captured
a large white butterfly

A deadly implement: the predatory fore-leg of a mantis

Courtship rivalry: two male stag-beetles in conflict

Barbed stinging-hairs of the ruby tiger-moth's caterpillar

Conspicuous bull's-eyes on the hind-wing of a South American Catagramma butterfly

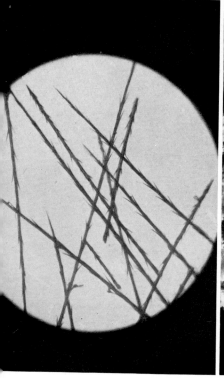

[Plate IX

Warningly
coloured
caterpillars
of the
mullein moth

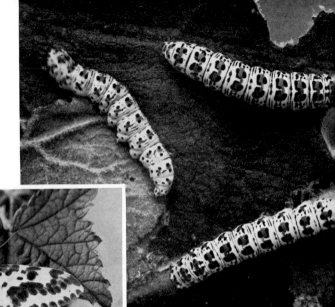

Easily seen : the magpie moth
resting with outspread wings

The orange and black banded
caterpillars of the
cinnabar moth on ragwort

The N. American Monarch
butterfly (*top*) mimicked
by a compatriot, the Viceroy

A colony of greenfly—or aphides—on the underside of a plum leaf

The glow-worm beetle and its larvae prey on snails
Here is one of the latter attacking a victim

[Plate XI

Pupae of the large
white butterfly "holed" by the
Pteromalus parasite shown
magnified (*inset above*)

[*Plate*

The *Apanteles* parasite (*left*),
the destroyer of
the large white butterfly's
caterpillars and (*below*) one
of its victims

(*Left and below*)
The so-called "mask" of the dragon - fly's nymph can be shot out rapidly like a lazy-tongs at its victim

The strange-looking larva of the may-fly (*left*). The fringe along the sides of the abdomen are its gills

The voracious larva of the diving-beetle—known colloquially as "the water devil"—has sharp-pointed tubular jaws through which it sucks the juices of its prey

Plate XIII

Many insects, e.g. bees, butterflies and two-winged flies, visit flowers to gather pollen and nectar and this promotes cross-fertilization. (*From left to right and down*) A wild bee entering the tubular corolla of a foxglove. A tortoiseshell butterfly attracted by michaelmas daisies. A hive bee visits a bluebell. Humble-bees are very fond of red clover. A large white butterfly thrusts its delicate proboscis into the knapweed's florets. A hover-fly sucks pollen grains from the stamens of a wild rose.

[Plate XIV

(*Top right*) The brimstone butterfly hibernates in the recesses of an evergreen, which is usually holly or ivy

(*Centre right*) The caterpillars of the powdered wainscot moth thatch their cocoons with short lengths of reed specially cut

(*Below right*) The grayling butterfly's caterpillars pass the winter among the roots of the grasses on which they feed

(*Above*) Naked chrysalides of the English swallow-tail butterfly suspended on reeds where they remain throughout the winter.

[*Plate XV*

Crude cantharadine, the dried bodies of blister-beetles or "Spanish flies" from which the drug comes

Flannel on which caterpillars of the case-making clothes-moth have been feeding. (A case is shown greatly enlarged at the foot of plate VII)

Part of an old beam from Westminster Hall riddled by grubs of the large death-watch beetle

(*Inset*) Beetle magnified

[*Plate*

(*Above*) The curiously shaped maggot of a house-fly. The mouth is at the pointed end

(*Above right*) The adult house-fly is capable of lay-ing from 800 to 1,000 eggs during its short life

(*Centre right*) A large shield-bug which abounds on trees and bushes in the autumn where it preys on caterpillars whose juices it sucks

(*Bottom right*) The Cheops flea which transmits the germs of bubonic plague (shown magnified) from rats to men

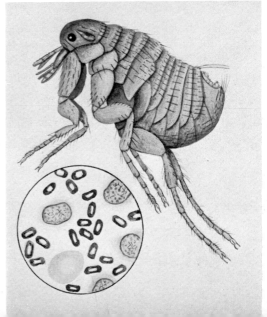

[*Plate XVII*

Remarkable sex-dimorphism. The bird-winged male butter-fly of paradise above, the female is below

The South American skip-jack beetle, with well developed wings and large luminous spots on its thorax, figures as the local firefly

(*Below*) Praying mantids are inveterate fighters, the victor usually eats the vanquished.

[*Plate XVI*

The giant Hercules beetle carries his inamorata—won in fair
fight with rival suitors—to a safe honeymoon retreat

The nuptials of a pair of hawker dragon-flies, the climax of
the so-called "tandem flight"

Photo by G. E. Hyde

[Plate XIX

A house-fly done to death
by a fungus

A sundew leaf captures a fly
which it will digest

[Plate

The Venus's fly-trap: a plant with leaves fashioned
like gins to capture unwary insects

transformed into galls, whose rotting interior provides food and shelter for a dozen or more white larvae.

Very few of the conventionally fly-like Diptera cause galls, but one example is sufficiently conspicuous to attract notice. This is the bulbous swelling, sometimes the size of a walnut, to be found at the top of the stem and sometimes at the nodes of the creeping thistle, where it arrests growth and becomes a focus for the ascending sap. The larvae, usually four in each gall, work their way downward into the juicy tissue, each excavating and keeping to its own burrow, where pupation eventually takes place. If these galls are collected in the autumn and kept in a glass jar until the following June the pretty little flies will be seen emerging.

A fair number of aphides or green-fly rank as gall-causers at one stage of their complicated life-cycle. As an example the red, blister-like excrescences on the leaves of currants, especially the black currant, may be cited, in the hollows beneath which the insects safely feed and multiply. During the summer winged individuals migrate to wild Labiate plants—notably the dead-nettles and hedge woundwort, where they continue breeding until the autumn, when they fly back again to the currant bushes to lay the eggs which hatch in the following spring.

Another aphis is responsible for the pear-shaped "purse galls", about the size of a hazel-nut, on the petioles and midribs of black poplar leaves. Each is a hollow chamber and houses a family of aphides which issue when mature through a sort of snout with an opening at its extremity. In this instance migration is to the root-crowns of lettuces, sow-thistles and allied plants, where no galls are formed, but the insects secrete a white, mealy substance under which they shelter.

A third aphis-caused gall is the familiar "false-cone" or "pine-apple" of the spruce, in the production of which it seems possible that more than one species may be concerned. The details of the life-story are unusually intricate, and can only be briefly summarized here. In the spring wingless, parthenogenetic females which have hibernated on the spruce lay their eggs at the tips of young shoots, thereby inducing the growth of the characteristic galls which when fully developed may contain a hundred or more chambers, each with its family of aphides. These creep out in June, develop wings, and for the most part fly to other conifers, usually larch, but also pine and silver fir. A few, however, remain on the spruce and eventually give rise to a new brood of wingless, hibernating females

E

which on their part become parents of some of next spring's galls. No galls are formed on the larch, etc., to which the migrants resort, but their presence is made manifest by the flecks of white woolly matter—looking like snow—with which they cover themselves. Several generations are passed through on the "alternative host trees" as they are called, and in July of the second year winged forms again develop which fly back to the spruce, where they start a fresh revolution of this involved life-cycle.

The nipple-like excrescences on the roots of turnips and certain other cruciferous plants which result from the egg-laying of the little black "turnip gall-weevil" are not likely to be overlooked, if only because they are frequently available for study in our kitchens. But the most interesting British beetle-caused gall is that of the smaller of the two poplar longhorns. In the early summer the female of this insect rests head downward on a young poplar stem—choosing most frequently the aspen—and with her jaws makes shield-shaped cuts in the bark, depositing a single egg at the base of each. Subsequently the stem forms swellings at these points, in which the larva feeds, first eating a circular galler round the sapwood, but during the second summer boring upwards and downwards in the pith. It changes to the pupa within the gall at the approach of autumn, and the perfect insect appears at the end of the following June, or in early July—making its escape by boring a hole through the stem on the side opposite to that on which the egg was laid. Economically this insect ranks as a minor forestry pest, since the larvae feeding in the stems stop the full growth of the leaves, which are consequently small, while the stems themselves, being weakened, are apt to break off in a strong wind—the result being a dwarfed shrub instead of a well-grown tree.

The resin gall-moth is likewise apt to be destructive in pine plantations, although in Great Britain it is uncommon outside Perthshire and Inverness. In this instance it is the systematic labours of the caterpillar which frame the gall, the parent doing no more than lay an egg near the terminal bud of a pine twig. This occurs in May, and the newly hatched caterpillar by boring into the pith induces a flow of sap which eventually coagulates into a hard nodule about the size of a pea, within which the winter is passed. Feeding is continued during the following spring, and the gall rapidly develops into a conspicuous object, as large as a walnut. When split open it is seen to be divided into two chambers, in the larger of which the caterpillar lives and ultimately pupates, and into the other discharges its excreta. In May of the second year the empty black pupa-skins may be seen protruding from the now tenantless galls. Not infrequently the shoot above the resinous mass is destroyed and numerous lateral shoots appear below it, so that in the case of young trees serious stunting results.

Chapter Seven

GIANTS AND DWARFS

THE opinion is widely held that all insects are small creatures. This, of course, is true in one sense of the term, for the largest insect looks diminutive when contrasted with the vast bulk of a whale or an elephant. But a comparison of this sort is unfair, because insects have scarcely anything in common with the vertebrates—save that both are living animals. One might almost as reasonably place a lady's wrist-watch beside a locomotive engine and proceed to argue that no such thing as a large watch has ever been made. When judged fairly in their proper sphere and among their own kith and kin we find that insects cover a range of size which is truly astonishing. Of terrestrial vertebrates the largest living example is the African elephant, while the smallest is the pigmy shrew—a tiny, mouse-like creature some six of which are needed to balance an ounce in the scales. A wide gap certainly separates these two types, but that between the largest and the smallest insect is even wider. Some are smaller than the largest Protozoa—the one-celled animals of primitive pattern; others are much larger than the smallest vertebrates, the shrews and mice.

In point of bulk the most imposing of all living insects are the Goliath beetles of Africa and the elephant beetle of South America. The latter measures rather more than four and a half inches from the tip of its forward-projecting horn to the extremity of its abdomen. The male Hercules beetle, also from South America, may be more than two inches longer, but well-nigh half of its length is accounted for by the huge pointed prong which springs from the thorax. A good idea of the relatively vast proportions of these giants may be gained by comparing them with one of our native ladybirds; yet these are by no means small beetles as beetles go. The real pigmies of the Order belong to a family bearing the unwieldy name *Trichopterygidae* —meaning "hairy-winged". Some of our British species measure barely the one-hundredth of an inch in length, and could easily creep through the eye of an ordinary sewing needle.

Whether these tiniest beetles are the smallest of all insects or whether this distinction belongs to the so-called "fairy flies" seems still to be an open question among the experts. It is safe to say, however, that the smallest of the fairies—which, by the way, are not really flies, but members of the Order Hymenoptera, whose most familiar examples are the bees, wasps and ants—is a very small insect indeed, measuring, in any case, no more than the beetle from head to tail, and with a wing expanse of just about a millimetre. Moreover, when viewed under the microscope, these midgets are far more attractive than their beetle rivals. In a particular example the exquisite form and graceful curve of the fore-wing, together with its fringe of long hairs and iridescent colouring, give it the appearance of a miniature peacock's feather. This species happens to have a colloquial name—the "battledore-wing fairy-fly". Its hind-wings are vestigial, reduced to mere bristles—each, however, is attached to the corresponding fore-wing by three minute hooklets after the approved Hymenopterous fashion.

Turning now to the scale-winged insects, we find that the largest known examples occur among the atlas moths of India, some of which measure fully twelve inches from tip to tip of the extended fore-wings. It must not be forgotten, however, that this record is very nearly equalled by some specimens of the great owl or Agrippa moth, which is not uncommon in many parts of South America. But the greater wing-area of the atlas moths renders them more imposing, whether they are at rest or in flight. A comparison of one of these giants with the tiniest of the clothes-moths which work havoc in our wardrobes is striking; but the moth whose larva mines the bramble leaves is smaller than the clothes-moth, while the smallest of all British moths is said to be the common blackthorn pigmy, the microscopic caterpillar of which mines the leaves of the plant whose name it bears.

The bird-winged butterflies of New Guinea and the adjacent islands are the largest of their kind, and—in so far as the males are concerned—the handsomest; for the females, though they exceed their mates in wing-expanse by an inch or more, are garbed in shades of russet and brown, in place of the male's glossy green or orange or gold. Although not quite as large as these Old World beauties many of the Tropical American Morpho butterflies are truly magnificent both in dimensions and colouring—varying shades of lovely iridescent azure shot with palest purple. As in the case of our "blue" butterflies these ravishing tints are due in the main to the minutely striated structure of the scales clothing the wing membrane, aided in certain instances by a drab pigment comprised in their make-up.

When the light-rays impinge upon the striae they are refracted in such a way that all the colour-bands of the spectrum except the blue are absorbed.

As far as is known the giant atlas and owl moths have the largest and longest wings of any existing insects ; but some of the dragon-flies of the Carboniferous Period measured two feet from tip to tip of their expanded wings. This compares with the four-inch wing-expanse of our largest native species, the emperor, but in the South American tropics there are still dragon-flies whose outstretched wing-tips are six inches or more apart. One curiosity from Panama has a body ten inches long although its wing-span does not exceed four.

Among the bulkiest insects alive today must certainly be reckoned the giant water-bugs—the "electric-light bugs" as they are often called in the United States, because of their nocturnal habit of leaving the pools and lakes where they get their living to fly round powerful electric lights, especially when these surmount high buildings. They are gluttonous killers not only of fish, but of frogs, newts and other insects—indeed, of any sort of aquatic creatures that they are capable of mastering. When once they succeed in grip-ping their prey it seldom manages to escape. The bug holds on with its strong fore-legs, drives in its deadly beak, and sucks until the last drop of blood has been extracted from the victim's body. It is probable that this fiendish operation is not performed without an anaesthetic, for the copious flow of saliva entering the initial wound has been observed to produce speedy paralysis, and death is not long delayed.

Although the giant bugs of the United States and Canada seem enormous when contrasted with our British water scorpion—a not distant relative—they are not the largest of their kind known. For a sight of these we must journey to Brazil, Guiana or Trinidad, where in muddy pools and sluggish estuaries may be found at least one species with a head-to-tail measurement of nearly five inches, and whose wing-expanse of almost seven inches exceeds that of our smaller native bats.

The most long-drawn-out insects are found among the spectres, or "walking-sticks" as they are often called. Some attain a length of nearly a foot from head to tail, while if the outstretched legs are included the measurement is much greater. Set side by side with one of these lengthy apparitions a male specimen of our native stag beetle, measuring slightly more than two and a quarter inches from

Three stages in the emergence of a dragon-fly
from its nymphal skin

the tip of its wing cases to the apex of its overgrown mandibles or
"horns", is dwarfed into insignificance. But not all these phasmids
are attentuated and spectre-like. A remarkable prickly species from
Australia and New Guinea is not only long but bulky, and with its
hard armour-plate integument and formidable array of spikes looks
a decidedly dangerous customer. One learns with a feeling of relief
that its tastes are exclusively vegetarian. Nevertheless, it should not
be handled incautiously, since it has a way of kicking so that the spurs
of its hind legs are driven into the flesh and cause nasty wounds.

Walking-stick insects belong to the Order Orthoptera, which also
includes the grasshoppers, crickets, locusts, cockroaches and their
relations. Among the members of this numerous company are some
which may certainly be classed as giants of the insect world. Some
of the largest cockroaches come from South America and the West
Indies, where they are known as "drummers" because of the noise
which they make at night. They are extraordinarily flat, and can
creep into narrow cracks in woodwork and flooring, where they
harbour during the hours of daylight; but they have an immense
wing-expanse, extending in some instances to six and a half inches.
On several occasions in the past specimens of these Brobdingnagian
"black beetles"—which in sober truth are honey-coloured with dark
spots and blotches—have made their appearance in Britain, doubtless
transported hither from their native land along with timber or other
merchandise.

Some of the largest and most grotesque of the grasshopper
fraternity are quite wingless in both sexes, even when adult. The
female of a species found throughout the warmer regions of Europe,
more especially in Greece and Turkey, attains a length of three inches,
if the short, sharp-pointed ovipositor is taken into account. It is
worth noting that these uncouth-looking prodigies find their true
affinity among the long-horned grasshoppers which include all the
so-called tree-grasshoppers and katydids. Apart from their long,
thread-like antennae, these insects may be distinguished from
members of the short-horned family by the fact that their tarsi or
"feet" are made up of four joints each, whereas three is the number
among the short-horns, which comprise the little meadow grasshoppers as well as the migratory locusts—the most devastating of all
insect pests, since their raiding swarms completely obliterate the
crops of a countryside on which they alight.

A solitary locust is neither a very large nor a very imposing insect.
The terrible destruction caused by the various species in the course

of their wanderings is due to the well-nigh incredible numbers of which the invading hordes consist. These not uncommonly cover areas of from two to five miles and are probably of about this density, while swarms of 100 square miles or more in extent are reported from time to time. The estimated weight of the larger swarms may be 50,000 tons or more!

The majority of Hymenopterous insects—i.e. the bees, wasps and their kindred—are comparatively small, but among the solitary spider-killers we find some notable exceptions, several of which measure more than two inches from head to tail, and withal are exceptionally strong and vigorous, as befits their vocation. Even the formidable bird-eating spiders—grim and hairy monsters with fearsome fangs—are attacked and destroyed. It should be remembered, however, that these wasps do not themselves devour their prey but store it in cunningly contrived caches for the benefit of their offspring, which they will never see. The spider-killing wasps of temperate regions behave in exactly the same manner, but naturally choose prey that is proportionate to their own size and strength. Yet even in these instances the audacity and adroitness of the killers are remarkable, for in almost every case the victim, if weighed, is found to be several times more bulky than its assailant. Other solitary wasps provision their nests with crickets, beetles, flies, caterpillars and so forth, all displaying the utmost prowess and intrepidity in their hunting expeditions.

Probably most insects are stronger and more enduring in proportion to their size than vertebrate animals, but during their adult life many of them are almost continuously active, and this ceaseless, often rapid, movement necessarily imposes a serious tax upon their physique. This doubtless accounts for the fact that the imaginal stage of their lives, unless prolonged by hibernation, is nearly always brief. The aerial life of some may-flies lasts only a few hours; others survive for one or two days, possibly a little longer. It is said that the average worker hive-bee literally wears herself out and dies after a few weeks of toil for the benefit of the community which she serves, first as a nurse, later as a food-gatherer and comb-builder.

Before concluding this chapter something may be said as to the advantages and disadvantages attendant on extremes of size. Minute insects obviously need little food to maintain them and can creep for safety into the tiniest niche or cranny. On the other hand they are very much at the mercy of the elements, perishing quickly by desiccation in a dry air, and liable to be blown hither and thither by all

the winds of heaven. Rain also may wash them out of existence—
although, if you have good eyesight and watch a bevy of gnats in
a heavy shower, you will see that they are seldom, if ever, over-
whelmed, but pushed aside by the cushions of compressed air in
front of the falling drops.

The probable reason why comparatively few insects have attained
truly gigantic proportions is the peculiar way in which they breathe,
namely through openings or spiracles communicating with a system
of tracheal tubes whose final ramifications are microscopic capillaries.
Through these atmospheric air can penetrate only by diffusion, and
this process slows down rapidly as the calibre of the capillaries
becomes finer and their distance from the spiracles increases. Hence,
if an insect were to become much more massive than, say, a Goliath
or an elephant beetle, we should expect it to be virtually incapable
of movement owing to oxygen starvation. This doubtless explains
why large, rapidly flying insects such as dragon-flies have long,
narrow bodies, since by this means all their tissues are kept close to
the surface.

Our bulkiest British insect is the silver-bellied water-beetle, but
a fine male example of the stag-beetle is a close runner-up, and
actually looks larger because of its projecting antlers. Our largest
wasp-like insect is the hornet, whose wing-span may be $2\frac{1}{4}$ ins.; our
largest two-winged fly the great ox gad-fly, of which the like measurement is slightly less.

Chapter Eight

SOME BODILY ODDITIES

SINCE the days when Charles Darwin proclaimed his famous theory of evolution by the agency of natural selection a tendency has manifested itself in many quarters to assume that all mystery has been brushed aside—that we now understand "all about everything". Yet in point of fact we are still faced with numberless problems that have so far baffled all attempts at solution, and this is notably the case where insects are concerned. Some aeons ago, Nature—so to say—conceived the idea of making a few of these jointed, six-legged creatures, and for an inexplicable reason the notion seems to have pleased her. We are entitled to draw this conclusion since she has been busily inventing new kinds of insects from then onward to the present day. What the grand total of her output to date may be is a matter for guessing, but experts estimate that the figure cannot be less than a million, probably a great many more. As we have seen, all the members of this vast array are built up on the same ground-plan, all having when adult neither more nor less than six legs and displaying a close similarity in the broad outlines of their get-up. Yet each distinct kind or species of insect is unlike all the others. Now, in very many instances it is plausible, and probably quite correct, to argue that the peculiarities of a given species of insect are closely related to the manner of life which it lives. For example, some look so much like the leaves or twigs of the plants which they frequent that their enemies pass them by unnoticed. Others figure as living aeroplanes, submarines, bulldozers, excavators and what not—every detail of their structure seemingly designed to promote the one end. But when all has been said that can be said under this heading there remain many insects whose *raison d'être*, from the orthodox scientific standpoint, is inscrutable. They seem to set explanation at defiance—to slap common sense in the face! Surely Nature must have been in jesting mood when she turned these oddities out of her workshop!

Consider, as a typical example, the common crane-fly or "daddy-longlegs", well known to most people by sight. Someone has said that this cannot be the original of the ancient nursery rhyme—the old daddy-longlegs who "would not say his prayers", because any attempt to "take him by the left leg and throw him downstairs" would be futile, since the leg in question would assuredly have come off as soon as seized. Indeed, the lengthy and easily detached legs of the crane-fly are a standing puzzle to naturalists, who so far have failed to account for them on utilitarian principles. As the eminent entomologist Dr. David Sharp said, they break off with great ease, and the insect appears to get on perfectly well without them! On the other hand, the suggestion has been advanced that the ease with which the crane-fly gets rid of its legs enables it to escape if one of them becomes hopelessly entangled among the grass blades, where it spends much of its time. But why long legs at all? Obviously the absence of a disease renders a remedy superfluous. In other words, if this insect had been furnished with short legs entanglement would be unlikely to occur and they need not be sacrificed.

When the bishop in the poem, anxious to ascertain the number of legs possessed by a caterpillar, put the question to the school-mistress, she answered that she considered such things were "not proper for girls". But science has no such blushes, and no excuse need be offered here for calling attention to two other examples of excessive legginess. One of these is the South American harlequin beetle which frequents the forest regions of Brazil and elsewhere, and is said to be extremely fond of the thick, white sap of the Bagasse tree. It is one of the long-horn tribe, and like most of its relatives has remarkably lengthy "feelers" or antennae. But its enormously outstretched fore-legs are its most arresting features. Some say that these assist it when traversing the branches of the trees in which it lives. If so, why in the name of common fairness has Nature failed to grant similar aids to the thousands of other tree-dwelling insects that are found in the same country? To this question science has no answer to give.

Our next oddity—one of the flag-legged bugs from tropical America—claims attention on account of its hind-legs. These are not merely disproportionately lengthy, but the shin of each is expanded and flattened in a manner suggestive of a leaf. These expansions are adorned with gay colours different from those of the body and wing-covers. Indeed, the whole effect is distinctly festive—as if the insect had bedecked itself with a couple of flags in celebration of some occasion of popular rejoicing. But what it signifies, or whether it signifies anything at all, nobody knows.

The antennae of insects are admittedly important sense-organs which combine the functions of fingers, nose, and possibly ears into the bargain. But there are some antennae which no pretext seems to justify. Those of certain long-horn beetles, such as the male timberman, for instance, are four times as long as the creature's body. It is a common insect in Sweden and Lapland and occurs as a rarity in Scotland; yet nothing is known of its habits to suggest a reason for this eccentricity. Again, there is the male of a Mexican cockchafer—a near relation of our British may-bug—whose antennae resemble two monstrous fans with curved slats. They seem hopelessly heavy and out of place—just as if the poor creature had been fobbed off by an unscrupulous outfitter with a pair many times too large.

Even more remarkable and mysterious than any of the foregoing are the so-called "lantern-flies" of the tropics, which have enormous hollow projections carried forward from the head—like a grotesquely outsized nose. These nebs or beaks or whatever else they may most fittingly be called were formerly supposed to be luminous—emitting, it was said, a brilliant phosphorescent radiance at night. In some of the older natural history books you may read graphic descriptions of these living torches and their dazzling refulgence. Yet all this seems to have been based on mere travellers' tales, for modern authorities deny that the lantern-fly is able to live up to its name. Of course there are plenty of real fire-flies, and very beautiful they look when they engage in their mazy dances in the warm darkness of the forest glades; but their kinship is with the beetle-folk, and they are in no way connected with the lantern-flies popularly so named. When all this became known, some ingenious soul suggested that the "beaks" of these latter oddities might be used for leaping—the insect being assumed to press the process against the ground or the branch of a tree and so hurl itself into the air like a skip-jack. But so far as the present writer has been able to discover, no one has ever seen this alleged feat performed.

The stalk-eye flies indigenous to tropical Asia and Africa certainly rank among the oddest of oddities. As their popular name implies, their eyes (also their diminutive antennae) are situated at the ends of two stalks, which stand out one on each side of the head. A somewhat similar device is adopted in the architecture of the snail; only the mollusc's eye-stalks are flexible and retractile, whereas those of the fly are perfectly rigid. In all other respects these insects seem quite normal, and why Nature should have seen fit to equip them with such queerly placed organs of vision is a profound mystery. Likewise, no explanation has been offered as to why the males of

the East Indian stag-horn flies have antlers of various shapes and
lengths springing from the sides of their heads. But in this connexion
it should be said that when a peculiarity of structure is confined to
one sex of a species it is almost certainly related to the business of
courtship and mating, although in what way we may not be able to
conjecture. A good example of extreme "sexual dimorphism" is the
Chilean stag-beetle. The male's sawlike jaws are enormously enlarged, while there is a corresponding elongation of the fore-legs,
which are also armed with teeth. Compared with this formidable-
looking prodigy the female appears insignificant. As is the case with
our British "stags", the males of this species fight when courtship and
mating are in progress, although they seem seldom, if ever, to injure
one another. In some other instances the englarged jaws, antlers,
prongs and so forth sported by male beetles are believed to serve as
weapons when rival suitors meet, or as grasping organs by means
of which the victor may carry off his spouse to a safe honeymoon
retreat ; but in others the extravagant shape of these putative weapons
and implements and the positions which they occupy on the owner's
head and thorax put any such theories out of court.

   Quite a number of insects seem veritable six-legged jokes which
might have walked straight out of Alice's "Wonderland" into every-
day life ! Try how you will you cannot take them seriously ! One of
these laugh-provokers inhabits the Malay Peninsula, Java, Borneo
and Sumatra, where it lives together with its grubs in the interior of
large, hollow fungi attached to decaying tree-trunks. It is perfectly
flat, fiddle-shaped in outline (whence its popular name of "fiddler"),
while its colour and texture exactly resemble the confection known
as "brandy snaps" or "jumbles". Those who doubt the accuracy of
this description may see specimens of the creature preserved in the
Insect Gallery of the British Museum (Natural History). Its scientific
name of *Mormolyce* is appropriate, derived as it is from the Greek
root signifying a hobgoblin.

   For sheer whimsicality of design, the particular family of long-
nosed weevils known to naturalists as Brenthids are probably
unsurpassed. In these aberrations the head and thorax (especially of
the males) are often extraordinarily long and narrow, and the
creature presents a most weird appearance. Dr. David Sharp states
that the males of some species fight, but do not injure their oppo-
nents, only frighten them away, which is not difficult to credit !
Representatives of the family are found in most of the warm regions
of the globe. They are probably all wood-feeders, burrowing into

decaying trees. In many instances the females' appearance differs little from that of a normally constructed weevil of the more slender type.

The unaccountably odd males of two other beetles call for mention here. First, the double-tailed weevil from Java and some of the adjacent islands has not only, like a Brenthid, an immoderately long head and snout, but adds to this a remarkable duplex tail or fork at its posterior extremity. Then we have the giraffe weevil from Madagascar, whose head and thorax are both drawn out, forming together a "neck" not unlike that of its mammalian namesake.

In Northern India, and in the warmer regions of the American continent, there are some gigantic relatives of the fisherman's alder-fly, belonging to the genus *Corydalis*. The males have enormous curved mandibles that project in front of the head like horns. Yet these formidable-looking creatures are perfectly harmless and have never been seen to make use of their overgrown jaws—except as forceps for grasping their mates. The same cannot be said of the Seroot flies, which render some districts of Nubia uninhabitable for three months of the year because of their passion for human blood. In their case it is the females that are exceptionally endowed, each being equipped with an immensely long, piercing proboscis sticking straight out in front of the head—this instrument being used by its owner to puncture the skin of its victims. In this respect they resemble our British gad-flies, to which they are nearly related. But the perplexing question is this : why are the proboscides of these Seroot flies long while those of their near relatives—no less blood-thirsty in their day and generation—are short and seem to serve the required purpose equally well ? No really satisfactory answer to this question is forthcoming—though we are told that these vampires can operate while hovering on the wing, and will pierce the human body even through clothing of considerable thickness. Ironically enough the males are said to suck the juices of flowers !

A catalogue of bodily oddities drawn from the insect world might be extended almost indefinitely, but one more example must suffice to bring this chapter to an end—a very curious flightless insect that we may call the mole-beetle found only in a small area of Brazil. It has no near relations living but is generally supposed to be distantly connected with the Longicorns, although some regard it as the last surviving representative of an ancient and more primitive race. The enormous development of the thoracic region containing the leg-muscles, the powerful digging-legs, the downward-directed, pick-like jaws and the short antennae all fit it for the subterranean life which, in fact, it leads, feeding on roots. Superficially it resembles a mole cricket, and together these insects, differing widely in the details of their structure, are a good illustration of what is called "parallelism" or "convergence": that is to say, both—in the course of their evolution—have been adapted along the same lines to fit them for similar conditions of life.

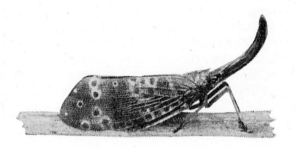

Chapter Nine

INSECTS AS FLYING-MACHINES

FLIGHT in Nature is a vast topic only to be tackled adequately by the professional physiologist with a sound knowledge of aerodynamics to guide him. But it presents certain aspects of interest to which a layman may venture to call attention without trespassing upon the domain of the expert. In the first place it should be noted that Nature's aeroplanes are *living* mechanisms—a fact, too often overlooked, which imposes far-reaching restrictions on the manner of their construction and mode of working.

Apart from jet-propulsion—which, by the way, has been used from time immemorial by various aquatic creatures such as squids or cuttle-fishes and the nymphs of dragon-flies—the motive power in flight is generated by the screw-propeller, which, mechanically considered, combines the principle of the wedge with that of the inclined plane. Anyone who has driven a screw into wood and then withdrawn it has some practical knowledge of how the device works. There is a forward or backward thrust according to the direction in which the shaft with its coiled flange or blade is rotated. Substitute air—or water—for wood and the results are the same though the resistance is less.

Primitive propellers constructed with several complete whorls of the spiral round the shaft were found to require a highly wasteful expenditure of energy for their rotation, and the necessary economy was effected by substituting two or more separate blades for the original "screw". This served admirably for the needs of human invention. But in the realm of animate nature the use of the screw-propeller, as such, is obviously a physical impossibility. How could an organ attached shaft-wise to a living body be caused to revolve without fatally constricting the blood-vessels, nerves and muscles passing through it, and upon which the maintenance of its activity must depend? It would be just as nonsensical to suggest that animals might have been evolved to run on wheels instead of legs! What has actually happened is that the essential operation of the screw-propeller is reproduced by a very complex series of movements on the part of special organs, such as we see exemplified by the tail of a fish or the wings of birds and insects. The fisherman who propels his boat by means of a single oar skilfully manipulated through a notch in the stern has learnt something of the fish's secret, but the flight of birds and insects has so far eluded all attempts at imitation. Moreover, according to Professor J. B. S. Haldane, even if man should succeed in fitting himself out with functional wings he would almost certainly be unable to fly with them : he would be too heavy !

Throughout the long history of animal life upon the earth only four groups—pterodactyls, birds, bats and insects—have developed the capacity for flight. The pterodactyls or "flying lizards" which flourished during the Secondary or Mesozoic Epoch, but long ago became extinct, had wings bat-like in structure. The wings of insects, however, are in no way comparable to those of either bats or birds, which are essentially modified fore-limbs. Membranous outgrowths from the second and third thoracic sub-divisions (the meso- and meta-thorax), they are supported and strengthened by a framework of veins or "nervures", which are often connected by cross-pieces or "veinlets" to form a network. Fossilized remains from the Carbo-niferous Period indicate that some of the earliest winged insects had also wing-like extensions springing from the pro-thorax, as well as similar but smaller ones from the sides of the abdominal segments. These discoveries strongly support the conjecture that the organs which now function as true wings were evolved from more or less rigid expansions originally serving as planes, enabling their owners to glide on a current of air after launching themselves from some point of vantage, such as the branch of a tree. Later, as those on the meso- and meta-thorax developed hinged joints and became capable of controlled muscular movement, the others dwindled and disap-peared. So, at least, runs the theory.

In all insects the wing-muscles are very numerous and com-plicated, but those which actuate the flight-mechanism when the creature is once launched into the air are of two classes. In the first the action is direct, the elevator and depressor muscles being attached to the base of the wing itself, the former just within, the latter just without, the fulcrum—i.e. the point at which the wing hinges upon the thorax. In the second class the action is indirect, the movements of the wings being effected by muscles which are attached at both ends to the exo-skeleton of the thorax, which, being flexible, can be altered in shape by their contraction or expansion. In consequence of the change of curvature thus produced the wing is raised or

lowered. The direct muscles of dragon-flies are those chiefly concerned in flight; in locusts and the majority of their kindred direct and
indirect muscles are about equally developed; but in most other
insects the indirect muscles are the largest in the body, the direct
being relatively feeble.

This is an all too scanty account of a very marvellous mechanism,
many details of which still await elucidation. Indeed, the aerobatics
of some insects literally beggar description, to say nothing of explanation, and are far more astonishing than those of any bird. Certain

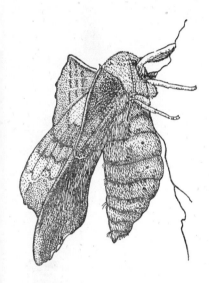

A poplar hawk moth
resting on a tree-trunk
to dry its wings after emerging
from the pupal skin. Note
the small openings—spiracles
or "breathing holes"—on
the abdominal segments

bees, flies and moths often remain poised motionless before flowers,
their wings vibrating so rapidly as to be scarcely visible. Then they
dart swiftly to a neighbouring bloom, which they adroitly plunder
without alighting and a second or two later are off again, repeating
these manœuvres with tireless energy as long as the sun shines. In the
early dusk of a summer evening the big "sphinx" moths behave in
much the same way, as those who have had the good fortune to
watch a convolvulus hawk-moth probing with its long trunk the
gleaming white chalices of the great bindweed can testify. Probably the
most accomplished of all insect aeronauts are the great dragon-flies,
whose long, narrow wings bear some resemblance to the propeller-
blades of a man-made flying-machine and can be moved separately,
while the lengthy abdomen serves both to maintain balance and as a
rudder. These insects not only hover and steer with marvellous

precision, but far outstrip all rivals in the accomplishment of flying backwards.

The rapidity of the wing-beat of different kinds of insects varies greatly and the comparative estimates arrived at by experimentalists have not always tallied. But it is probably a safe approximation to say that the wings of the hive-bee worked at full pressure vibrate at least 250 times per second, those of a hover-fly 190 times, those of the humming-bird hawk-moth 85 times, and those of the large white butterfly only 12 times. The speed at which insects move through the air has proved even more difficult to measure with any approach to complete accuracy, but the following figures may be regarded as sufficiently exact: hive-bee 5·7 miles per hour, hover-fly 7·8, humming-bird hawk-moth 11·1, large white butterfly 5·7. Some years ago wide publicity was given to a statement that the deer bot-fly of North America can achieve a speed of 800 miles per hour; but this is on a par with the assertion that if a flea were as large as man it could jump easily over the dome of St. Paul's Cathedral. Such misleading pronouncements were refuted by Miall and Denny, the nineteenth-century biographers of the cockroach, who showed that for muscles possessing the same physical properties the relative muscular force necessarily decreases very rapidly as the size of the animal increases. This is because the contractile power of the muscles, depending as it does upon the number and thickness of their fibres, increases as the square of their lineal dimensions, whereas the weight of the body, depending on its length, breadth and thickness jointly, increases as the cube. It follows that of two animals equally well equipped with muscles in proportion to their size the smaller will be capable of feats of strength far more spectacular than those which the larger can perform. But in each case capacity will be limited by the contractile force exerted by the muscles themselves, and it is obviously impossible to pack more of these into a body than it can accommodate. Hence, it is farcical to suggest that a creature no bigger than a small humble-bee when on the wing can exceed or even equal the top speed of a bird like the swift, which is estimated to be 70 miles per hour.

Weight is essential for flight, not only in its relation to momentum but also as providing the leverage needed to develop the downward and backward thrust of the wings. Moreover, since the resistance of the air opposed to each element of the surface of the wing increases as the square of the velocity of that organ, a large animal can sustain itself with fewer strokes than would be necessary for one of smaller size. It follows, however, that if of two animals approximately equal in weight one is required to fly more swiftly than the other a considerable reduction in the surface area of its wings must be effected. In other words, for swift and well-controlled flight long and narrow wings exactly proportioned to the weight of the body are indispensable. Compare, for example, the flight of a bee or a hawk-moth with that of a butterfly, and at the same time contrast the area of their respective wings. Furthermore, it is noteworthy that increased efficiency in flight seems to be gained when the wings are reduced to one pair, or to two pairs functioning as a unit. As we have seen, this reduction has been effected most completely in the case of the Diptera or true flies, whose hind-wings are replaced by little stalked knobs called balancers or halteres which appear to serve chiefly as sense organs stabilizing in function. All the other highly specialized four-winged insects have the two wings of each side joined together during flight by a mechanical device. This, in the case of the bees, wasps and their relations, takes the form of a row of minute hooks on the anterior margin of the hind-wing which engage a corresponding fold in the hinder margin of the fore-wing—a particularly neat device recalling our hook-and-eye mode of fastening. Many bugs and their kindred have a sort of clip on the hind-wing which unites during flight with a fold of the fore-wing; while in water-bugs there is a single hook near the back of the fore-wing which fits into an upwardly directed flange on the front edge of the hind-wing. The wings of many moths—but not of butterflies—are held together by a kind of safety-pin arrangement, consisting of a process known as the "frenulum", arising near the base of the hind-wing, which fits under a strap-like "retinaculum" on the underside of the fore-wing. As a rule, the frenulum of the female consists of three separate bristles, but in the male it is usually a long, curved spine.

Some insects, notably dragon-flies, have both pairs of wings nearly alike in size and shape, but frequently the fore-wings are larger, broader, or in some other respect different from the hind-wings. Cockroaches, grasshoppers and crickets, for example, usually have the former thickened or "leathery" in texture, and they serve as covers to protect the latter, which when not in use are folded fanwise beneath them. Fore-wings so modified are known technically as "tegmina" to distinguish them from those of beetles, which are usually hard or horny, and are termed "elytra". In both instances these "covers" or "cases" appear to play some passive part in flight, either by serving as planes or gliders or it may be only to maintain equipoise. Stag beetles and cockchafers, for example, hold their elytra well up when flying, but the great West African Goliath beetles and our own rose-beetle keep them folded above the back, never raising them more than is necessary for the hind-wings to slip out under their outer edges. In the great family of the rove beetles or "cocktails" the elytra are very short, covering less than half the abdomen, the hind-wings being folded both lengthwise and across—as, indeed, is customary with all beetles—before they are packed away beneath. Earwigs also have these short wing-cases; but the structure and folding of their hind-wings are very different. Each consists of a thickened basal portion from which radiate numerous veins or nervures supporting the delicate membranous area. By a fan-like radial closing and two transverse folds the whole structure is packed neatly into small compass and tucked—usually by means of the forceps or nippers—out of harm's way beneath its corresponding cover. Typical bugs have only half of the fore-wings thickened and opaque, the apical area being transparent like the hind-wings, and when not in use the two pairs are folded one above the other and lie flat on the back.

The manner in which an insect closes it wings when it settles to rest is interesting, and often serves as a guide to relationship. The larger dragon-flies, clinging with their legs to the leaves of an over-hanging branch after a hawking cruise, keep their wings spread out horizontally, as if ready for immediate service. This also is the habit of most "carpet" and "pug" moths, although some of them hold the wings in repose more or less upright and pressed together like the pages of a closed book, while may-flies, the majority of butterflies and all the smaller dragon-flies do the same. On the other hand, caddis-flies, alder-flies, stone-flies, lacewings and most of the larger moths slope their wings roof-wise over their backs; but a few moths, mostly the smaller kinds, wrap their wings round their bodies when they come to rest with the edges tucked underneath, so that they look like fallen bud-scales or withered and crumpled leaves.

Little is known at present as to the precise influences which prompt flying insects to engage in migratory journeys, but we may safely infer that one—perhaps the most important—is the impulse to seek for food. We in Britain are happily beyond the range of the hordes of marauding locusts—although in 1869 one species reached our south-eastern counties in some numbers which spread northward and eastward into the midlands; but vast flights of white butterflies periodically cross the English Channel and North Sea to our south and east coasts, whence they spread far inland to raid our cabbage gardens. Certain other butterflies and moths, including several of great rarity, come to us in this way. The red admiral and the painted lady, though rightly regarded as British butterflies, would be quite unable to maintain their footing here without annual replenishment from North Africa *via* the Continent; and probably much the same is true of the famous death's-head moth, which is a powerful flier, and on many occasions has landed on the decks of ships far out at sea. The painted lady butterfly is a great traveller whose range nowadays is well-nigh cosmopolitan, except for South America, where its place is taken by a closely allied species. The largest of all the butterflies to which the epithet "British" can by any stretch of courtesy be applied—the monarch or milkweed—comes to us from America, usually it is said as a stowaway on some ship, but occasionally by its own powers of flight. Its appearance in this country was first recorded in 1876, in which year three specimens were captured, since when, up to the time of the present writing, more than 150 others have been claimed as seen, 62 having been caught. Besides butterflies, moths and locusts, certain other insects are known to engage in regular or occasional migratory flights, the most notable example being the four-spotted darter dragon-fly, swarms of which have sometimes been seen approaching the Kent and Sussex coasts.

All that has been said above concerning strong, well-controlled flight obviously applies only to large and medium-sized insects. The very small ones of all kinds, being completely at the mercy of winds and atmospheric currents, are often carried willy-nilly over long distances or high into the upper air, to be deposited later, perhaps, far from their place of origin. This may mean disaster for the individuals concerned, but in certain circumstances it may assist the geographical distribution of the species. Evidently the old-time gardener who used to predict that the east wind would bring "blight" from the Continent to his roses and vegetables knew what he was talking about. But the most astonishing happening of this sort was recorded some years ago when a large number of spruce aphides and their parasitic hover-fly suddenly turned up in Spitsbergen, eight hundred miles in a straight line from the Kola Peninsula of northern Russia—the nearest part of the mainland where grows the spruce on which the aphid lives and breeds.

All the great Orders of insects include some flightless members, usually the females of the species, examples being the common cockroach and the glow-worm beetle, certain moths, ichneumons and the "neuters" or "workers" of ants. Most external parasites, such as fleas, lice and the spider-flies, are wingless in both sexes; while a few beetles, including the "cellar" or "churchyard" beetle, are without hind-wings although their elytra are well developed, often fused together along the middle line, thus serving as a protective shield over the abdomen.

To account on evolutionary lines for the loss of organs so apparently advantageous as functional wings is far from easy, but in the case of insects spending much of their life in underground nests or among close-growing herbage these organs would be of little use, and might even prove detrimental. The male and female ants, often seen in vast swarms during the summer months, actually discard their wings immediately after pairing. Again, parasites born and bred in close association with their "hosts" can dispense with wings, having no need to travel far afield. Likewise, the flightless females of moths mostly emerge from the pupa either upon or close to the food-plants where they must lay their eggs, and as this usually happens during the winter months, when winds are often boisterous and temperatures low, the absence of wings may well be advantageous rather than the reverse, since the feebly fluttering males are less likely to miss finding their mates.

As a general inference, therefore, we may feel fairly certain that an insect having once acquired wings in the course of its evolutionary history would not lose them unless it had ceased to depend upon flight for food-getting or mating: otherwise it would long ago have been extinguished as a species by natural selection. As a matter of fact, in only one Order—the Aptera—is the wingless condition primitive or original. All other flightless insects appear to have descended from ancestors which once had wings but for some reason or other have subsequently dispensed with them as superfluous.

Chapter Ten

CAMOUFLAGED INSECTS

To SAY that one-half of animate nature flourishes at the expense of the other half is axiomatic. Everywhere, from the tropics to the poles, the working of this law is clearly apparent. The sparrow chases the butterfly, but the sparrow is chased by the hawk. The roach feeds on worms and insects, but the pike is ever ready to make a meal of the roach. In short, the problem of life is two-fold. It is not only necessary to eat ; it is necessary also to avoid being eaten. Yet if organic evolution is to run its appointed course the population of the earth must be maintained : so we see that every creature is equipped with a means of defence calculated to render the attacks of its enemies less frequent or less deadly. One of these—perhaps the most important—is what we term "camouflage" or the "protective resemblance" of the animal to its customary environment ; and of all living things insects are probably better equipped in this respect than any others. The protective resemblance may be either general or special. That is to say, it may result simply from an approximation of the creature's coloration to its normal surroundings when at rest, or from its deceptive likeness to a definite object commonly present in those surroundings.

No better examples of general protective resemblance could be advanced than the very numerous moths and other insects which rest during the hours of daylight on rocks, tree-trunks and similar situations, where, although they are fully exposed to view, they can only be detected by the closest scrutiny. Moths like the red underwing fold their fore-wings—which harmonize with the background —roof-wise over the back ; but most of the "carpets", many of whose wings display a greyish or drab tinting, spread them out horizontally against the surface on which they repose. Certain butterflies settle by preference on the ground, and some of these—e.g. the grayling— have the habit of dropping suddenly after a short flight and leaning over at a sharp angle—a manœuvre which not only displays the concealing coloration to best advantage, but minimizes—or perhaps completely covers—the shadow that might otherwise betray the insect's presence. Other butterflies, including some of our gayest, such as the peacock, have the underside of the wings dark brown or blackish; and these insects habitually hibernate in such places as wood-piles, among the rafters or under the eaves of barns and out-buildings, or in the hollows of tree-trunks. The wings of the green hairstreak butterfly are uniform chrome green on the underside in accordance with the leaves of the bramble-bush that is visited for egg-laying. The well-known orange-tip butterfly when in flight is very conspicuous; but as soon as it settles among herbage it seems to drop out of existence, for the reason that the underside of the hind-wings, between which the fore-wings are folded when they are not in use, is mottled with green and white in a manner suggestive of an in-florescence, such as that of the common garlic-mustard or "Jack-by-the-hedge"—one of this insect's food-plants.

The majority of butterflies rest with the wings folded together over the back, so that the protective or concealing coloration of their undersides is exposed to view. But there are several interesting exceptions to this rule. According to the late L. W. Distant, a com-mon and widely distributed African butterfly (*Hamanumida dedalus*) sits in South Africa with its wings spread out horizontally, showing their brownish-grey upper surfaces which are in harmony with the colours of the rocks in that region; whereas in West Africa it folds its wings over its back after the common habit of butterflies, in which position the tawny tinting of their undersides—in accord with the general tone of the local soil—is displayed. Again, certain forest-frequenting butterflies of South America settle with outspread wings on the trunks of trees in exactly the same attitude adopted by the "carpet" moths. The upper surface of the wings thus exposed exhibits a very complicated bark-like pattern in various shades of grey, diversified by numerous circular spots which resemble holes drilled by wood-boring insects.

Many resting insects simulate patches of lichen or lichened twigs, one striking example being the marvel-du-jour moth; but this type of coloration is of common occurrence and not confined to any one Order. A Malagasy weevil is a veritable walking facsimile of a lichen tuft. The same may be said of the caterpillar of our Brussels-lace moth, only in this instance the likeness is to a twig encrusted with the identical grey-green lichens on which it feeds. The cater-pillar of the related scalloped hazel moth is very variable, usually ashy grey or pale brown when associated with twigs on which no lichen is growing, but irregularly blotched with pale green when this is present. In all such cases it is noticeable that the sharp outline of the insect is blurred by a subtle disposition of dark and light shades ; and this is all-important, because even if the insect matches to perfection the background against which it is seen, a clearly defined profile will inevitably betray its presence.

No hard and fast line can be drawn between general and special resemblance. The likeness of a brimstone butterfly to a sere and yellow leaf of the holly bush in which it is hibernating is due partly to the peculiar tinting of the wings on the underside, partly to their

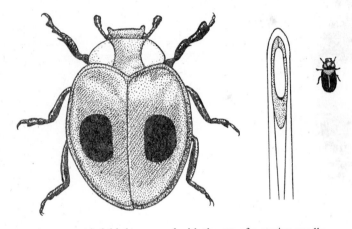

A two-spot ladybird compared with the eye of a sewing-needle and a pigmy beetle—one of the smallest insects known

angular shape. The number of butterflies which, thanks to the shape and coloration of their folded wings, are able to pose as leaves in various stages of decay is legion, but the most spectacular example is the Indian leaf-butterfly. Experienced naturalists tell us that they have often been at a loss to discover the exact whereabouts of one of these insects after having watched it settle on a branch. This marvellous capacity for masquerade is due to a combination of features. The tip of the fore-wing is pointed and the hind-wing terminates in a sort of tail, like a leaf-stalk. On the underside all the wings display shades of buff, brown or tawny, crossed by dark lines simulating the skeletal framework of a leaf, and often with irregular blotches such as might be caused by the growth of moulds. Moreover, at the centre of each fore-wing a small clear spot looks as if a hole had been bitten by a caterpillar.

The most marvellous of all "leaf insects" are members of the

Phasmid family. They occur only in the tropics of the Old World and have a marked penchant for living on islands. The females are much more leaf-like than the males because the tergmina or wing-covers (often absent or reduced to mere scales in other members of the family) are large and foliaceous, although in this sex the hind-wings are absent. In both sexes the body and joints of the legs are remarkably flattened, while the males have functional hind-wings. The green colouring matter which permeates the tissues is said not to differ from chlorophyll or leaf-green when subjected to spectral analysis; which suggests that it may, in fact, be chlorophyll taken into the system with food but left over from digestion. This conjecture seems borne out by the experience of J. J. Lister, who noticed that captive specimens of these insects when short of food "nibbled pieces out of one another, just as they might have done out of leaves . . . but confined their depredations to the leaf-like appendages and expansions", so that no serious injury resulted. On an earlier page we have noted that the eggs of these insects bear a close structural resemblance to the seeds of plants.

With the exception of these "green-leaf insects" Phasmids are almost always more or less stick-like in guise. Unlike their relatives the Mantids, or "praying insects", they are vegetarians, feeding voraciously on the leaves of plants during the hours of darkness, but resting by day when movement might betray them to their numerous enemies—monkeys, birds, lizards and so forth. Some tropical species are a foot or more in length, irrespective of their legs, with bodies jointed or knotted in exact imitation of the bamboos, canes or rank grasses which they frequent. Others, found on thorny bushes and scrub, reproduce the spines and prickles on the surface of their own bodies. Many species are wingless, but when wings are present they fold up so tightly as to be scarcely noticeable when not in use.

One group of Phasmids—attractive, fairy-like creatures for the most part with exquisitely tinted wings—resemble grass blades rather than twigs when at rest. Their bodies, legs and antennae are "as green as grass". The fore-wings are reduced to a pair of scales; but the hind-wings when spread are extensive and gauzy, with a fan-like manner of folding. A narrow strip of the anterior margin is thickened and green in colour, in pleasing contrast with the delicate main area, which is usually bright pink. After a flight the whole of this flimsy portion is packed away under the narrow marginal strip, the folding being so close that a casual observer might fancy that the insect had suddenly become wingless, with the result that it is transformed into the counterpart of a grass-blade, its legs and antennae being too slender to attract notice.

Caterpillars furnish innumerable examples of protective resemblance achieved in many different ways. Some rely solely upon their coloration. Those which feed on grasses or the needle-like foliage of coniferous trees are commonly marked longitudinally with strongly contrasted dark and light striping. No more striking instance of this type could be advanced than that of the pine beauty moth. Then there are the caterpillars of the "puss" and "prominent" moths, a motley crew as to colours, mostly of curious form, and often assuming very singular postures when at rest. These characters in conjunction serve to disguise their owners in the most wonderful ways when they are among their normal surroundings—although if one sees them for the first time as captives in a cardboard box one finds difficulty in crediting this statement. In a box the caterpillar of the pebble prominent seems inexplicably outlandish; but in its natural setting it becomes to all intents and purposes an integral part of the leaf that it is eating with a realistic brown patch representing decay into the bargain. The resting caterpillar of the lobster moth might be mistaken for a dried and crumpled leaf; but when disturbed it poses as a sort of hobgoblin—concerning which habit more must be said on a later page. Specially interesting also is the caterpillar of the puss moth, not only because it, too, in the last stage of its larval life, throws itself into a "terrifying attitude" when alarmed, but likewise on account of the remarkable changes which take place in its appearance after each successive moult. In its infancy it feeds almost exclusively at night, resting by day in full view on the upper surface of a leaf, where—by reason of its dark colour—it resembles a slit or tear, because real holes in the leaves and the gaps between them look black or nearly so when the foliage is seen in a strong light. But if the perforation of the leaf is more than a narrow slit, recently made, the margin is likely to be somewhat curved, highly lighted and probably bordered with brown, or reddish brown, where the tissue is dead or dying; and these changes are faithfully reproduced in the coloration of the caterpillar during its middle life. Then, in its last stage, the now corpulent caterpillar hangs back-downward from a petiole or leaf-edge when it is not engaged in feeding. Its third thoracic segment rises into a Punch-like hump, while the hind-body tapers sharply to a pair of tails, which are normally held in close contact so as to appear as one. The sides and ventral area are a beautiful pea-green, with a broad, white-edged dorsal "saddle" varying in colour from purple to purple-grey or cream. From this description one might suppose that the puss moth's caterpillar when full grown must be a very conspicuous object, but in fact the reverse is the case. When attached to its support at a high angle and seen laterally, as it might be by a passing bird, it resembles two green leaves limned against a background of purplish bark or shadow; but if viewed horizontally the dorsal saddle figures as an accurate copy of the slightly upturned tip of a foreshortened leaf. These imitations are so convincing that persons to whom these caterpillars have been pointed out at a distance of only two feet have failed to distinguish them from the surrounding foliage.

Other caterpillars—for instance, those of the Kentish glory moth —resemble in their shape and colouring the catkins of the trees whose leaves they eat; others, again, look like the blackish flower-spikes of the plantains, or the bennets of grasses. That of the swallow-tail butterfly exemplifies yet another type of coloration, in which we have bright green barred and spotted with black—a combination which, seen against a white or pale background, is glaringly con-spicuous; but among the much-divided foliage of the umbelliferous food-plants it serves admirably as a disguise. It is worth noting that caterpillars coloured after this fashion are not found on trees or herbs of the broad-leaved sort. Those that are usually have lateral rows of light oblique stripes which diverge from the longitudinal axis of the body at the same angle as the veins diverge from the mid-rib in the leaves of the food-plant. The large, vividly green caterpillars of the privet hawk moth have seven such stripes, tinged above with purple, on each side of the body; while the quaint anal spine, or "tail", which characterizes the larvae of this family heightens the leaf-like effect by suggesting a petiole or leaf-stalk. In late summer and early autumn they are common enough on privet and lilac in parks and gardens, yet are seldom seen except by those whose eyes have been trained to detect their presence. Incidentally, these large caterpillars—like those of the puss moth—hang back-downward from a stem or leaf-edge when at rest.

In the great family of the "carpet moths" the majority of the caterpillars—known popularly as "loopers" or "measurers", in recognition of their characteristic manner of progress—are stick-like in guise and habits. Having, for some unexplained reason, dis-carded all but their two hindermost pairs of pro-legs, these creatures move by first grasping a twig or leaf with their six thoracic legs, then bringing the pro-legs forward until they nearly touch the thorax, thus throwing the body into a strong curve or loop as each "step" is taken. Most of them feed at night, and when daylight comes take a firm hold upon a twig with their pro-legs and stretch out at an acute angle. To ease the strain that this posture imposes not a few of them spin a silken thread from the mouth to the stem on which they rest. It was the late Sir E. B. Poulton, when describing some of these "stick caterpillars", who first called attention to a principle in natural coloration, now termed "shadow neutralization", by means of which the protective resemblance of an animal to its immediate environment is greatly heightened. He pointed out that the slight furrow on each side of the caterpillar's body where it is in contact with the branch to which it is holding is commonly filled up by a number of light-coloured fleshy tubercles, the tell-tale shadow which would betray the furrow being thus obliterated. Similarly, he showed that the pupa or chrysalis of the purple emperor butterfly, that simulates the sallow leaves among which it is suspended, looks flat —instead of rotund, as in fact it is—by reason of an elaborate disposition of tiny white dots over its surface—a process which an artist would describe as stippling.

These observations provided an important clue to a better understanding of the conditions that are indispensable for successful disguise; but their significance was not fully realized until the American artist-naturalist Abbott H. Thayer called attention to the fact that the presence of an animal may be betrayed to its enemies by the sharpness of its outline, or by the shadow which it casts, even if its coloration accords perfectly with that of the background against which it is seen. He reminded us that an artist, by shading—i.e. by a painting in of shadow—produces an appearance of relief or solidity on his flat canvas, and made the plausible suggestion that Nature often achieves an exactly opposite effect by simply reversing this method. He constructed a model, replicas of which are nowadays exhibited in most up-to-date museums, in which two dummy ducks are mounted, strongly illuminated from above. Both are covered with the same neutral grey material with which the back and sides of the container is lined. One is otherwise uncoloured, and is rendered very conspicuous by the light falling on its back and the heavy shading of its under-surface—thus proving that mere identity of colour between an animal and its surroundings does not in itself promote protection, but rather the reverse. The other dummy is skilfully painted with a dark tint above graded through increasing

paleness to white beneath, so that an effect of flatness and unreality
is produced. At a distance of four feet it can scarcely be distinguished,
even by those whose sight is faultless.

A recognition of this principle of shadow neutralization—or
"Thayer's law", as it is often called—enables us to explain satisfac-
torily many peculiarities in the coloration of living creatures which
were formerly obscure. Take, for example, the following instances.
The full-grown caterpillar of the brimstone butterfly rests by day
outstretched on the upper surface of the buckthorn leaf that it has
been eating—usually along the midrib, when it is very difficult to
detect. The colouring of its back is almost identical with that of the
leaf, but is much paler beneath, thus compensating for the penumbra
which would reveal its presence. In the case of the similarly green
caterpillar of the orange-tip butterfly the ventral surface is light and
the dorsal dark. Why? Because when not feeding it has the habit of
lying along one of the stiff seed-vessels of its food-plant, in which
position the upper part of the body—thanks to the virtual effacement
of its underside—appears to be part and parcel of the immediate
surroundings. The pupae of both these butterflies are scarcely if at
all less difficult to discover than their larvae. That of the orange-tip
is very extraordinarily shaped, the extremities being remarkably
elongated and pointed, so that it rests against the stem of its food-
plant—where it remains throughout the winter—without causing an
abrupt prominence that might betray its presence.

Many protectively coloured insects, notably caterpillars, habitually adjust themselves in relation to the angle of maximum light
intensity. If, for instance, we take a caterpillar of the poplar hawk
moth at rest on a small branch of its food-plant, the stalk of which
is inserted into a bottle of water, we may place the latter upon a
turntable that can be rotated without disturbing the insect's repose.
Whenever this is done, we shall find that the caterpillar curves or
bends its body, this way or that, as the need may be, so as to bring
itself into a particular relation with the window through which the
strongest light comes. Evidently this complex reaction has become
stereotyped as an "instinct" in the course of the insect's evolution,
so that the colour scheme on which its safety largely depends may
always be presented to the best advantage. In the same way observation in the open strongly suggests that many insects—e.g. moths
whose wings simulate lichen-encrusted bark—instinctively come to
rest whenever possible on an harmonious background. If this is not
so, why are cases of glaring incongruity so rarely seen? Moreover,

the theory that adjustments in a specific colour scheme to harmonize with changes in the environment can only be brought to pass very slowly by natural selection is now obsolete. In this connexion the peppered moth has often been cited, its formerly scarce melanic or "nigger" variety having in living memory all but replaced the black-and-white prototype in the neighbourhood of our large towns and manufacturing centres where the polluted atmosphere has blackened the tree-trunks and killed the lichenous growths which once flourished thereon. Doubtless this has happened because the old camouflage was no longer effective. The pepper-and-salt individuals against the darkened background of the tree-trunks on which they rested, being clearly visible, were picked off and destroyed in large numbers by their bird-enemies, whereas the "niggers", less easy to see, more often escaped detection, and so were left free to perpetuate their kind. The same tendency towards protective melanism has been noticed in many other tree-frequenting insects in districts where smoke and chemical vapours are poured constantly into the air.

In times past no reason could be given for the frequent presence of conspicuous pale-coloured spots or markings—usually centrally placed—on the wings and bodies of insects in other respects adequately concealed. Examples are the white, kidney-shaped patch on each fore-wing of the dot moth and the silvery "C" in the middle of the hind-wing on the underside which gives its name to the comma butterfly. Thayer was able to demonstrate convincingly that all such insignia, far from detracting from the concealing value of the coloration, actually enhance it by tending to efface the creature's contour. The sensitive retina of the observer's eye is so powerfully stimulated by them that it fails to perceive adjacent details reflecting less light. These marks may also imitate a hole illuminated from behind, or the sparkle of a dewdrop.

Two common British moths whose protective resemblance invariably excites astonishment when pointed out to the uninitiated are the lappet and the buff-tip. In repose, the former might easily be mistaken for a few withered and crumpled oak leaves, the illusion being heightened by the unusual manner in which the wings are folded. The buff-tip, on coming to rest, wraps its wings closely round its body, and when seen thus presents the appearance of a small piece snapped off the end of a dry and rotten twig such as may often be seen by the score lying on the ground under trees. Successful concealment is achieved in an almost identical fashion by certain large moths of the Indo-Malayan region. These are related to our

G

wood-leopard moth, whose caterpillars burrow in the stems and branches of trees, and sometimes do much damage in orchards. One from the forests of Assam known as *Duomitus leuconotus* resembles a decayed and mouldy stick so closely that even the cutest bird or monkey could hardly be supposed capable of detecting the deception.

A few insects gain protection by their resemblance to flowers. Reference has already been made to the orange-tip butterflies, which when at rest are difficult to distinguish from clusters or umbels of small white flowers seen against a green background. Several of our common "blue" butterflies have their hind-wings spotted on the underside in a manner which suggests the stamens of plantain-heads or grass-blooms, among which these butterflies commonly settle to roost an hour or so before sundown. The most curious case of flower simulation so far recorded, however, is that vouched for by Professor Gregory and described in his book *The Great Rift Valley*. The insects in question are a species of *Flata*, and although in appearance remarkably like butterflies their true affinity is with the lantern-flies. Moreover, they are dimorphic—some individuals of each sex being bright pink, others bright green, while the larvae are queer-looking objects draped with long filaments of a waxy secretion, like the feathery appendages of air-borne fruits and seeds. Their habit is to sit motionless on the stems of plants, feeding on the sap; and they were observed frequently to group themselves so that the green individuals were uppermost, then the pink, and lowest of all the larvae—in this way imitating the appearance of a flower-spike. Professor Gregory relates that he was completely deceived by the first cluster that he came across, and attempted to gather it, when the mock flowers and buds jumped off in all directions.

Clearly, protectively coloured creatures, if their disguise is to have "survival value", must be able to keep still. Experiments conducted early in the present century by a Russian biologist, Peter Schmidt—at that time Privat Dozent in the University of St. Petersburg—indicate that certain insects pass periodically into a state of self-hypnosis or catalepsy. A common Palaearctic Phaemid or "stick insect" was the subject of these investigations. It feeds only at night and during the hours of daylight rests motionless with extended limbs among the twigs of its food-plant, when its stick-like form and green or brown colouring render it inconspicuous. Schmidt was able to demonstrate that this diurnal tranquillity, until then regarded as normal slumber, is really cataleptic—or "auto-catalep-

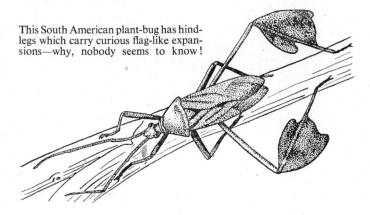

This South American plant-bug has hind-legs which carry curious flag-like expansions—why, nobody seems to know!

tic", as he termed it, since the condition arises from inherent causes', and the insect cannot be hypnotized artificially, as is possible with rabbits, crayfish, etc. The muscles during the period of inactivity were found to be in the state that physiologists term *flexibilitas cerea*, or wax-like flexibility: i.e. they are strained, but not extremely so, and if further stretched remain in the new position. Moreover, the insects show no signs of animation, even when mutilated, and only "come to life" again after sundown. The same wax-like flexibility of the muscles coupled with nervous insensibility is observable in the artificially induced hypnosis of the higher animals, including man.

These investigations seem not to have been followed up—unfortunately, because they afford strong presumptive evidence that insects of other kinds pass on occasion into states of self-induced trance. It may be, for example, that the apparently dormant moth is actually comatose and temporarily incapable of responding to stimuli of any kind. Anyone with the time and patience necessary to pursue this line of inquiry seems likely to make some interesting discoveries.

Experiments initiated by Sir E. B. Poulton and carried on by other observers have shown that many caterpillars are able to adjust their coloration in accordance with that of the immediate environment. Thus, caterpillars reared exclusively among green leaves and shoots remained green from first to last, whereas most of those supplied with dark brown twigs bearing only a few leaves nearly all became brown, although one or two per cent took their cue from the leaves and continued green. Such changes result from the stimulus of reflected light upon nerve-endings in the skin. They take place slowly, and cannot be accomplished more than two or three times during the caterpillar's life; but—as we have seen in the case of the emperor moth—the tint of the silk with which the cocoon is spun may be predetermined in this way. So, also, with the chrysalides of butterflies : they are found to agree more or less closely in colour and markings with the surroundings of the caterpillar when it rests motionless, as is its habit, prior to pupation. The metallic areas displayed by the chrysalides of some Nymphaline butterflies, such as those of the small tortoiseshell, are supposed to harmonize with recently fractured rock-surfaces which present such glittering minerals as mica ; but it seems just as likely that they simulate the gleam of dewdrops or the light reflected from the surface of a newly wetted leaf.

So far as is known, no adult insect has this chameleonic capacity of adapting its colours to a particular environment; nor is this surprising when we remember that in the adult state the integuments are usually hard and lifeless. But, through the agency of natural selection, different races of the same species with habits and a coloration appropriate to the localities which they frequent become established. We have seen, for example, how the *Hamanumida* butterfly rests with outspread wings in South Africa, whereas in West Africa it folds them over its back—matching in each instance the prevailing colour of the soil. This is an example of stereotyped habit. One of stabilized coloration, mentioned by Poulton, is that of a very abundant grasshopper which is invariably reddish brown, like the earth, on Heligoland, but always sand-coloured or green on the flat, sandy Düne, separated by only three-quarters of a mile of sea.

In addition to these obvious adaptations to the surroundings among which they live it is noticeable that certain insects which normally accomplish two or more generations in the course of the year are differently coloured and marked in the successive broods. This phenomenon, known as seasonal dimorphism, may be seen in our own white butterflies, individuals of the spring brood being less heavily marked with black than their descendants of the succeeding summer brood ; while the wet—and dry—season forms of some exotic butterflies differ so surprisingly that they were at one time thought to be distinct species. The significance of these changes is by no means clear, although, according to Poulton, "in northern latitudes the differences between the early and late broods of the same species sometimes correspond to differences in the surroundings, and thus promote concealment. In tropical countries the dry-season forms are often better concealed than those of the wet season, when the struggle for existence is less severe." The causes of seasonal variation are scarcely less obscure, but temperature seems to be important. The application of artificial cold suffices to produce spring forms from summer pupae, while more rarely summer forms are obtained from winter pupae which have been kept in a hot-house. "Yet" (to quote E. B. Ford) "temperature is only one of the agents which may make the environment of an early brood unlike that of a later one, and any or all of them may play a part in the production of seasonal variation."

Chapter Eleven

INSECTS THAT WEAR MASKS

B ESIDES the very numerous insects whose form and coloration "match" and "blend with" their customary environment so perfectly that the eye of the observer often fails to detect the deception, there are others whose disguises do not depend on bodily get-up but are constructed by the creatures themselves, just as an artilleryman piles up turf, brushwood and so forth to hide the location of his battery from the enemy. Many of these "masked insects", as they have been called, make a portable sheath or case which they drag about with them in their wanderings and into which they withdraw for repose or when danger threatens. Much of the material employed is in the nature of silk secreted in a viscid state, but frequently a considerable quantity of foreign matter is incorporated, such as pieces of leaves, grass or heather, or perhaps grains of sand. The tiny caterpillar of the case-making clothes-moth uses minute scraps of the woollen fabric on which it feeds, felting them together very cunningly into a tough little tube, to the ends of which additions are made from time to time as more length is required, while to increase its girth slits and cuts are made in the sides and gussets inserted.

Certain outdoor case-making caterpillars are known as "basket-worms" because the results of their labours resemble more or less closely the basketry of primitive peoples. Unfortunately, we have few of these interesting insects in Britain, and those which we have, being mostly small, are apt to be overlooked. One species, however —known colloquially as the black muslin sweep—which occurs in the New Forest and in certain localities in Dorsetshire, constructs a case that may be as much as two inches in length. The inner, silken tube is covered externally with short pieces of twig or ling, placed longitudinally. The male insect, whose case is smaller than that of the female, develops finally into a reddish-grey moth with a wing-expanse of about an inch and a strong, swift flight. The female, on the contrary, is grub-like and helpless, even when mature. She never leaves her case but is courted there by her mate, and it eventually becomes her tomb—though not before she has laid a large batch of eggs from which the next season's generation of caterpillars hatch out.

We have also in Britain a host of tiny or minute case-making caterpillars which, if they are searched for, may be found during the summer months on a great variety of trees and shrubs. The majority of these belong to a genus called *Coleophora*—literally "sheath-bearers". The newly hatched caterpillar usually feeds for a time as a "miner", burrowing between the upper and lower cuticle of a leaf and battening on the soft inner tissues. Later, it creeps out, constructs its case, and when hungry adopts a very unconventional method of feeding. Standing more or less on its head, it fixes the mouth of its case to a leaf or seed-vessel, bores its way through the layer of epidermal cells and so gains access to the succulent nutriment within. When it has exhausted the possibilities of one opening or shaft it moves slowly away and sinks another, leaving behind a tell-tale pale blotch with a round hole in the middle—"which" (says the authority Edward Mayrick) "distinguishes the mines of this genus from all others".

The adult moths of this interesting group are often extremely similar in appearance and hard to separate as species, but the larval cases are nearly always perfectly distinct and easily identified. In many instances they are covered externally with minute atoms of the food-plant—bits of the leaves, petals, seed-husks and so forth characteristically arranged; but not a few of the caterpillars make their cases entirely of spun silk, adding no foreign matter. The shape and colour of these silken cases vary greatly according to the species. Some are pale, others dark—almost black; some cylindrical, others curiously proportioned. Certain of the most remarkable resemble pistols—the length of the "barrel" being a guide to identification. The longest of these is made by one called in English "Scar large case", whose food-plant is dyer's greenweed or woad-waxen.

The pretty little brown china-mark moth claims special notice because its caterpillar's case serves not only as a protective disguise but also as a sort of diving dress. It feeds on several kinds of aquatic plants, and when young adopts no special precautions to keep itself dry. But later in life it cuts two oval pieces of leaf and deftly joins them with silk to form the case in which it thereafter resides. Through a cleft at one end the caterpillar pokes out its head to feed, but thanks to the architect's skill no inrush of water occurs, since the edges of the cleft are elastic and yield only to pressure from within; so we have the remarkable spectacle of an air-breathing animal constantly submerged and subsisting on water-weeds, yet never wetting the hinder part of its body.

The most noteworthy aquatic case-makers are the numerous species of caddis-worms, of which almost any pond or stream will provide examples. Their cases or sheaths are familiar objects to the keeper of an aquarium, but comparatively few know what the creature inside really looks like, because it objects strongly to vacate its portable house, and all attempts to persuade it to do so by the front door prove futile. But insert gently a fine grass-stem through the rear opening and the owner of the castle shuffles hastily into view. Thus seen the larva is more like a caterpillar than a grub; but its six thoracic legs are very long, and it has no pro-legs on the abdominal segments. A pair of strong hooks at its tail-end fixes it to its case. Noticeable also are tufts of soft white filaments along the sides and back, these being the tracheal gills by means of which oxygen is extracted from the water.

Naked caddis-worms dropped into an aquarium and supplied with building material soon start work on homes for themselves, and if hard pressed will utilize almost any objects of suitable size that may be given them—beads, small pieces of coloured glass, china or metal, to say nothing of scraps of cloth, fragments of paper and vegetable débris. But in normal circumstances each species evinces a characteristic conservatism and builds only with materials that its ancestors have used, following also a time-honoured plan. Thus, while some of the cases are of tiny stones, or of mixed stones and shells of molluscs (sometimes still tenanted by their owners!), others are formed of pieces of leaf or grass, either arranged length-wise or obliquely. Then there are flattish productions made by fixing several largish fragments of leaf together, and others, again, of cylindrical form laboriously constructed of sand grains, with the invariable addition of a trailing bit of twig or reed—this, probably as Réaumur suggested, for the purpose of adjusting the specific gravity of the case to that of the water in which it is immersed. In this way the transportation of the case, already nearly floating, is rendered easy, and the larva clambers nimbly among the stems of plants, and over stones, oblivious to the fact that it is dragging a load which, in the air, would prove all too heavy for its utmost exertion. Those species whose cases are made wholly of heavy materials, such as gravel, never leave the bottom of their stream or pond. Perhaps the most wonderful of all these caddis-worms' cases are those which consist of innumerable sand grains pieced together to form an elegant, curved tube not unlike the elephant's-tusk shell of the sea-shore.

The cement used by caddis-worms for fixing together their building materials is a secretion of the salivary glands indistinguishable in essence from the silk spun by caterpillars and similarly issues in a viscid state from a "spinneret" situated just behind the mouth.

A few kinds of caddis-worm build fixed cases of mud or sand grains, usually on the underside of stones in swiftly flowing streams. In some instances several of these larvae work together to construct a common shelter in which they subsequently cohabit on terms of good-fellowship. But the most distinctive fact relative to these socially inclined caddis-worms is that—unlike their solitary relations—they are largely carnivorous and spin webs in which their prey—aquatic animalcules—become entangled.

A cocoon, by definition, is the envelope constructed in advance by the larva for its protection after it has changed to the pupa ; but cocoon-making and case-making are evidently closely related activities, and when the feeding period is ended the owner of a case generally converts it into a cocoon by closing the openings at each end. In the restrictive sense of the word, cocoons, in their simplest form, may be no more than a delicate silken network such as that woven by the caterpillar of the diamond-back moth, but frequently they are so artfully constructed or tricked out that the living contents is effectually hidden from potential enemies as well as shielded from inclemencies of the weather. The iron-hard fastness of the puss moth has already been described. Another specially interesting cocoon is that of the powdered dagger moth, which in Britain is confined to the marshes of our eastern counties. The caterpillar first draws together the edges of the sedge or reed-mace on which it has been feeding, spins a pure white cocoon in the groove thus formed, and then, with much neatness and skill, roofs in its work with a thatch of leaf fragments cut specially for the purpose. This thatch serves both to carry off excessive moisture and to mask the glaring whiteness of the cocoon, which, during the long winter months, might easily attract birds in search of a snack. The cocoons of the figwort weevils are not less remarkable as instances of successful camouflage, their peculiar effectiveness as protective masks arising from the fact that the fully nourished larva habitually shifts its quarters from the leaves to the immediate neighbourhood of the very numerous seed-vessels just before it prepares for pupation. The cocoon is globular, semi-transparent, and in tint and texture the exact counterpart of the seed-vessels among which it is situated. Incidentally, the perfect weevils are also well protected by their form and colour. In repose, with their legs retracted, they resemble small nodules of soil or the droppings of birds. But the grubs, when still feeding upon the leaves, might be mistaken for little dark-coloured slugs, because they cover their identity under a cloak of slime—a mode of self-protection adopted by other larvae, notably those of the pear saw fly, known to gardeners as "slug-worms", which in some seasons do damage to the foliage in pear and cherry orchards.

Many aphides and scale-insects live concealed under a waxy exudation from the skin. Sometimes, as in the case of the woolly aphid or "American blight", or the felted beech coccus, this congeals to form a white flocculence, and the individual insect separated from its fellows resembles a tiny flake of snow, easily wafted hither and thither by the breeze, and probably often carried in this way from one situation to another. In other instances the substance hardens into a shell, which may counterfeit in miniature that of a mollusc, examples being the mussel scale and the oyster scale, both of which occur commonly as "pests" on the bark of the apple and other trees. Other species—i.e. the cottony cushion scales—in addition to their brown shells secrete such vast quantities of white woolly material that their colonies in the hedgerow or on currant bushes in the garden are not likely to be overlooked. Lac insects exude a resinous liquid so copiously that when it hardens it completely covers the insects and the twigs upon which they are living under a thick, impervious crust. This, the lac of commerce, is largely used in the manufacture of varnish and sealing-wax, as well as in the making of gramophone records, and in India and elsewhere its cultivation has grown to be a native industry of considerable importance.

The masking methods employed by some insects' larvae are fantastic, almost beyond belief. The so-called "aphid-lion", the juvenile form of a lacewing, feeds—as its name suggests—chiefly on plant-lice or green-fly, and as each victim is sucked dry its empty skin is hoisted up and lodged among the stiff hairs of the slayer's back—the load of tiny pelts eventually serving as a complete disguise calculated to disconcert a would-be assailant. The immature frog-hopper, popularly known as the "cuckoo-spit insect", is housed in one of those blobs of frothy moisture which are familiar objects in hedgerow and garden during the early summer. The tiny pale green insect hidden in each sucks the sap of the plant upon which it finds itself, and the old theory was that the froth was simply a discharge of surplus moisture. But analysis has shown that it is a mixture of sugary sap, wax and a little digestive ferment whipped up with air into a kind of soap-suds by means of a sort of bellows contrivance on the under-surface of the creature's abdomen. In this way, to quote Sir J. Arthur Thomson, the frog-hopper's larva contrives to "live under water and yet in the air, conspicuous and yet concealed, in the sunshine and yet cool". Then there is the larva of the "masked bug", which tricks itself out with particles of dust until it resembles the accumulations of fluff in neglected corners of rooms —where, in fact, these oddities usually reside. Such habits fail to correspond with our ideas of hygiene; but since the insect in question is a reputed foe of the detestable bed-bug we need not be too critical of its eccentricities.

Mention must also be made of certain larvae which habitually mask themselves with filth. Typical are those of the tortoise beetles that retain their ordure as a shelter, held in place by a forward-inclined, two-prong fork. The incredulous may find these curiosities upon thistles—their food-plants—during the summer and early autumn.

Of all masked insects, however, the most astonishing belong to a family whose members, being closely related to the frog-hoppers, have been styled "devil-hoppers" by some writers and "nightmare insects" by others because of their unearthly appearance. Only two species occur in Britain, but many hundreds inhabit the warmer regions of the globe, more than half of this number being natives of South America. Mostly insignificant in size—the largest scarcely exceeding half an inch in length—their peculiarity is due to a very abnormal development of the pronotum—the dorsal area of the first thoracic section—which may extend as a sort of bonnet completely covering the rest of the body, or rise high above the back in a fantastic display of knobs and spikes. Often the significance of this extraordinary outgrowth—assuming that its has one—completely baffles conjecture; but in certain instances it obvious mimetic likeness is calculated to stand its owner in good stead as a protective disguise. This is clearly the case with species which not only mimic a leaf-cutter ant but also the piece of leaf which the ant carries! Also, the effectiveness of the disguise of the Brazilian "thorn bug" speaks for itself, as does that of the numerous kinds which resemble fruits, seeds, bud-scales, and suchlike items of their normal environment. Then there are those that mimic insects which bite, sting or are objectionable on account of their unpleasant taste, while a few

of the most outlandish might be mistaken for two or more antagon-
ists in deadly combat—a spectacle which might well be supposed to
warn off intruders. The point to bear in mind is that all these curiosities, being palatable and defenceless, are liable to hostile attack;
and we may feel fairly certain the race would have suffered extermination long ago but for the "survival value" which they enjoy in
virtue of their misleading or awe-inspiring masks—hollow shams, to
be sure, but none the less effective safeguards.

Chapter Twelve

PIOUS FRAUDS OF THE INSECT WORLD

THE common European praying mantis, which ranges northward as far as central France, occurs in two distinct forms or
varieties, one green, the other brown, and whereas the former commonly frequents verdant foliage, the latter is habitually associated
with withered and decaying leaves, so that in each case the insect
corresponds with its surroundings and is difficult to detect. When
the Italian naturalist Cesnola reversed the natural order by tethering
green mantids on brown foliage and brown on green he found that
the death-rate immediately rose steeply—proving the "survival
value" of camouflage in the never-ending struggle for existence
among living creatures great and small. But mantids, with the
possible exception of dragon-flies, are the most ravenously predacious of all insects, devouring enormous numbers of unwary
butterflies, bluebottles and the like, which they catch and hold with
their fore-limbs. Furthermore, in common with most carnivores,
they are physically incapable of long-continued abstinence and soon
perish if unable to obtain constant supplies of nourishment. Hence,
and although a percentage of Cesnola's captives were probably discovered and destroyed by birds, lizards and other enemies, we may
fairly assume that many—probably the majority—died of starvation; since, being forcibly retained against an inappropriate background, they would be as plainly visible to their potential prey as
to their foes.

Mantids form collectively a large family represented in all the
warmer regions of the earth. The majority are cryptically coloured
—to use the technical term, many being green or brown, while the
tinting of others accords with lichen-encrusted twigs or bark. There
are also numerous leaf-like mantids, the shape and coloration of
whose tergmina or wing-covers, as also of certain outgrowths from
the thorax, give them a deceptive resemblance to foliage. In general,
they are sluggish in their movements, as if aware that their interests
will be better served by tranquillity than effort. They usually sit
motionless in the sunshine, barely distinguishable among their surroundings—and wait. At most their activities consist in a stealthy

stalking until they come within striking distance of their victims. The first pair of legs is useless for walking, but wonderfully modified to serve as prehensile organs—somewhat similar in principle to the clap-nets employed by sparrow-catchers—in the use of which the owner is extremely adroit, not only seizing insects resting on near-by leaves, but even capturing them while still on the wing. The rows of sharp spines with which the modified femur and tibia are armed make escape impossible for the prey, once it had been grasped. When not in use these fearsome limbs are held erect in a posture suggestive of piety and devotion—hence the English popular name of "praying mantis". The American equivalent of "rear-horse", while sufficiently descriptive, is less ambiguous.

The above remarks are based mainly on personal observations of imported specimens of the European mantis, which, if housed in a roomy cage and adequately fed, can be kept alive and healthy in our climate during the summer months. Those who have enjoyed the opportunity to study mantids in their native haunts, more especially in tropical countries, tell us that some species attract or allure their prey by their resemblance to flowers. The bright colours which promote this likeness may be restricted to certain areas of the body or suffused over its whole surface; and when these mantids assume their characteristic attitude of expectation among vegetation the deception is often so perfect that nectar-seeking insects fly to them as readily as they do to real flowers, thereby sealing their own doom.

Among the earliest of these "flower simulators" to be described was the so-called rose-leaf mantis of southern India, a species which had been known to naturalists for upwards of three centuries, but whose astonishing habits and manner of life remained obscure, until the following particulars, embodying first-hand information supplied by the late Dr. J. Anderson, were published in the *Proceedings* of the Asiatic Society. "On looking at the insects from above they do not exhibit any very striking features beyond the leaf-like expansions of the prothorax and the foliaceous appendages of the limbs, both of which, like the upper surface of the insect, are coloured green, but on turning to the under-surface the aspect is entirely different. The leaf-like expansion of the prothorax, instead of being green, is a clear, pale lavender-violet, with a faint pink bloom along the edges, so that this portion has the exact appearance of the corolla of a plant, a floral simulation which is perfected by the presence of a dark, blackish-brown dot in the centre, over the prothorax, and

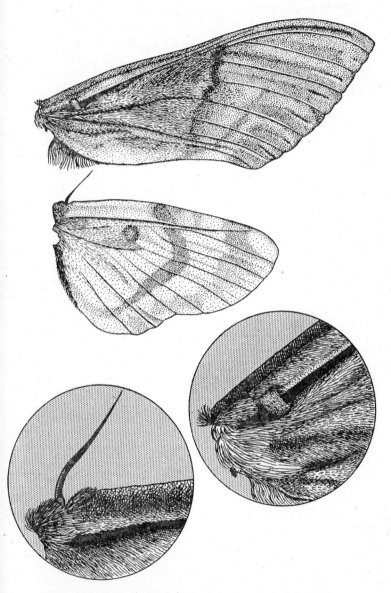

The wings of the death's-head hawk moth, seen from beneath,
showing the "safety-pin" attachment of the hind-wing to the fore-wing.
Magnified pictures of the frenulum and retinaculum are below

which mimics the opening of the tube of a corolla. A favourite position of the insect is to hang head downwards among a mass of green foliage and, when it does this, it generally remains motionless, but, at intervals, evinces a swaying movement as of a flower touched by a gentle breeze; and while in this attitude, with its fore-limbs banded violet and black, and drawn up in front of the centre of the corolla, the simulation of a papilionaceous flower is complete. The object of the bright colouring of the under-surface of the prothorax is evident, its purpose being to act as a decoy to insects, which, mistaking it for a corolla, fly directly into the expectant, sabre-like arms of the simulator."

Dr. A. R. Wallace, Darwin's distinguished contemporary and fellow-worker, mentioned a Malayan mantis called by the natives "kanchong", which "exactly resembles a pink orchis-flower" and allures and devours butterflies. Detailed information concerning its habits have been given by Nelson Annandale, who states that it usually ensconces itself at the centre of a flower-cluster of the so-called Straits rhododendron (*Melastoma polyanthus*). The thorax is held upright with the predatory legs in the erect attitude customary in the family; but the other two pairs of legs—parts of which are remarkably flattened, so that they resemble petals—are symmetrically disposed round the axis of the body, while the abdomen is turned upwards and forwards, as if in imitation of a floral hood. The tinting and texture of this insect so closely resembled the blossoms among which it posed that it was impossible to "tell exactly where the animal tissue commenced and where the flower ended".

In the above instance the form and coloration of the whole insect combine to produce the flower-like appearance. But in the case of the Indian rose-leaf species previously described only a small part of the body—the prothorax—contributes to this end; and this applies also to a mantis, called the diabolical spectre, from Mozambique—another of these pious frauds that, judged by human standdards, get their living by methods scarcely less depraved than downright parasitism. When the creature poses, the underside of its thorax combines with the flattened parts of the fore-limbs to produce a flower-like effect, the coloration being a broad band of violet across a pale or whitish ground. The rest of the body, including the wing-covers and legs, is greenish or brownish, in harmony with the foliage by which it is partly hidden when the insect lies in wait for a meal.

Other naturalists in the course of their travels have come across remarkable mantids which they claim to be flower-like in appearance when lying in wait for prey; but precise information as to their habits is lacking. In the region of the Pilcomayo River where Paraguay and Argentina join there are tree-frequenting species which resemble tufts of lichen so exactly that they can only be detected when they move. Members of yet another genus counterfeit the droppings of large birds, and by this means—so it is said—attract filth-loving flies to their destruction. H. W. Bates, well known for his record of journeyings in the Amazon basin, brought home from Para a mantis so like a phasmid or stick-insect that only an expert entomologist could tell the difference. It was found in company with true stick-insects, on which—in Bates's opinion—it probably fed. Assuming this surmise to be correct, we have a particularly interesting example of what has been called "aggressive mimicry"—the trick of assuming a friendly guise the better to perpetrate enemy action.

Adult mantids seem possessed by a veritable mania for slaughter. With their terrible fore-limbs, which are hinged and spiked in such a manner as to combine the flail and the shark's-teeth sword of the Pacific Islanders, they clutch and hold their victims. Quite often only a portion of the catch is consumed, the rest being cast aside; for mantids are not only voracious but wasteful. Moreover, the species whose habits have been studied closely are inveterate cannibals, and it is said that no two individuals ever come face to face without fighting; nor is the contest a mere display of skill, but a duel to the death. Sooner or later one of the combatants gains a momentary advantage and seizes its opponent, of which it begins at once to make a meal. These affairs are by no means confined to the members of one sex, for the female often tires of her accepted suitor; and when this happens she rushes upon him with menace. The male attempts to defend himself, but as he is smaller and less robust than his spouse, the contest is unequal, and he is generally defeated. Then the female proceeds calmly to make a meal of her quondam mate.

That implements of prey so highly specialized as the mantis's fore-legs should have been duplicated in insects of a widely distinct family is an interesting example of what has been called parallel evolution or convergence—meaning the acquirement by unrelated creatures of similar organs as a result of similar modes of life. So close is the likeness that the mantis-flies were actually classified with the true mantids by the earlier systematic entomologists. Yet in point of fact they are members of the Order Neuroptera and have a

H

close affinity with the snake-flies and lacewings. In particular, all four wings are nearly equal in size and shape and are traversed by a complex network of veins. We have no British species but several occur in southern Europe and many more in the warmer regions of the earth. They are all dull-coloured and rather small insects, the largest having a wing-expanse of slightly more than two inches. The adults frequent herbage and the lower branches of trees, where they stalk the small fry on which they feed. In most cases information is still to seek concerning the youthful stages of the metamorphosis. But the complete life-history of one species has been observed, and in this instance the young larva tears a hole in the egg-cocoon of a spider and nourishes itself on the contents.

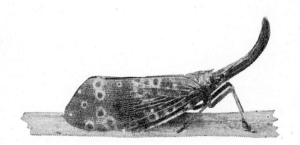

Chapter Thirteen

DEFENCE AND DEFIANCE

THIS chapter is to deal with the more obvious ways in which insects—apart from a deceptive likeness to their surroundings —evade, hoodwink or do battle with their enemies. Many adult insects, and some youngsters, avoid threatened danger by running or jumping out of harm's way. The remarkable leaping powers of grasshoppers, fleas and certain beetles are accounted for by the great size and muscular development of the hind-legs, but the precise means by which the frog-hopper achieves its no less spectacular bounds are less easy to explain. A skip-jack or click-beetle is equipped with a peculiar apparatus consisting of a spine-like projection from the underside of the thorax which fits into a corresponding cavity, enabling the creature when it falls on its back not only to right itself, but also to jump to a distance of several inches from its starting point. In the case of the tiny springtails of the Order Aptera, the leaping mechanism takes the form of a two-pronged fork which when not in use folds under the hind-body and is held by a retaining catch. Certain larvae also display considerable agility when alarmed, a specially intriguing instance being that of the little cheese-fly— known popularly as the "cheese-hopper"—which by gripping its tail-end with its mouth-hooks and then suddenly letting go jerks itself into the air.

Less active insects, and those of sedentary habits, often escape destruction by quiescent means, such as the trick known as "playing possum" or "feigning death", the effectiveness of which is more often than not enhanced by a protective resemblance to adjacent objects. Both these attributes are exemplified by the all-too-common clay-coloured weevil, which gnaws the tender shoots and developing flower-buds of our raspberries, frequently to the serious detriment of the fruit crop. When alarmed, it instantly draws in its legs and antennae and allows itself to fall to the ground, where it exactly counterfeits a nodule of soil. Even more remarkable in this respect are the pill beetles, of which there are three British species. At the first hint of danger the head is retracted into the thorax, against the side of which the antennae are closely folded, and at the same time the joints of the legs are doubled back on one another so that each limb can be fitted snugly into a groove on the underside of the body. As a result, the beetle becomes to all appearances a small, round stone which when handled or rolled about betrays not the smallest sign of life.

Certain other insects, when exposed to hostile attack, assume a menacing or repellent attitude. The devil's coach-horse curves its abdomen scorpion-wise over its back, simultaneously exuding a fœtid substance from glands in its tail-end; nor is this exhibition wholly make-believe, for it will attack savagely with its jaws if given the chance. The common earwig brandishes its forceps in much the same manner, holding the tips wide apart, ready to nip any object, alive or dead, that they may encounter. Similarly, the male stag beetle adopts a threatening attitude if molested, holding its over-grown mandibles wide apart, although the bite which they can in-flict is feeble by comparison with that of its mate, whose much smaller jaws are far more powerful. In this connexion, however, it should be said that many of the organs of insects which look most like weapons are least deserving of the name, or at most are used for purposes of defence and offence only against rival suitors at the period of courtship and mating.

Some insects when startled confront the assailant with a show of bluff, assuming what has been described as a "terrifying attitude". An example is the strangely shaped caterpillar of the lobster moth, which, as we have seen, convincingly imitates when at rest a withered and crumpled leaf. But in addition it has an active means of defence at its disposal; for should it be disturbed by a rustling of the foliage in its immediate neighbourhood, it promptly rearranges itself in a guise suggestive of something highly objectionable and forbidding, the while its abnormally lengthened thoracid legs are waved in a threatening manner, as if to warn off intruders. When posing thus it has been likened to a hobgoblin spider, and experiments have shown that the sudden transformation is very disconcerting to birds and other insectivorous creatures, which evince signs of disgust or alarm at the sight. Probably this caterpillar's spider-like appearance acts also as a safeguard by warding off the attacks of its most in-sidious enemies, the ichneumons and parasitic flies, when bent on egg-laying.

In the final stage of its development the caterpillar of the puss moth defends itself against the assaults of ichneumons by squirting an intensely acid fluid from a special gland situated just below the mouth, the while it lashes out with a pair of pink, whip-like filaments extruded from its twin tails. Moreover, to the slightest stimulus— such as a light touch with a grass-blade, or a puff of the breath—it responds by drawing back its head into the first body ring so that the semblance of a grotesque face is produced, two intensely black, white-rimmed spots suggesting eyes.

Such eye-like marks probably enable their possessors to trade on

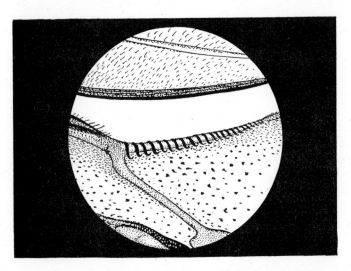

Row of hooks on the margin of a humble-bee's hind-wing.
In flight they engage a fold on the hind-margin of the fore-wing,
so that both wings move in unison

the evil reputation of noxious creatures, such as snakes and lizards. A South American caterpillar mentioned by H. W. Bates startled everyone to whom it was shown because it resembled a dangerous reptile; while there can be no doubt that those of our native elephant hawk moths gain protection in like manner. When quietly resting among the leaves of their food-plants they are concealed by their brown—more rarely green—colouring; but if alarmed by a rustling of the surrounding herbage, the head and the three following segments are suddenly withdrawn into those behind. As a result of this telescoping the front part of the body swells out, looking like the head of some animal, with four enormous, awe-inspiring eyes. This description applies to the caterpillar of the larger species. In the case of the smaller the posterior pair of eye-spots, though present, are not very conspicuous, so that the caterpillar in its terrifying attitude appears to have only two eyes. Birds in captivity exhibit signs of alarm when shown these caterpillars, and will not venture to approach their favourite seed among which one of them has been placed.

Monstrous eye-spots occur on the thoraces of certain Central American beetles. Since they are portrayed upon the insect's hard integument they cannot be altered in shape or rendered more obvious by any contortions of the body. Yet their power to inspire awe is greatly enhanced when the owner, after the manner of "skip-jacks" the world over, first hurls itself through the air and then lies doggo for an indefinite period. For when discovered by a hungry bird these beetles not only jerk themselves out of immediate danger but also prepare a surprise for the enemy in the event of pursuit and discovery. With their legs and antennae tucked snugly out of sight they look like outlandish reptiles, presumably poisonous; and the hungry but now thoroughly disconcerted bird turns away in search of a more inviting meal.

Among insect bogies none is quainter than the so-called alligator bug of tropical America. It has a huge hollow projection from the front of its head; and this, when seen from the side, looks like a miniature alligator's snout—eye, nostril and a formidable row of teeth all being pictured, together with a dark line to represent slightly opened jaws! As Dr. Julian Huxley says, "A bird or a little monkey picking over the foliage and coming suddenly upon what looks like a grinning and repulsive reptilian head would scarcely be encouraged to continue its explorations."

The significance of eye-spots on the wings of butterflies and moths has been much debated. Outstanding examples are those on the underside of the fore-wings of the South American "owl butterflies". They are especially conspicuous when the insect is at rest, seeming to stare at the observer, and are calculated to scare away inquisitive birds and reptiles.

August Weismann, a staunch supporter of Charles Darwin's teaching, believed that they do, in fact, benefit their owners in this way, and instances in particular the eyed hawk moth, which rests with wings folded in leaf-like fashion, but when alarmed spreads and elevates them so that the eye-spots on the hind-wings are exposed to view, conveying to the beholder the impression of "the head of a much larger animal". A similar explanation has been advanced to account for the eye-spots of the emperor moth, particularly those in the middle of the fore-wings, which—in conjunction with the pendulous and pointed abdomen, supposed to figure as the beak of an imaginary bird of prey—present an apparition likely to discourage closer investigation during the critical period following emergence from the cocoon, when the wings, though fully expanded, are still too limp for flight.

As for the small eye-spots often so numerously depicted on the wings of our dull-coloured "browns" and "ringlets", these may, by simulating dew- or rain-drops, enhance the protective disguise of these butterflies when, as so often happens, they settle among dead leaves or decaying vegetation at or near the ground level.

Darwin himself put forward the plausible conjecture that, in certain instances, eye-spots and similar conspicuous markings may stand their owners in good stead by serving as foci or "bull's-eyes" likely to attract assailants as points at which to strike; for if a bird chasing a butterfly or moth were to pierce one of its eye-spots, or even tear a piece out of the wing, little damage would be done and the insect would gain time to evade its pursuer; whereas its fate would almost certainly be sealed if the bird struck at and mutilated any part of the body. "A lizard" (writes Dr. E. B. Ford) "has been observed to pick out the 'eye-spot' of a small heath which had just settled. The insect escaped, since butterflies can fly with surprisingly large areas of the wings missing. The grayling combines this type of marking with concealing colours in a very successful way. On settling, it at first displays the eye-spot on the fore-wings so that any predator which has observed it come to rest may attack it in a non-vital part. Having allowed time for such an event, it assumes, with remarkable accuracy, the appearance of the soil, or of the bark of a tree, by covering the eye-spot with the hind-wings and leaning over at a sharp angle so as to reduce its shadow: it then becomes practically invisible."

The wings of many butterflies and moths besides those mentioned above carry eye-spots, in some instances small and oft-repeated, in others large, solitary and staring. Perhaps the most curious variety is that which has the centre perfectly transparent—looking just as if a small piece of glass or talc had been let into the wing. This is seen, for example, in the tusser moth of India, whose caterpillars produce a strong, coarse silk of commercial importance. Some South American butterflies have completely transparent wings —save for the supporting veins and conspicuous eye-spots—so that the leaves and twigs among which they settle can be clearly seen

through them. This may help them to escape discovery by their
enemies; but the strange "80" and "88" designs on the under-wings
of other South American butterflies have so far baffled all attempts
at explanation. They may be purely decorative, for when concealment is not imperative Nature is often lavish in her embellishments;
but it is always possible that such apparently unimportant features
fulfil some useful purpose which one of these days may be found
out.

In the opinion of A. H. Thayer the disproportionately large
wings of butterflies, though at first sight disadvantageous, have in
reality a life-saving value. Weight for weight a medium-sized butterfly has about twenty times the wing-expanse of a bee, and in consequence its flight is jerky, tortuous and relatively slow. Yet if
chased in the air by a bird it stands the better chance of making
good its escape because its body bobs up and down between the
wings in a disconcerting way, and is moved forward in an erratic,
zigzag course that nine times out of ten completely baffles its pursuer.

"Swallow-tails" is the name bestowed by popular fancy on a
group of butterflies represented in all the warmer regions of the
globe; and although many of the species have rounded wings con-
forming to the more ordinary butterfly type, the "tailed" kinds are
sufficiently numerous to confer a marked character on the family.
These appendages vary greatly both in shape and in length, and we
do not know how they originated or what function, if any, they may
have served in the remote past. But today Papilios are by no means
the only butterflies which sport them, while they occur also in several
families of moths and among certain relatives of the lacewings,
classed as *Nemopteridae*, in some of which the hind-wing is so long
and narrow that it can be aptly described as "all tail". Not infrequently the tips of the tails are dilated and rumpled, so that when
trailing behind in flight they waggle in a way likely to attract attention. Often the colouring is quite different from and more conspicuous than that of the wing in general; and in all likelihood
they benefit their possessors, just as do eye-spots, by diverting the
attacks of pursuing birds from more vulnerable parts of the body.
Moreover, after a number of futile snaps, all aimed at the eye-spots
or tails, the assailant might abandon the chase in disgust.

The extreme hardness of certain insects no doubt stands them
in good stead if they are pecked at by birds. There are some weevils,
for example, whose armour can only be cracked by a sharp blow
with a hammer. Other insects, notably caterpillars, are protected

by a formidable array of spines or prickles, or by stiff stinging-hairs, planned somewhat on the lines of those of the nettle. Filled with poison and very brittle, they fracture when touched so that the broken ends penetrate delicate skins, causing intense irritation, or even a painful rash. It is said that these stinging-hairs defend their possessors from almost all birds except cuckoos, which seem able to swallow them with impunity—just as donkeys and camels can thrive on thorny scrub.

The poison-injecting sting, the most formidable of all the weapons of insects, occurs only among the bees, wasps and ants, and is most perfectly developed in the more highly evolved members of these families. As we have seen, it is confined to the female sex, being a modification of the ovipositor, which—once a channel for the effusion of fresh life—has been transformed into an instrument of death. Its structure varies considerably in different species, but if we examine that of a wasp an understanding of its make-up and working may be gained. First the whole apparatus must be carefully teased out with the point of a needle and transferred to a glass slip. This done, we shall see with a lens that our trophy consists of (1) the poison reservoir or bag, and (2) a muscular mass from which protrudes the sting proper, flanked by its two palpi or "feelers". The muscles, together with six hardened plates which they enwrap and to which they are attached at various points, supply the force and leverage operating the whole mechanism; but their movements are far too complicated to be described in detail here.

The actual sting, which can be protruded from or withdrawn into the apical part of the abdomen as occasion dictates, consists of a pointed sheath or "director" within which slide two barbed darts or "needles". The first thrust is administered by the director, whose function is to open a wound. The needles then strike alternately with a rapid, plunging movement, and thus drive deeper into the flesh beyond the director's tip. Meanwhile poison is forced between them by muscular contractions of the bag in which it is stored. If time permits the palpi are used to ascertain the most vulnerable point of attack; but when alarmed the wasp dispenses with this preliminary and stabs at random. In the case of wasps and bees two glands, the secretion of one acid and of the other alkaline, supply the poison, for although the injected liquid is acid in reaction an alkaline admixture appears to be necessary to render it lethal. The alkaline glands of digger-wasps and the like which need only to paralyse their prey are functionless or abortive. Also, in these insects and most other stinging Hymenoptera the needles are much less strongly barbed than in the worker hive-bee, and so can be readily withdrawn after use; whereas the bee commonly leaves her weapon sticking in the wound, and thus suffers a fatal rupture. She is usually too much agitated to perform the slow spiral move-ment—similar to withdrawing a corkscrew from a cork—by which the barbs can be released.

A few of the smaller British ants have stings, but the large ones of our fir woods have not, although their poison glands secrete a considerable quantity of formic acid which can be squirted from the tip of the abdomen to a distance of ten or twelve inches. As may be imagined, when a nest is disturbed and thousands of the inmates rush out in defence, the atmosphere for yards around is redolent of the pungent fumes. Moreover the individual ants viciously bite any foes with which they may come into contact and eject the acid into the wounds.

Many insects discharge evil-smelling or poisonous secretions from their bodies when touched or annoyed. An example is the common bloody-nose beetle, which on the slightest provocation ejects a large drop of red, acrid fluid from its mouth. The bombardier beetle is preyed upon by larger members of its own family, and when chased squirts from its tail-end a small quantity of very vola-tile liquid that instantly vaporizes, forming a tiny cloud of "poison gas" which discomforts the pursuer and gives the quarry a chance to dart into safety under a stone. The caterpillars of swallow-tail butterflies are equipped with a retractile Y-shaped process behind the head, which is shot rapidly out when the owner is alarmed and diffuses a strong, acrid odour.

A very frequent protective device among insects is a repellent smell or taste, due, it may be, to the secretion of glands situated on different parts of the body, or to the composition of the blood itself. The metallic green beetle known as the Spanish fly provides phar-macy with the potent blistering agent cantharidine, which is said to be an almost perfect safeguard against the attacks of birds, reptiles, etc., on account of its extremely caustic properties. Ladybirds and many other beetles, a number of bugs, moths, butterflies and their caterpillars all derive benefit from their disagreeable odour or—if seized—unpalatableness; and it is noteworthy that the majority of these insects, in common with those which possess poison-injecting stings, are coloured conspicuously and are at no pains to hide them-selves as do those whose safety depends upon a protective resemblance to their surroundings. For example, the caterpillars of our large white butterfly are conspicuously marked with numerous black spots on a pale greenish or yellowish ground colour and rest on the upper surface of cabbage leaves, where they are plainly visible to birds, but are not molested because of their offensive smell. By contrast, those of the small white, lacking this first line of defence, are green like the leaves under which they lurk, when they do not bore into the heart of the plant. In the next chapter we shall find occasion to refer again to this topic of "warning coloration".

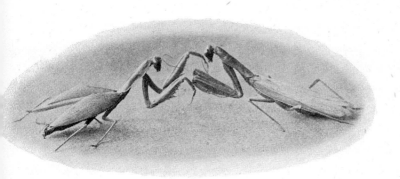

Chapter Fourteen

WHAT MIMICRY MEANS

EVEN careful writers on natural history matters occasionally
state that such-and-such an animal "mimics" a leaf, a twig or
a tuft of lichen. What is really meant, of course, is that the creature
in question bears a "protective resemblance" to the object named,
thereby eluding the prying eyes of its enemies. Strictly defined, the
scientific conception of mimicry is based on the antecedent theory
of "warning coloration" advanced by Darwin's distinguished contemporary Alfred Russell Wallace to account for the conspicuous-
ness of certain creatures in their natural surroundings, by contrast
with those others whose appearance is indeterminate—or "cryptic",
to use the word favoured by the late Sir E. B. Poulton. Very many
insects, as we saw in the last chapter, seem to court attention. Clearly
they are not coloured to be hidden but rather that they may be
readily seen. Examples of distasteful, warningly coloured caterpillars are those of the magpie, mullein shark and cinnabar moths.
Experiments with these and other conspicuous insects have shown
that newly hatched chicks and young monkeys will sample them,
but having done so once or twice avoid them afterwards—the conclusion being that they have learnt to associate the garish coloration
with unpalatableness.

The fact that an insect, regarded as an individual, is unsuitable
for food will not save it from molestation. But if it is garbed in a
manner so striking that its appearance is not forgotten by its
attacker, a distinct advantage to the species is likely to accrue; and
where Dame Nature rules supreme the individual is always sub-
ordinated to the species. As Tennyson wrote:

> So careful of the type she seems,
> So careless of the single life.

Obviously a considerable number of conspicuous insects must
fall victims each year to young and inexperienced assailants. But
these unavoidable sacrifices can hardly fail to benefit a noxious or
unpalatable species if its appearance is such that its members will

be readily seen and recognized when this stage of "experimental tasting" has passed, and the young have learnt their lesson.

The strongest testimony to the "survival value" of warning coloration is afforded by the similarity of many harmless and edible insects to others that are harmful or disagreeable. The most striking examples occur among tropical butterflies. When the naturalist H. W. Bates returned from his travels in South America he brought with him a large collection of these insects, among which were some

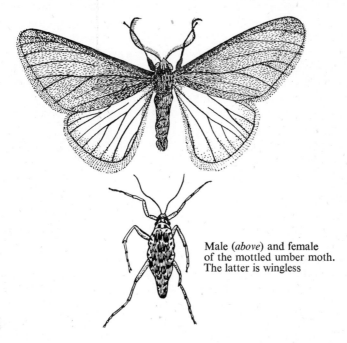

Male (*above*) and female of the mottled umber moth. The latter is wingless

that he had placed together, believing them to be of the same species. Closer inspection revealed the astonishing fact that the supposed identity was superficial; that species belonging to perfectly distinct families were so much alike in the shape, colour and markings of their wings as to be indistinguishable without detailed examination by experts.

The point to grasp is that whole families of butterflies are rendered unfit for food by reason of pungent juices which permeate their tissues, whereas other families comprise species which are perfectly edible and, in fact, much sought after by insectivorous creatures. By mimicry, therefore, we mean that one of the latter (the "mimic") resembles one of the former (the "model") so closely in get-up that its predacious enemies are deceived, once they have learnt to recognize the coloration as ill-omened. It is as if an ox should pass muster as a lion, or a rabbit as a weasel!

Not infrequently the sexes of a butterfly differ so remarkably in colour and pattern that the casual observer would certainly mistake them for distinct species; and when this is the case with a distasteful butterfly that has become a model for mimicry, the respective types of colouring are sometimes reproduced with the utmost fidelity by the males and females of the mimic. There are other instances in which only the females of a species are mimetic, the males retaining the ancestral coloration; while one and the same species may have two or more distinct types of female each coloured and patterned in imitation of a separate evil-tasting model. This state of things is explicable on the grounds that the females are comparatively slow in flight and exposed, when engaged in egg-laying, to dangers from which the males are exempt. A particularly interesting case of the kind is that of a butterfly, *Hypolimnas misippus*, not distantly related to our purple emperor. Its headquarters are in India, but it has a wide range in the Eastern Hemisphere and is common in tropical Africa. Wherever it occurs its females are almost indistinguishable at first sight from the common distasteful Danaine models of the district. Frank Finn, when in India, proved to his own satisfaction that while as a species it is liked by birds and monkeys if they can be induced to sample it, they fight shy of its models.

Still more remarkable is the case of certain swallow-tail butterflies of Africa and Madagascar. They are usually spoken of collectively (*Papilio cenea*) as if they were one species, but there are many local forms and sub-species each of which has been provided with a separate scientific name. The males have always angular wings with black markings on a cream ground, and each hind-wing terminating in a longish tail. But the females usually have rounded wings, without tails, and their colours resemble those of various distasteful butterflies found in the locality. This is the rule. The Malagasy representatives, however, as well as one or two of the East African forms, have black-and-cream tailed females, almost identical with their males in appearance. Why have these isolated races failed to participate in the colour changes from which their congeners elsewhere presumably derive benefit? The question is not easy to answer. Yet in the absence of contradictory evidence it seems likely that the non-mimetic races have suffered less hardship and persecution than those in which the females, in the course of their evolution, have adopted the showy liveries of the distasteful models with which they fly. In the case of the Malagasy race this view is certainly plausible, and was adopted by Sir E. B. Poulton. "It requires a very slight exercise of the imagination," he wrote, "to picture the steps by which these marvellous changes have been produced; for here the new forms have arisen at so recent a date that many of the intermediate stages can still be seen, while the parent form has been preserved unchanged in a friendly land, where the keen struggle of continental areas is unknown."

Since Bates made his initial discovery thousands of examples of butterfly mimicry have come to light, chiefly in tropical countries where the "struggle for existence" is most acute. In South America, for example, species related to our wood white are so like some of their gaudy, warningly coloured associates that they can only be told apart by experts. Sometimes a mimetic butterfly is modelled on a moth with a reputation for unpalatableness, one of the most remarkable instances being that of a swallow-tail from New Guinea and the Aru Islands. It has greenish-black wings crossed by slightly bluish-green bands, the hind-wings having short, whitish tails. In all these respects it is "as like as two peas" to a moth in association with which it is found. Of butterfly mimicry in temperate regions probably the most convincing case is the "Viceroy" of North America, whose model is the well-nigh ubiquitous, evil-smelling "Monarch". The "Viceroy" is first cousin to our white admiral; yet the coloration of both these butterflies, model and mimic, is rich tawny with black markings and white spots. Their only obvious difference is that the former is somewhat larger than the latter on the average.

In Britain we have no butterfly mimics; but several species of "clearwing" moths, as well as a number of two-winged flies, are deceptively like bees, wasps and other insects with stings, both in their general get-up and mode of flight. That these similarities were observed long ago by the non-scientific public is witnessed by such popular names as bee hawk moths, hornet clearwings and bee-flies. Even more interesting is the plant-bug, which, in its early or nymphal stage, mimics the ants in whose company it is usually found. Bugs and ants run about together over leaves and stems, and since they are similar in size and the colouring of both is blackish they cannot be distinguished without close inspection. It then appears that the broad, basal part of the bug's hind-body, having a pale—nearly white—patch on each side, is almost invisible, save for a narrow dark mark in the middle which in outline resembles the ant's attenuated "waist".

Then we have our wasp beetle, whose mimicry may not be completely convincing to human eyes, but is doubtless sufficient to hoodwink the less critical judgement of the average insectivorous bird in search of a meal. A more realistic counterfeit is the rather rare chafer, which is chiefly found in Scotland, where it is called the "bee beetle" because of the long tawny-and-yellow hairs which clothe its thorax and wing-cases. Once on the wing it keeps the latter folded together above the abdomen, so that when flying, as it does, round thistle-heads in the hot sunshine it looks exactly like a humble-bee. Several species of humble-bee are mimicked by a two-winged fly, which occurs in two distinct varieties, one red-tailed, the other yellow-banded ; while the carder-bee fly is an almost perfect copy of the small fulvous carder-bee from which it takes it name. The narcissus-fly would also pass muster as a humble-bee with anyone save the expert, while the drone-fly is almost always mistaken for a denizen of the hive by those without entomological knowledge.

Thus far we have been dealing with what is usually referred to as "Batesian mimicry"—the protection which an edible insect gains from its superficial likeness to one which is commonly avoided because it is dangerous to attack or repulsive as food. The complementary theory of "convergent mimicry" originated with Fritz Müller, a German naturalist resident in Brazil, who showed that it must also be advantageous for noxious and unpalatable species to resemble each other for the reason that none of them is absolutely exempt from hostile attack, since young insectivorous creatures do not inherit a knowledge of what they may eat with impunity and what to avoid. On the contrary, as we have seen, they have to learn by actual tests as they grow from youth to maturity ; and this means that a certain percentage of individuals will be victimized each year of even the most repulsive species, no matter how glaringly conspicuous its warning coloration may be. But it is clear that if several such species resemble one another so closely as to be practically indistinguishable the relative loss sustained by each will be greatly lessened.

Müller's estimate was essentially as follows : Assuming that the birds and other insectivorous creatures of a given region have to destroy 1,200 butterflies of a distasteful species before it becomes recognized as such, and that there exists in this region 2,000 individuals of a species A and 10,000 of a species B ; then, if these two species are *different* in appearance each will lose 1,200 of its members annually; whereas if they are deceptively alike this loss will be divided among them in proportion to their numbers, so that A will lose 200 and B 1,000 each year on the average. Thus, while the relative numbers of the species is as 1 to 5, the relative advantage derived from their resemblance is as 25 to 1.

It would seem, therefore, that certain types of coloration having been established as danger signals, the subsequent tendency of natural selection has not been to go on multiplying types indefinitely, but rather to draw together under those already in existence increasing numbers of species to share in the protection which they offer. Thus, in a given locality we find that the colours and markings of a variety of unrelated insects approximate more or less closely to a common pattern. A good example is the yellow or orange-and-black banding exemplified by so many wasps, beetles, flies, moths and even caterpillars, such as those of the cinnabar moth. Our largest British robber-fly has joined this charmed circle by donning the conventional livery of a hornet. It is a ferocious ruffian, pouncing upon and destroying any flying insects that it is strong enough to master, including wasps and bees; and it has been suggested that its resemblance to a hornet may assist it in its murderous enterprises by enabling it to approach its Hymenopterous prey without arousing suspicion. But this theory of "aggressive mimicry", as it has been called, lacks the support of convincing evidence; nor is it easy to believe that so swift and agile a fly stands in need of any such aid. It is therefore more reasonable to assume that the mimicry is really protective, serving to defend the insect against the attacks of its own foes.

Although every kind of defensive device is valuable, none can avail at all times and in all circumstances, nor are insectivorous creatures the only destructive agents that insects have to counter. Far more formidable, though less evident, is the ever-present threat of starvation. For insects, like all other animals, must eat to live, and there is never enough food to satisfy an inflated demand. Hence, in normal circumstances, the numerical status of every species is constantly maintained in stable equilibrium. In other words, of all the progeny of a single pair in each succeeding generation two only, on the average, can reach sexual maturity and become parents on their own account. Many of the others are doubtless destroyed by enemies, accident or inclemencies of the weather, while the rest perish from hunger. In respect of survival, therefore, each species is,

I

so to say, on the horns of a dilemma. Either it must—like the green-fly or aphides—follow the primitive practice of producing offspring in sufficiently vast numbers to offset the inevitable massacre of the innocents implicit in the principle of natural selection, or—if it inclines to birth restriction—it must evolve such self-defensive precautions as protective disguises, warning coloration, mimetic similarities and so forth, which, if sufficiently successful, serve to restore the balance and prevent extinction.

Chapter Fifteen

FOOD AND FEEDING

INSECTS as a class are omnivorous in the most comprehensive sense of the term. A substance may be bone dry, as hard as metal, and in every other respect uninviting, yet so long as it traces its origin to the animal or the vegetable kingdom at least one species of insect is likely to find in it the wherewithal of subsistence.

In an earlier chapter something has been said about the ways in which certain insects get their living; but the topic is well-nigh inexhaustible, the feeding habits of insects being almost as diverse as the kinds of food which they eat. A few widely distributed species, such as the common cockroach and the house cricket, feast on any edible substances to which they can gain access. The house-fly is equally catholic in its appetite, but owing to the structure of its mouth-parts must take its nourishment in liquid form. The adults range from sweet juices to those of filth and decay, while the larvae, in the absence of their special preference—stable manure—have been found feeding in many kinds of fermenting organic matter, including kitchen refuse. But the vast majority of insects in the larva stage of their existence are either exclusive vegetarians or exclusive carnivores, although several instances have been recorded in which a remarkable change-over takes place in the course of the life history, one of the most surprising being that of the caterpillar of the large blue butterfly, which begins by eating the flowers of the wild thyme and ends by being carried by ants into their nest, where it preys on the helpless grubs. Most of the caterpillars of butterflies and moths, however, as well as nearly all saw-flies and the grubs of many beetles, feed openly on herbage or the foliage of trees, and are occasionally so numerous that they denude the plants of their leaves, or by devouring the soft tissue between the veins reduce them to mere skeletons. The latter mode of devastation is well exemplified by the work of the rose slugworm; but in this instance the lower skin of the leaf is frequently left intact, eventually becoming brown and shrivelled. The wholesale destruction wrought by leaf-feeding larvae is largely accounted for by the fact that most of them derive their nourishment solely from the juicy cell-contents. They secrete no digestive ferments capable of disintegrating cellulose, so that the cell walls and other hard constituents pass unchanged through the intestines to be discharged in the form of the dry pellets called "frass".

The larva of our British "jerking-disk" saw-fly makes blotch-mines in the leaves of sycamore and maple in June and July, usually working at the apical part of one of the lobes. As the time to pupate approaches it cuts a circular piece out of the upper epidermis, and on the under-surface of this weaves a silken cover, thus forming a sort of sleeping-bag, close sealed against intrusion, in which the winter is passed. When all has been made secure, the least breath of wind suffices to dislodge the little fastness, and it falls lightly to the ground. Then it begins to jump perceptibly and with persistence. Hugh Main has described these saltatory disks very happily as "animated confetti"! But why do they do it? Experiments have shown that the effective stimulus is heat—heat and, perhaps, intense illumination. For the jumping continues more or less vigorously so long as the temperature is high; but when the disks chance to jerk themselves into a cool and shady place they lie still. Now a cool place, screened from the sun's rays, is likely to be a sheltered place—a harbour of refuge, a hiding-place from the prying eyes of birds and other insectivorous creatures.

The same explanation seems also to fit the case of the so-called "jumping beans" which are brought to this country from Mexico in considerable numbers as curiosities, and may be purchased at some London shops and stores: for each of them contains a larva —this time the caterpillar of a small moth. Strictly speaking they are not "beans" at all, but sections of the triply divided fruit of a shrubby spurge. Each is about one-third of an inch long, with three sides—two flat and one rounded. The most interesting point about these objects, however, is their jumping proclivities. When placed near a fire, or upon a plate that has been previously warmed to blood heat, they jerk and roll in the most surprising fashion. They can leap as much as one-eighth of an inch from the ground, at the same time altering their position by about a quarter of an inch. As with the saw-fly's disk, a high temperature stimulates to exertion, which is discontinued when a cool spot is reached.

The life history of this moth begins when the parent lays her eggs on or near the developing fruits of the spurge. Each tiny caterpillar on hatching bores its way into a segment of a young fruit, which at this stage is small and soft. As the segment swells the insignificant opening is completely obliterated, so that by mere inspection it is impossible to tell which sections are vacant and which tenanted; but as the latter grow the occupants eat up the seeds and pulp which surround them until nothing remains but an empty husk, in which the caterpillar changes to a pupa, after first cutting a circular trap-door in the side through which the adult moth eventually pushes its way to liberty.

The jumping-bean moth is closely related to several moths found in Britain, including the notorious codlin moth, whose caterpillars feed in the centres of apples, and are a world-wide orchard pest.

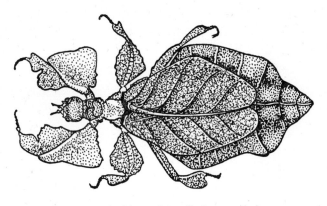

The green leaf-insect from Ceylon: a relative of the phasmids or "stick-insects"

The caterpillars of other species bore into walnuts, acorns, chestnuts and beech masts, but none of these causes the attacked fruit to "jump".

Among our native seed-eating insects the pea-and-bean beetles deserve special mention. The females glue their eggs on the pods of leguminous plants. For a short time the young larva burrows in the substance of the pod, but soon makes its way into one of the developing peas or beans. Once established therein it loses its legs and becomes a podgy grub incapable of locomotion. The puncture due to its entry is slight and soon heals over; so that we are presented with the curious phenomenon of a pea or bean, apparently healthy and well-favoured, which has, nevertheless, a despoiler within. Yet a single seed provides much more than sufficient nourishment for the development of its lodger, which consumes only a part of the cotyledons, and rarely if ever touches the embryo; so that although mutilated it remains capable of germination, and—in favourable circumstances—may develop into a healthy plant.

Before changing to a pupa the grub gnaws its way to the surface of its pea, scooping away everything except the thin outer skin, which it leaves intact; so that when the adult beetle is ready to emerge it has only to push up this diaphragm in order to gain the open air. This habit of the grub makes it possible to detect infested peas and beans before the occupants have escaped, since the tell-tale circular patches may easily be recognized.

Bugs, hoppers, aphides and so forth are nearly all sap-suckers, but a few bugs suck the juices of other insects or the blood of verte-brates, and so much be classed as carnivores, the most notorious of these latter being the cosmopolitan bed-bug. In all these instances the mouth-parts are modified for piercing and pumping. The equiva-lents of the mandibles and first maxillae are long, slender stylets which work to and fro within a kind of grooved sheath (termed the rostrum) which is formed by the union of what must primarily have been the second maxillae. The whole constitutes a lengthy proboscis which when not in use is bent backwards beneath the body and lies between the coxae of the legs. When one of these insects feeds it first brings the tip of its rostrum into contact with the organism— plant or animal as the case may be—that is to be attacked. The sharp-pointed stylets are then driven into the tissues, and saliva flows down the rostrum into the wound, so that coagulation of the blood or sap is arrested, allowing it to be imbibed freely.

Many aphides and scale insects exude a sweetish substance known as "honey-dew", consisting of undigested sugar and other materials, and this is greatly relished by ants, bees and certain other insects, which lick it greedily off the leaves whenever opportunity offers. Some species of ants, indeed, rely upon aphides for a con-siderable part of their food supply, taking almost as much care of them as they do of their own grubs, and receiving in return the sugary sap which they cannot obtain in any other way. They even collect aphides' eggs in the autumn, store them in their nests during the winter, and with the return of warm weather carry out the newly hatched young and place them on the proper food-plants. In short, the ants keep and tend the aphides just as human beings keep cows for the sake of their milk !

Carnivorous insects may be roughly classified in three groups, viz. the predators, the blood-suckers and the parasites. These last will be dealt with in the next chapter; but the blood-suckers, though they are often spoken of as "temporary parasites", have more in common with the predators, since while they are dependent on their victims for food they do not live within or constantly attached to their bodies, as is the case with "permanent parasites". Many predacious insects rank as benefactors in the eyes of economic entomologists because each season they destroy in the aggregate a vast total of insects and other creatures which are inimical to the interests or well-being of mankind—such as agricultural and forestry pests and the carriers and disseminators of diseases. Nearly all the "ground beetles" and their kindred—of which upward of 700 species are found in Britain—spend the whole of their active life as larvae and adults hunting prey either on or just below the surface of the soil, although several—e.g. a very common, dark-brown species—have been convicted of gnawing mangolds and other roots, and of invading strawberry beds with baleful intent; but such lapses into vegetarianism are probably only temporary, perhaps due to excessively dry weather or a scarcity of other food.

Our five species of "tiger-beetles" are likewise predators, so also are most of the water-beetles and water-bugs; but the larvae of tiger-beetles, instead of chasing their victims, lie in wait for them in burrows. Their shape is very abnormal, yet well adapted to their peculiar mode of attack, namely to jerk themselves backwards upon the prey, which when seized is dragged to the bottom of the lair.

Some ground beetles subsist on snails, notably a small, dull-black species, whose head and thorax are disproportionately slender by contrast with the rest of its body so that they can be thrust some distance into the spiral corridor of a mollusc's shell. Two other snail-eaters are the glow-worm and the rare *Drilus*, which has no English name. The nature of the glow-worm's food had long been known, but the precise manner in which the prey is attacked and consumed was described by Fabre, whose essay on the subject was among the last penned by this great naturalist. The larval glow-worm, in common with many other insects, has hollow mandibles—instruments somewhat resembling in structure the poison fangs of a snake, though with a very different function, since through these grooved jaws the creatures in question imbibe their food in a liquid state. But the glow-worm does more than this. It injects into its victims first an anaesthetic poison which speedily ensures immobility, then a serum capable of liquefying the tissues. Fabre graphically describes the mode of attack, which may be witnessed by anyone who has sufficient time and patience at his or her disposal, for glow-worms can be easily reared in captivity. It often happens that several larvae join forces, with the result that the carcass of the victim, even if a large one, is soon reduced to the requisite consistency. These larvae have at their tail-end an unusual organ which has been described as a "rosette of twelve fingers" that "do not seize, but stick". Its chief function is to assist the insect when climbing, especially on smooth surfaces. But it is also used in moments of leisure after a feast to polish the body from end to end, thus removing the last traces of viscidity remaining from contact with the snail.

The larva of the other snail-killer mentioned above has a different mode of attack from that of the glow-worm, first reconnoitring its victim, and then—if need be—manoeuvring it by blandishments and pushes into a secluded position where the meal, which may last for from eight to sixteen days, will not be interrupted. It then eats its way into the shell, where it resides until the feast is finished, though coming frequently to the opening to eject refuse. The banded garden snail is the chief sufferer, three or four individuals being destroyed by each larva during its career. In the autumn it pupates within the last shell of the series, the orifice of which is neatly barricaded with its cast skin. The females of both these snail-killing beetles are totally different in appearance from their males, being much more like overgrown larvae than adult beetles.

Ladybirds and their larvae, as every gardener knows, are among the most important "natural enemies" of aphides, but in this respect they are ably seconded by the lacewings and other Neuroptera, also by the hover-flies. The curious snake-flies and scorpion-flies are likewise predatory, but their hunting-grounds are chiefly in wooded areas.

Few insects trap their prey, but this is done by the larvae of ant-lions. Unfortunately we have no native species, but the common European one has long been studied by naturalists, the first accurate account of its habits having been given by Réaumur. The larva is a strange-looking creature, thick-set and somewhat oval in contour, having a flat head and curved, grooved mandibles, and its hinder-most pair of legs short and stumpy. These larvae make their pits in fine dry sand, usually choosing a sheltered situation with a sunny aspect. First a furrow is made to correspond with the circumference of the finished excavation. Then the worker ploughs round and round in diminishing circles, the while it jerks out the sand with its shovel-like head, the final result being a funnel-shaped hollow, in the bottom of which the maker lies buried with only its jaws visible. Any small insect that chances to set foot over the edge of the pit slides helplessly downward, its descent being hastened by the jets of sand hurled up by the impatient owner.

The uncertainty of the ant-lion's food supply appears to govern the duration of its larval life. In propitious circumstances—i.e. when meals occur with reasonable regularity—the pit-making episode continues for two years; but when provisions are scarce the period may be greatly lengthened. Sooner or later, however, the larva burrows more deeply into the sand and constructs a spherical cocoon of white silk, the most notable feature of which is its smallness when compared with the adult, dragon-fly-like insect which it cradles.

A very extraordinary creature which has been called the long-necked ant-lion frequents the sand-strewn chambers and galleries of Egyptian tombs and pyramids, though what it finds there to eat is not stated. Appearances suggest that it is a sort of Paul Pry of the insect world, for its neck—really a rod-like extension of the prothorax—is longer in proportion to its body than that of the giraffe, so that it can poke its flat head into cracks and crevices of the masonry from which, presumably, it picks out hidden kickshaws of one sort or another, and so contrives to make a living. When first found this oddity was regarded as a fully developed insect, but it is now known to be the larval form of one of the elegant long-tailed Nemopterids mentioned on page 120 of Chapter Thirteen.

Dragon-flies, both when winged and during their aquatic larval life, are indefatigable hunters; so, too, are the robber-flies, whose grubs are found burrowing in damp earth, where—so it is said—they batten on the grubs of other insects which frequent similar situations. The adults have been stigmatized as "inhuman murderers . . . savages of the insect world, putting their captives to death with merciless cruelty". Like dragon-flies they have noticeably large eyes, which enable them to mark down their victims from a considerable distance and to swoop upon them with the directness of a hawk. They attack every kind of flying insect that they are strong enough to master, including wasps and bees, nor do they spare their own kind. It is even said that the males are frequently seized and eaten by their mates!

By contrast, mature hover-flies are decorous and peaceable, feeding for the most part on nectar and pollen filched from the flowers, often in company with bees and wasps, which some of them resemble closely in appearance. Most of those that frequent our gardens lay their eggs on plants in the neighbourhood of aphides, whose juices the maggot-like larvae suck. Not all, however, serve the interests of horticulture. The grubs of a particularly bee-like species—the narcissus-fly—burrow into bulbs and cause much mischief both in this country and in Holland. In another genus the larvae are found in the nests of bees and wasps, where they were formerly believed to prey upon the grubs, but are now said to act as scavengers.

In addition to the few bugs already mentioned, blood-sucking insects include a number of two-winged flies, the lice of the Order Anoplura, and the fleas. Of the last-named upwards of forty British species have been described, the largest being one which infests moles and field-mice. In general each kind of flea is associated with a particular mammal, while several attack birds; but this does not hinder them from experimenting elsewhere should occasion offer, as when stray cat, dog or fowl fleas, as sometimes happens, make themselves a nuisance to human beings. Most notorious of all fleas is the "chigger", happily confined to tropical countries. Its particular nastiness is the habit of the gravid female of burrowing under the skin of beasts and of men, giving rise to painful tumours. In this position her body becomes enormously distended, and at intervals she discharges a number of eggs which fall to the ground. Although adult fleas are blood-suckers their larvae have biting mouth-parts and, as far as is known, feed on the organic constituents of dust accumulated in the nests or runs of their "hosts". This is certainly the case with the human flea and other species whose life histories have been investigated. When full grown the larva spins an oval cocoon, wherein it changes to the pupa.

The objectionable insects called lice fall naturally into two groups, namely the blood-suckers and the "bird-lice" or "biting-lice", although some modern authors treat them as a single Order in disregard of distinctive characters which suggest descent from widely different ancestors. The former, which may possibly be the degenerate issue of some long-extinct bug-like stock, are small, wingless insects which spend their whole lives on the bodies of mammals, whose blood they suck. In other words, they are total but superficial parasites. The same may be said of the biting-lice, only they are not blood-suckers, but feed on the scurf and organic detritus which accumulate among the feathers or hairs of their hosts. One species is a common resident on dogs, others on sheep, cattle and horses, but by far the larger number live among the feathers of birds. They are small, large-headed insects with mandibulate mouth-parts, and have obvious affinities with the familiar book-louse, which is often numerous in houses, especially if they are somewhat damp; and this insect, again, seems to be a poor relation of the termites, or white ants. Both kinds of lice fix their eggs to the hairs or feathers of the creatures which harbour them, and with both metamorphosis is slight, the young differing little from the parents except in size.

Most of the blood-sucking two-winged flies belong to one or another of four distinct family groups, namely the gnats and mosquitoes, the midges, the gad- and horse-flies, and the so-called "spider-flies" already referred to in Chapter Three; but the stable-fly—sometimes called the "biting house-fly"—is a member of yet another family, the *Muscidae*, as also is the rather dingy-looking blow-fly, which lays its eggs in the nest of birds (mostly sparrows, larks and swallows) in order that its maggots when they hatch may suck the blood of the nestlings. The sanguinary habits of the Nubian Seroot-flies with their immensely long proboscides have already been referred to in Chapter Eight.

Many of the midges are harmless, but certain species of one genus are inveterate blood-suckers and are chief among the nuisances that haunt our gardens in the summer twilight. People often say that they have been "stung" by one of these insects, or by a gnat or mosquito, when "bitten" would be the better word, since these pests have no stings, but use their marvellously modified mouth-parts to puncture the victim's skin. Moreover, this is not done in self-defence, but to draw blood—although only the females make these sanguinary attacks, the males—if they feed at all—imbibing the juices of flowers. The popular names "gnat" and "mosquito" are really synonymous, but the current belief that some of these insects are more dangerous than others is justified to the extent that the spotted-winged members of the genus *Anopheles* and their near allies are responsible for the spread of the parasite which causes malarial fever in those countries where this disease is endemic.

The proboscis of a gnat or mosquito consists of a grooved sheath enclosing no less than six needle-like lancets, all employed in opening the wound, into which a slightly poisonous secretion from the salivary glands is injected—probably to retard coagulation of the blood, and to stimulate its flow. When the needles are being driven into the flesh of the victim only the tip of the sheath encircles them, the rest loops back under the insect's head. The mouth-parts of most other blood-sucking two-winged flies are similarly planned, but with great diversity of detail. The largest and most ferocious of these insect vampires are the gad- or horse-flies, some twenty-eight species of which are British natives. The habits of one of the commonest—the cleg, stoat-fly or rain breeze-fly—are graphically described by Richard Jefferies in the following passage: "With a low hissing buzz, a long, narrow and brownish grey insect settles on your hand as you walk among the hay, and presently you feel a tingling sensation, and may watch (if you have the patience to endure the irritation) its body gradually dilate and grow darker in colour as it absorbs the blood. When once thoroughly engaged, nothing will frighten this fly away; you may crush it, but it will not move from fear; it will remain till, replete with blood, it falls off helpless into the grass."

The stable-fly calls for special mention on more than one count. The vast majority of the flies in the family to which it belongs have— like the common house-fly—soft, sponge-like mouth-parts adapted for mopping up liquid food. But in a very few—of which the stable-fly and the dreaded tsetse-flies of the African continent are outstanding examples—the proboscis has been modified into a horny stylet which projects stiffly from beneath the head. Unlike other sanguinivorous flies, both sexes of these exceptions bite and suck blood. The stable-fly is very similar in general appearance to the house-fly, with which it is frequently confused. That it seldom enters houses except when a storm is imminent accounts for the popular conviction that "flies only bite when it is going to rain".

Chapter Sixteen

GUESTS, HANGERS-ON AND PARASITES

No OUTLINE of the feeding habits of insects would be complete without reference to the numerous hangers-on of various grades that get their living at the expense of, or in association with, other species without being parasites in the strict sense of the word. The intimate connexion of many ants with aphides on account of the sweet substances secreted by the latter has already been noted ; but Donisthorpe has enumerated more than 250 invertebrates, nearly three-quarters of them insects, which occur more or less constantly as residents in the nests of British ants. Eric Wasmann, whose investigations extended over a wider field, and whose list included nearly 1,200 of these ant-satellites, arranged them in four categories, namely :

1. Welcome guests, which are fed and tended by the ants, often, if not always, because they yield some dainty coveted by these insects.

2. Tolerated inmates, being as far as is known not disliked by the ants, or at least not actively molested by them.

3. Baleful lodgers, recognized as such by the ants, but nevertheless successful in maintaining themselves as inmates despite persecution—frequently by lying up in some sequestered situation withdrawn from the main current of the nest's activities.

4. Complete parasites, dwelling in or attached to the bodies of the ants or their larvae.

In many cases, however, these distinctions cannot be maintained with strictness, while the ants themselves are often deceived in their preferences. For instance, they show the greatest solicitude for the well-being and safety of certain beetles whose presence in the nest is in fact highly undesirable. One of these is a little blind and wingless species found most commonly in the earth mounds—like mole-hills covered with grass—raised in meadows by the common yellow ant. The reason for its popularity with the ants is that they greatly relish an aromatic substance that it excretes in small quantities from glands hidden among tufts of hairs on its back. If a nest is disturbed, the ants show as much anxiety to remove these beetles to the safety of its lowest galleries as they do to protect their own larvae and pupae. They also feed and furbish them with equal punctiliousness, and occasionally give them pick-a-back rides. In short, were it not for the care of its hosts this beetle would probably have become extinct long ago, since it appears to have lost all capacity for independent existence, and has never been found outside ants' nests. Yet—such is the obliquity of Nature unadorned— this accomplished sponger is believed to prey as a larva on those of its life-long benefactors.

Another beetle, which lives in the nests of the slave-making blood-red ant, is certainly guilty of this dastardly imposition; and the strangest aspect of the business is that the ants cherish and feed the alien's offspring, allowing them to eat up their own grubs without the smallest sign of resentment. The result of this misplaced philanthropy is not difficult to foresee. The ant population declines steadily season after season until in the end it is so much depleted that the colony can no longer maintain itself in being. It is then that the beetles—which, fortunately for the survival of their race, still retain their wings—migrate to other ant-communities, there to carry on their nefarious practices.

Ants feed these and other special favourites among their numerous associates in the same intimate manner in which they feed one another, namely by opening the mouth, causing a drop of liquid to appear on the lip, and remaining passive while the recipient partakes of the proffered *bonne bouche*. By contrast, when feeding their larvae, the nutriment is forced without ceremony into the youngster's open mouth.

In addition to the caterpillars of the large blue butterfly previously mentioned those of several related species are cosseted by ants, especially during the last stage of their larval life. At this time a "honey-gland" on the seventh abdominal segment—the tenth behind the head—begins to function, and the ants are very partial to its sweet secretion. They are in constant attendance upon the caterpillars, often caressing them with their antennae, and treating them with as much care as they bestow upon aphides. As we may suppose that their presence serves to ward off the attacks of ichneumons and parasitic flies, this would seem to be an instance of mutualism—or benefit received for benefit conferred. But in the case of the large blue the association has become much closer and withal one-sided; for—as we have seen—its caterpillar, after the third moult, is transported bodily by one of its attendants to the ants' nest, where it completes its feeding by preying upon the grubs.

Most of the "tolerated inmates" of ants' nests appear to be scavengers or feeders on refuse of one kind or another. An example is the disk-shaped larva of a fly so flattened that the ants can run easily to and fro over its back in their passage along the galleries. To all appearances they are quite unaware of its presence, for it is neither molested nor petted, but they may recognize it as an asset in their domestic economy, which in fact it is, since by clearing away excrement and other organic residue it promotes the sanitation

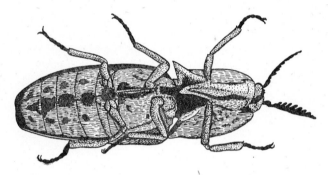

The underside of a skip-jack beetle, showing
the spike and socket mechanism by means of which it rights
itself when it falls on its back

of the nest. The larva of the pellucid drone-fly or wasps'-nest fly resides on similar terms in the subterranean abodes of wasps, where —according to Fabre—it fills a double rôle by clearing the cells of the cast skins and excrement of the grubs and ridding the nest of its dead. "Thus the fly is welcomed peaceably when it penetrates into the burrow to lay its eggs, and thus in the very heart of the dwelling, where no stranger may wander with impunity, its larva is tolerated and even respected."

The gregarious caterpillars of a tiny moth—a near relative of the webbing clothes-moth—are found only in the nest of wood-ants, where they spin silken tunnels among the accumulated vegetable refuse, on the choicer portions of which they feed. Their activities are not sufficiently extensive to interfere with the architectural arrangements of the ants, and they are never molested. The honey-comb moth, in its larval stage, is a regular inhabitant of hives, and is one of the major pests of bee-keeping. During the summer months the female moths enter the hives in the evening or at night and lay their eggs in crevices on the comb, into which the caterpillars burrow, eating what they gnaw away, and lining the galleries which they make with silk. Many bee grubs are destroyed by pressure, and eventually masses of dense, firm cocoons are spun among the wreckage. The lesser honeycomb moth is often very destructive in old hives, where it works in a similar fashion, while a third species —the green-shaded honey-moth—is normally associated with wasps and humble-bees, though it occasionally invades hives.

The fat grubs of the metallic green rose-beetle are most often found feeding in heaps of leaf mould or in the wood-soil which collects in the hollows of trees, but they sometimes occur as lodgers in ants' nests made of vegetable refuse. So far as is known the ants ignore them—perhaps because they are too little in the way to attract their attention! Another beetle which we may christen the four-spotted clythra—something like a large, elongated ladybird in appearance—passes the whole of its larval and pupal existence in the nest of the wood-ant. The females make up their eggs into packets that look like bits of twig and drop them from overhanging branches upon the nest in which the larvae subsequently take up their abode. Like caddis-worms, they construct and live in cases which they decorate externally with fibrous fragments and drag about with them, the head and legs protruding from the narrow end. They are scavengers with vegetarian proclivities and do more good than harm as tenants, yet they seem only to be tolerated while disguised; for when the perfect insects appear the ants attack them, and they have to run the gauntlet to escape from the nest.

An example of lodgers recognized as intruders and disliked by the ants, but which manage to maintain their footing in the nest by lying low and hiding, is a little wingless insect related to the "silver-fish" of our larders and store-cupboards. It takes food from the very mouths of ants which are in the act of feeding one another. When workers, filled with nectar or other juices, return home from an expedition they are often solicited for food by their fellows that have not left the nest. If this happens the two stand face to face and the forager disgorges a small drop of liquid, which is absorbed by the other. While a pair of ants are thus engaged, the interloper grabs the drop, and hurries with it to its sanctuary. These impudent robbers are constantly chased by the ants from one corner of the nest to another, and if caught killed.

A curious complication of ant-life is the keeping of slaves by certain species. There are degrees of turpitude in this habit. The blood-red or British slave-making ant makes occasional sallies on the nests of smaller species—usually those of the negro ant, stigmatized by Donisthorpe as "a shy and cowardly ant, fleeing before danger"—whence, after overcoming such resistance as may be offered by the owners, a supply of larvae and pupae are carried away. These are carefully tended by the raiders; and when the adults appear they make no attempt to escape but take part in the activities of the alien nest as if it were their own; and when, as sometimes happens, the masters change their quarters the slaves trek—or are carried—to the new abode.

The European Amazon ant is almost completely dependent on its slaves, by which it is carried about from place to place, and periodically fed—being unable, or too indolent, to feed either itself or its young, even when surrounded by food. Thanks to their fierce and warlike disposition these insects seem never at a loss to secure as many slaves as they need.

Strangest of all is the case of the dark guest ant, of which the worker caste no longer exists, while the males and females are only found in the nests of the turf ant, where they are carried about and fed by the owners, being unable to eat without assistance. Exactly how this strange association originates is at present uncertain. It seems probable, however, that a gravid female of the dependent species manages somehow to enter the nest and so to ingratiate herself with its worker population that they kill their rightful queen in favour of the intruder; for, according to Donisthorpe, she is hardly strong enough to do the killing herself. Be this as it may, she is eventually established as queen-mother of the stolen kingdom; but her triumph must be short-lived, for when its workers die—which they must do in the course of a year or so—her reign and her life end. But meanwhile she has laid many eggs, from which males and females of her kind are reared; and the latter, after pairing, disperse to find other turf-ants' nests, where—if they succeed in establishing themselves—the whole sordid business is re-enacted.

The extraordinary behaviour of these ants seems to be an extreme development of what is known as "the cuckoo-habit" that prevails among certain genera of bees and wasps, which neither make nor provision nests of their own but lay their eggs in those of industrious species, so that the alien grubs may take a share—not infrequently it is the lion's share—of the food provided by the owner for the benefit of its own offspring. For example, a

K

leaf-cutting bee, after shaping and provisioning a cell, lays an egg in it and then goes off to collect the material needed for the cap. During her absence, a cuckoo—which has been awaiting the opportunity—lays an egg side by side with that of the leaf-cutter; and since the timing is so contrived that its egg is the first to hatch, the cuckoo's grub devours most of the food while the other is starved. There are reasons for thinking that in some instances these cuckoo-bees' grubs so far forget themselves as to kill and eat the lawful occupant of the cell after robbing it of its food.

Cuckoo-bees in general are deficient in the specialized appliances—e.g. feathery hairs and "baskets" on the hind-legs—characteristic of those species whose females punctiliously perform their parental duties. On the other hand, they are usually much more conspicuously coloured: and might easily pass muster as small wasps. This is not the case, however, with the cuckoo humble-bees, some of which are so nearly like their dupes in appearance that it is difficult to tell them apart without close scrutiny. Thus, one, when on the wing, is almost indistinguishable from the large red-tailed humble-bee, except that its humming is noticeably softer. When at rest on a thistle-head its identity is at once made known by the smoky tone of its wings, by comparison with those of the dupe, which are pale amber-coloured.

The queens of these particular cuckoos, of which we have six British species, make their way into the nests of authentic humble-bees to lay their eggs. Apparently the intruders have suave manners, for the alarm and resentment aroused among the workers by their entry soon gives place to harmony; and eventually the reigning queen is stung to death by the usurper, so that no more true humble-bee's eggs are laid. Not only are the alien grubs, when they hatch, fed and tended by the humble-bee workers, but the cuckoo adults—all males and females—when they appear consume much nectar from the common store. Moreover, because the supply of workers has been cut off, the population steadily declines, until by the late autumn it consists mainly of cuckoo princes and princesses, of which the latter, after pairing, hibernate to become next season's marauding queens.

Permanent or complete parasitism as practised by insects, when the body of the victim is invaded and its vitality impaired or destroyed, is usually periodical—i.e. it is confined to the larval stage of the life history, the adults being free-living. The larger ichneumon wasps—often, but misleadingly, styled "flies", of which we have

2,000 or more species in Britain—for the most part attack cater-pillars or the grubs of beetles, while an equal number of chiefly very tiny ones generally lay their eggs in those of other insects, or in aphides and the like small fry; but some specialize in pupae. Then there are the Dipterous ichneumons with some 200 or more British representatives—true flies, these, most of which lay their eggs on caterpillars, into whose tissues the maggots burrow. A large pro-portion of the above promote the interests of mankind by destroying annually myriads of the pests which despoil his crops. But the larvae of the bot-flies and warble-flies rank among the most revolting of all insect parasites, since they live and feed in the nasal passages, under the skin, or in the alimentary canal of vertebrate animals—sheep, deer, oxen and horses according to the species in question.

As an example of the wasp-like ichneumons the common Pimpla parasite of the large white butterfly may be cited. The female, by means of her ovipositor, implants her eggs in the caterpillars of this pest, whose numbers are thus considerably thinned, since few if any of those which have been "stung" survive. Caterpillars of the same butterfly are even more frequently done to death by the tiny Apan-teles ichneumon. This time the number of eggs deposited in each is so large that the space between the digestive organs and the skin, normally occupied by a layer of fat, is soon completely packed with the alien grubs, which eventually eat their way out and spin a mass of small yellow cocoons round the shrivelled remnants of the slain. It might be supposed that when once a caterpillar has changed to the pupa the risk of attack by parasites would have passed, but this is by no means the case. The pigmy Pteromalus parasite may often be seen waiting, perhaps for several hours, close to a white butter-fly's caterpillar about to pupate. When this event has taken place the insect mounts the newly formed pupa, stabs it with her ovipositor, and inserts a suitable number of eggs, with the result that the entire content is consumed by her grubs, and no butterfly appears. Many of these smaller parasites spin their cocoons in close contact, either within the empty skin of the victim—which they completely fill—or on a neighbouring leaf or stem, when the white cluster is often mistaken for a spider's nest.

Another group of these busy-bodies attack aphides or green-fly and in some seasons check appreciably their increase and spread. A single egg is inserted into the body of each and its soft tissues are subsequently consumed by the parasitic larva, which finally uses the empty skin as a shelter for pupation. The perfect insect makes its début through a neat, round hole. It is thus easy to see whether a defunct aphid still harbours its slayer, or whether the latter has emerged and flown away. If, however, the exit hole is not neatly circular but has jagged edges it will have been made by a "secondary parasite", whose grub did not destroy the aphid but the larva of the "primary parasite". In other instances this "hyper-parasitism", as it is called, is carried to even greater lengths, for some secondary parasites are victimized by tertiary parasites, while a few cases of quarternary parasitism have been recorded.

Ichneumon wasps, in the widest sense of the term, vary greatly in appearance. Some of our native species are relatively large insects, over an inch in length, but many are microscopically small. The more typical forms have attenuated bodies, narrow, transparent wings, and long, slender legs and antennae. The majority are remarkably active and inquisitive, as befits their avocation. The all-important ovipositor may be inconspicuous, but it often figures as a lengthy, auger-like instrument—notably in the case of species whose rôle is to reach wood-boring larvae such as those of the goat moth or the wood-wasps. The latter are parasitized by our largest ichneumon, which—guided at least in part by her sense of smell—locates the immured grub and drills a shaft down to it through an inch or more of solid timber. The egg then passes through a central passage of the slender ovipositor and is glued to the skin of the luckless creature, whose doom is thus sealed. The small, wingless ichneumons, which resemble ants, were formerly regarded as a sort of Amazonian race consisting exclusively of females capable of virgin reproduction; but it now seems probable that their authentic consorts have been mistakenly grouped as an all-male genus. Be this as it may, most of these matrons oviposit in spiders' egg-cocoons, but several have been found in the nests of ants.

Smallest of all these ichneumon parasites are the so-called "fairy flies", which have long-stalked hair-fringed wings destitute of nervures or veins, and whose eggs are laid for the most part in those of plant-bugs and frog-hoppers. A particularly beautiful example of these pygmies, which rank among the smallest of all insects, is known as the battledore-wing fly. Several related species enter the water to lay their eggs in those of aquatic insects; but these will be dealt with in the next chapter.

The Dipterous ichneumons or parasitic flies are very variable in their modes of egg-laying as also in their choice of victims. Those most commonly selected are the caterpillars of moths and saw-flies, but other insects, as well as members of other groups of animals, are attacked. Thus, one species penalizes the common earwig, another a particular kind of earth-worm, while the larvae of some others live in the bodies of snails. In the majority of instances the eggs are fixed to the back of the host and the newly hatched larvae burrow down into its body; but sometimes the female is equipped with a kind of awl at the end of her trunk-like ovipositor, and with this she pierces the skin and inserts an egg— or it may be a young larva. Again, many species lay large numbers of very minute eggs on the leaves of plants. These may infect caterpillars, which swallow them with their food; or the young larvae may lie in wait ready to attach themselves to any creature that happens to come along—just as land-leeches in a tropical jungle lie in wait for passing animals. Obviously the wastage in such methods of reproduction must be prodigious, since only a fractional percentage of the eggs laid is likely to promote the survival of the species. In this as in other matters the instinctive shrewdness of the wasp-like ichneumons far surpasses that of these parasitic flies. Not infrequently one of the latter will glue her eggs to the back of a caterpillar that is about to change its skin; and when this happens the caterpillar simply discards its old coat and the eggs along with it, thus escaping destruction. Moreover, these flies often attach three or four times too many eggs to their victims, with the result that a high percentage of the grubs perish for lack of food, while the remainder are half-starved and perhaps too feeble to pupate. Wasp-like ichneumons, on the other hand, scarcely ever make mistakes. They seem to know by a touch of the antennae whether a prospective victim has already been "stung" by an earlier visitor, and if this is so they rarely insert their own eggs; nor do they lay more eggs than the size of the host warrants.

Solitary bees and occasionally wasps are subject to the attacks of small parasitic insects of the genus *Stylops*, whose structure is so unusual that some entomologists treat them as a separate Order, although by others they are regarded as an outlandish type of beetle. The small elytra of the males are curiously twisted, but their hind-wings are relatively large and supported only by radiating nervures. After pupation they leave their "hosts" and fly about with much activity. The female, which differs little in appearance from the full-grown larva, spends her whole life within the victim's abdomen, and is visited there by her mate. The minute, six-legged larvae are produced viviparously in large numbers and congregate among the hairs of the host-insect, by which they are carried to its nest. Here, some of them manage to worm their way into the bodies of the bee- or wasp-grubs, as the case may be, when they change immediately to legless maggots. This parasitism does not end fatally; but, as O. H. Latter has pointed out, its effect is to transpose the distinctive secondary sexual characters: affected males fail to develop their usual masculine features, and assume some of the feminine; and *vice versa*.

Chapter Seventeen

INSECTS IN THE WATER

ALTHOUGH available evidence points to the conclusion that living things originated in the water, where conditions were peculiarly favourable to the inception and subsequent development of the small and fragile organisms which we believe these primitive creatures to have been, most experts nowadays agree that no insects as such trace their beginnings to an aquatic ancestry. In other words, this special type of animal seems to have evolved from more or less worm-like forbears which had already established themselves on the land, possibly during the Silurian Epoch of the earth's history, perhaps 350 million years ago. This conjecture gains strong support from the fact that in nearly all existing insects oxygen is conveyed directly to the tissues through a ramifying system of tubes or tracheae which ordinarily open on the outside of the body by valvular apertures—the spiracles. Even among the many kinds which have taken to the water by far the larger number are still dependent on atmospheric air and would soon drown like other denizens of the land if they did not come periodically to the surface to breathe. Hence, it may fairly be assumed that the oldest aquatic insects are the relatively few gill-breathers, which are capable of absorbing air dissolved in water.

Aquatic insects are not confined to any one Order but form in the aggregate a miscellaneous group drawn from many sources. Also, as we shall see, the manner and degree of their adaptation to this mode of life varies greatly, as also does their choice of habitat. Some prefer putrid water or wet and foetid mud. Some are found living in salt marshes, in subterranean streams and even in hot springs. Brooks and rivers, turbulent and slow-flowing alike, have all their characteristic insect populations; so, too, have lakes, pools, ponds and puddles of all sorts and sizes, not omitting static water-tanks and the flooded basements of bombed buildings. The larvae of one kind of gnat are found only in accumulations of water in holes of decaying tree-stumps. Others must be looked for in covered butts or dark receptacles, while still others may be found in the rain-charged cups formed by the paired perfoliate leaves of the teasel. In tropical regions, where stagnant water is scarce, some of the smaller dragon-flies undergo their metamorphosis in the fluid contained in the pitcher-like leaves of insectivorous plants, preying on the unfortunate creatures that chance to wander or fall into these death-traps. In rock-pools of the sea-shore the larvae of several species of midges live among the green algae, into whose fronds they burrow. Certain of the tiny wingless insects known popularly as "spring-tails" because of their hopping propensities disport themselves on the surface of water, both fresh and salt, and one at least can remain submerged for weeks on end. A very few marine caddis-worms are also known. Yet insects in general have fought shy of the ocean, although a peculiar genus of water-skating bugs (*Halobates*), not distantly related to those which skim over the surface of our village ponds, glide over the calm seas of the tropics, often hundreds of miles from land, and lay their eggs on floating objects such as scraps of drift-wood or the feathers of birds. On the other hand, a great number of insects, especially beetles, make their home on the beach and are often submerged twice daily by the tides. They lurk under stones or among weed, and the velvety pile which clothes parts of their bodies entangles sufficient atmospheric air for their needs until the water subsides.

For practical purposes most water-frequenting insects may be divided into three main groups, namely (1) the surface dwellers, (2) those that live in water or wet mud but have periodically to make contact with the surface in order to breathe, (3) those that are constantly submerged and—like fishes—soon perish if transferred to atmospheric air. It should be noted that the imago or perfect insect is never completely aquatic, and that even when it spends most of its time in water it is able to live on the land and in some instances habitually makes long flights.

The best-known examples of the first group are the pond-skating bugs—or "water-measurers"—which normally glide over the surface of stagnant pools and sluggish streams, although they make occasional excursions among the herbage on the banks. Their ability to move about—even to leap—on the water without being wetted is due in large measure to the fact that the molecules of the liquid when in contact with those of the atmosphere are in a peculiar condition of aggregation which simulates the physical properties of an extremely thin, elastic membrane. This surface-film, as it is called, having a rough resemblance to a delicate sheet of stretched indiarubber, offers resistance to the passage of solid

The little bombardier beetle, pursued by an enemy, ejects
from its rear-end a puff of acid vapour or "tear gas"

bodies, and can therefore support a weight so long as it remains
unbroken. The reason why the legs of skater-bugs do not break
through it is that they—and, indeed, the rest of the body—are
clothed with a velvet-like pile which repels moisture; so that even
when these insects are completely submerged they carry with them a
silvery envelope of air which the water cannot displace, and when
they come again to the surface they are quite unwetted.

Of our ten or twelve British skaters, all very much alike to
the uninstructed eye, the commonest may be found in the young
stages of its development from April to September. The adults do
not hibernate, but dart about on the water in all but the coldest
weather, laying their eggs, enveloped in mucilage, on submerged
plants during the spring. The fore-limbs are prehensile, the weight
of the body being supported by the long and slender middle and
hind legs, of which the former are used chiefly for locomotion, the
latter for steering. Some forms of this insect are wingless, while
those which have wings seem unable to use them. The nearly related
water-gnat or water-measurer is very different in appearance, with
all six legs long and slender and its head one-third the length of its
whole body. Its habits, too, are quite distinct, for its does no skating
or leaping, but creeps sluggishly on the surface-film or mud, and is
often found on merely damp soil among vegetation. Another
distinct but allied insect (*Velia currens*), which has no English
name, rejoices in the eddies and currents of swiftly flowing brooks
and streams, and may sometimes be seen to run, back downwards,
on the underside of the surface-film. Compared with the foregoing
it is more sturdy and thick-set, with much shorter legs. All these
surface-dwelling water-bugs feed chiefly by sucking the juices of
dead or dying insects floating on the water, though it is possible
that some of them occasionally capture living prey.

Other interesting surface-dwellers are the small whirligig

beetles, whose middle and hind legs are remarkably paddle-shaped, the efficiency of the latter being enhanced by a fringe of long, stiff hairs. They spend most of their time in mazy gyrations on the surface-film, but dive instantaneously if alarmed, carrying with them a bubble of air at their tail-end. They are also good flyers. Their fore-legs are very little modified and serve chiefly for seizing and holding food, which consists mainly of small dead insects; but in the case of the males they are used for grasping the opposite sex when pairing. Each compound eye is divided into two separate portions, one part directed upwards, the other downwards— which suggests that these insects can peer into the water and at the same time keep watch for any danger which may threaten from the air; but this attractive theory still lacks completely confirmatory evidence. The whirligigs may be said to live a double life, in the sense that their larvae are completely aquatic and breathe by means of gills. Thus, they really belong to our third group—not, like the adults, to the first. They live in mud at the bottom of pools and slowly moving streams, and are sometimes found in company with the larvae of alder-flies, to which they bear a superficial like-ness. When full grown they creep up the stem of a water-plant, and spin small, oval cocoons in which they pupate.

No better example of our second group of aquatic insects could be chosen than the common diving beetle. Its oval somewhat flattened body with the surface highly polished is streamlined to perfection. The hind legs are modified to serve as oars, and—by a peculiar keel-like extension of the thorax—are set far back, below the axis. Thanks to this arrangement, and the ample play allowed by their articulation, they can be brought at right angles to the body, thus making possible a strong and wide sweep. Normally, these limbs operate simultaneously, but they can be used singly for the purpose of turning in a confined space—just as an expert sculler uses one oar to manœuvre his skiff. Although somewhat clumsy at pedestrianism, these diving beetles can make shift to shuffle faster than might be expected over the ground, and their broad wings enable them to make long voyages through the air; so that if one pool or mere is not to their liking they quit it at night and fly to another, into which they drop vertically, sometimes from a con-siderable height, being guided, it is said, by moonlight reflected from the water—a supposition borne out by the fact that they occasionally land upon the glass roofs of greenhouses! The rapacious larvae, which are often called "water-tigers", have grooved jaws through which they suck the juices of their victims, having first injected a peptic fluid that liquefies the tissues. This method of feeding, termed "external digestion", is practised by a number of other larvae, including those of the glow-worm; but the adult diving beetle tears its food apart with its toothed mandibles and swallows it in solid fragments after the more ordinary fashion. When full fed the larva forms a cell in the bank, where it changes to the pupa. The adults emerge in the spring, at which season the eggs are inserted into the stems of rushes and other aquatic plants; but they live for more than one year, and except in the coldest weather remain active throughout the winter.

The spiracles are not placed along the side of the body as is usual with most terrestrial insects, but open on the back beneath the elytra. Moreover, the two posterior pairs are unusually large and the edges of the elytra fit closely against the abdomen, forming an air-tight chamber occupied in part by the folded wings. When the beetle needs to take breath it poises itself in the water, thrusts its tail-end through the surface-film, and slightly depresses the tip of its abdomen, with the result that air rushes into the four large spiracles, filling also the space between the elytra and the back. The chink is then closed tightly and the insect is ready for another diving excursion. Timing of specimens confined in an aquarium shows that males normally rise to the surface once in every eight minutes and twenty seconds on an average, but they are able to remain submerged for as long as nineteen minutes. Females, being less active than their mates, are more economical in their use of oxygen and so come up less frequently for a fresh supply. In the case of the larva all but the last two spiracles at the pointed extremity of the abdomen are obsolete, and from these water is excluded by the folding together of hair-fringed flaps, or cerci, which—when the creature comes up to breath—are spread out horizontally on the surface-film, allowing air to enter the tracheal tubes.

A quite different method of breathing is practised by the silver-bellied or great water-beetle, which is not uncommon in ponds and deep ditches throughout the southern and south-eastern counties of England. This is our bulkiest British beetle, although its length is exceeded by the stag beetle because of the latter's enormously elongated jaws. Like the diving beetle it has an air-reservoir between the elytra and the upper surface of the abdomen, but when submerged carries an additional supply in the form of a silvery breastplate. It comes head first to the surface to replenish its store of oxygen and its manner of doing this is very remarkable. The joints of the antennae are broad and hairy and serve as little ladles by means of which air is scooped down to velvety tracts on the underside of the body which communicate with the dorsal reservoir. The normal function of the antennae seems to have been taken over by the maxillary palpi, which are unusually long and resemble "feelers". The adult female is equipped with a silk-spinning apparatus conjoined with her ovipositor, with which she constructs a boat-like cocoon, complete with a little mast, for the reception of from 50 to 100 eggs. As an adult, this beetle's tastes are mainly vegetarian, but its podgy, slow-moving larva feeds on small water-snails. It takes in air through two spiracles at its tail-end, and when full grown quits the water to pupate in moist soil.

Apart from the surface-dwellers already dealt with, British water-bugs fall into two groups which may be designated the swimmers and the creepers. The best-known representative of the first is the common water-boatman, called also back-swimmer because of its habit of swimming upside-down. It is very active and agile, using its long hind-legs with the skill of a practised sculler, and carrying with it when submerged a supply of atmospheric air entangled among the hairs of its body. It feeds on any small aquatic creatures that it can capture, and should be handled with caution, since a stab from its sucking-beak is almost as painful as a bee's sting. So much air is taken down by this insect that it can remain below for a lengthy period and is so buoyant that when not actually swimming it must needs hold on to some support or it will rise like a bubble to the surface.

Several of the lesser water-boatmen, of which there are a score or more British species, might at first sight be mistaken for their namesake; but they swim back uppermost, and—since they are much less active than the true boatman—the supply of air which is carried down when they dive enables them to remain submerged for a much longer period. They spend most of their time among weeds at the bottom, where—after the manner of the diving beetle— the female inserts her eggs into the stems of plants. Furthermore, and unlike other water-bugs, they are supposed to be vegetarians, though there is still some doubt on this point. By rubbing their fore-legs together, or against some part of the head, certain of these insects are able to produce tolerably loud and sustained sounds, this peculiarity being shared by the tiniest member of the family, a midget only one-twenty-fifth of an inch long, which lives in the cavities of fresh-water sponges.

More beetle-like than any of the foregoing is the Naucoris, another bug whose "beak", though short, is strong and very sharply pointed, and capable of piercing the human skin. Although very common, it has no English name, but may be regarded as our nearest native relative of the big "fish-killers", some of which have already been referred to, since they rank among the giants of the insect world.

The creeping water-bugs are represented in this country by two insects very different in appearance, yet both members of the same family. These are the water-scorpion and the so-called water stick-insect. The former is flat and thick-set, the latter slender and long-drawn-out. Both, however, have the fore-legs modified for capturing prey, while the abdomen terminates in two long, slender half-tubes which when brought together interlock and form a channel or "syphon" through which air is conveyed to the tracheal system when the tip is thrust through the surface-film. Some exotic species, notably one from Lake Tanganyika, have remarkably long syphons and can reach the atmosphere while still resting on the bottom in fairly deep water; the rest must climb up the stem of a plant when they need to take breath. A curious fact about our native species is that although they have well-developed wings which look serviceable they are unable to fly because the principal wing-muscles have atrophied. Why this should be is hard to understand, since the Swedish observer Ossian Larsen has told us that during exceptionally severe winters in his country when the ponds have been frozen over for long periods the water-bugs that could fly escaped from them in time, whereas those which could not perished by suffocation.

In their larval and pupal stages the gnats and mosquitoes are incompletely aquatic, needing like the beetles and bugs already described to come periodically to the surface to breathe. The familiar "wrigglers" that are often numerous in water-butts and cisterns during the summer season are the larvae of the common gnat. Each is furnished with a respiratory tube near the tail-end, and this communicates with the tracheal system. When taking in air these larvae suspend themselves at an angle from the surface-film, whereas those of the spotted-winged species, which have no breathing-tube or syphon, but whose spiracles open on the eighth segment of the abdomen—lie immediately beneath it horizontally. In each case the method of feeding is essentially the same, minute, floating organic particles being swept together by a pair of brush-like appendages (or "fans") situated in the neighbourhood of the mouth and combed by bristle-beset jaws into the gullet. The curiously formed pupae float normally at the surface, breathing through a pair of funnel-shaped openings on the thorax; but they, too, are active and at the first sign of danger jerk themselves into the depths by vigorous flappings of their tails.

The larva of one species of gnat—although, like its relations, it is devoid of gills—contrives nevertheless to remain permanently submerged by obtaining its oxygen from plants, using its syphon— which has been specially modified into a pointed instrument—to pierce their stems and roots. Similarly, the grubs of the very attractive riverside beetles—resplendent in shades of metallic blue, green, purple and red—live buried in wet mud on the roots of various sedges and grasses. They have two sharp, tubular processes near the anal end of the body, which they drive into air-spaces of the plant's tissues and in this way extract sufficient oxygen for their needs.

We now come to three types of two-winged flies whose larvae aerate their tissues by means of outstandingly remarkable adaptations. The common drone-fly is one of a group of species whose larvae are the rat-tailed maggots that live by preference in dirty water. The distinctive "tail" contains an extension of the tracheal system and consists of three attenuated abdominal segments capable, like a telescope, of extension and contraction, so that in shallow pools the tip can always be kept just above the surface. If, however, the water should increase in depth to more than about six inches the maggot must either creep along the bottom to some point of elevation or allow itself to float upward, in order to maintain its communication with the atmosphere. These larvae and their habits are curiously paralleled by those of certain crane-flies, which are often numerous in the mud of shallow pools, from which they send up their whip-like tails to puncture the surface-film. They may be known apart by their more slender form and the fact that—unlike those of the drone-fly—they have small but distinct heads. The larvae of the handsome soldier fly and some of its near relatives, usually found in stagnant ditches, swim jerkily in the water or—when in need of oxygen—hang motionless with their tail-tips exposed to the atmosphere. At this extremity there is a circlet of about thirty branched filaments, the structure and function of which are described by

L. C. Miall in the following passage : "When this coronet is expanded it forms a basin open to the air and impervious to water, by reason of the fineness of the meshes between the component filaments. Were the larva provided with a basin of the same proportions formed out of continuous membrane it might float and breathe perfectly well, but would find it hard to free itself neatly and quickly from the surface-film when some sudden emergency rendered it necessary to descend. As it is, the plumed filaments collapse and their points approach ; the side branches are folded in, and the basin is in a moment reduced to a pear-shaped body, filled with a globule of air, and reaching the surface of the water only by its pointed extremity. Down goes the larva at the first hint of danger, swimming through the water by swaying and looping movements. . . . When the danger is past, it ceases to struggle, and floats again to the surface or swims upwards by a lashing movement. The pointed tip of its tail-fringe pierces the surface-film, the filaments separate once more, and the floating basis is restored." All these three types of larvae normally leave the water when their time for feeding ends and pupate in damp earth or under cover of decaying vegetation.

The insects so far mentioned in this chapter perish by suffocation if they are forced to remain submerged for more than a limited period. They are equipped, so to say, with a serviceable diving apparatus, but are entirely dependent upon a supply of atmospheric air. Those of our third group—the completely aquatic—can remain below indefinitely because they are able to utilize the air which is dissolved in water. In the very young nymphs of many species, such as may-flies and some dragon-flies, aeration of the blood is effected through the skin. But as growth proceeds specialized gills are usually developed. These are very diverse in form and situation, but in general they may be described as thin-walled outgrowths of the integument containing delicate branches of the tracheal system, into which oxygen extracted from the water penetrates—though exactly how this happens is not yet perfectly understood.

The larvae of whirligig beetles, of alder-flies and the nymphs of many may-flies, have branching or leaf-like gills at the sides of the abdominal segments. Other species carry their gills like tails at the end of the hind-body. The nymphs of some stone-flies—so called because they usually lurk under stones at the bottom of rapidly flowing streams—breathe cutaneously during the whole of their aquatic existence, but our largest representatives of the family, such as the twin-spotted species, develop after the earlier moults twelve tufts of gill-filaments beneath the thorax and two smaller ones at the extremity of the abdomen between the cerci. Some stone-fly lymphs might be mistaken for those of may-flies, but can easily be distinguished since they have only a pair of these tail-filaments, or cerci, whereas the may-fly nymphs usually have three. The larger dragon-fly nymphs have their gills in the posterior part of the alimentary canal, into which water is drawn and expelled, normally by a gentle pulsation of the abdomen; but in the event of alarm it may be ejected suddenly and with so much force that the creature's body is propelled forward to a considerable distance. The nymphs of the smaller or "demoiselle" dragon-flies carry their gills externally as "caudal appendages". During the later stages of their development, however, the thoracic spiracles of all dragon-fly nymphs are open and the insect obtains at least some of its oxygen by raising the front part of its body above the surface of the water.

With the possible exception of diving beetles and their larvae dragon-fly nymphs are the most rapacious of all aquatic insects. For the capture of their prey they are equipped with a unique development of the second maxillae or labium called the "mask", which when not in use lies folded back beneath the head, but can be shot out with great rapidity, the prey being seized by means of terminal hooks and then drawn back to the mouth, when it is torn in pieces by the powerful jaws.

Whirligig beetles and the common alder-fly live as larvae at the bottom of pools and slowly moving water, often hidden in the mud. They are predatory after a somewhat indolent fashion, whereas the larva of the strange little sponge-fly—a relative of the lacewings—resides in the cavities of fresh-water sponges, where it feeds as a parasite by probing their tissues with its long, needle-like jaws. All these larvae leave the water when full grown to pupate, but the nymphs of may-flies, stone-flies and dragon-flies simply creep into the air; after which the winged adults emerge. Gill structures are discarded when this last moult takes place, except in the case of the stone-flies, some of which retain these organs in the adult state, though whether or not they still function is uncertain. But the fact that they persist suggests that the aquatic habit of these insects may be of very ancient origin, going back, perhaps, to a period when the atmosphere was much more heavily charged with moisture than it is today. This supposition gains support from the discovery of fossilized gill-bearing adult insects, possibly ancestors of existing stone-flies, dating from the immensely remote Carboniferous Period.

A good deal has been said in Chapter Eleven concerning the case-making capabilities of caddis-worms. After feeding for several months the larva closes both ends of its case with a webbing of silk, thus converting it into a cocoon in which it changes to the pupa. Like the larva the pupa is equipped with powerful mandibles; but these are used only once—to cut a way out of the case—and are discarded with the pupal skin at the final moult. After effecting its escape, the pupa swims to the surface, using its middle pair of legs which are developed like oars for the purpose. It then climbs up some convenient stem or post, its skin splits down the back, and the perfect insect emerges.

A considerable number of small Dipterous larvae are completely aquatic, never coming to the surface for oxygen. Of these the following examples may be regarded as typical. The first, known popularly as the "phantom", completes its metamorphosis by changing into a small gnat-like insect. When full grown it is about half an inch long, yet but for its black eyes and two pairs of dark, air-filled flotation sacs at either end of the body it would be completely invisible when it remains motionless, as is its habit, in the clear water which it frequents. It feeds on any tiny living creatures that come its way, seizing them—of all things!—with its antennae, which are armed with sharp, curved spines for impaling the victims; and we may infer that its transparency and immobility are important factors in providing it with a plenitude of meals. Respiration must be effected through the skin, since at this stage of its existence the tracheal system is imperfectly developed, and there are no gills. But the pupa floats at the surface of the water and has a pair of breathing-funnels, not unlike those of the common gnat's, through which it takes in its oxygen.

Our second type of completely aquatic Dipterous larvae is exemplified by those of certain midges which go by the name "blood-worms" because of their bright red colour. Special interest attaches to these creatures which breathe cutaneously and inhabit tubular burrows in mud at the bottom of stagnant water, in view of the fact that their blood, like that of many other animals, including man, contains haemoglobin—a substance capable of forming what is termed a "loose combination" with oxygen, so that this vitalizing gas can be surrendered subsequently to the tissues of the body without

L

chemical decomposition. In short, the blood of these larvae plays a
part in respiration all but unique among insects, and its redness
enables them to profit to the utmost by the very scanty supply of
oxygen which their environment affords.

Completely submerged Dipterous larvae of a third type are
found among the sand-flies and black flies, better known in North
America as buffalo-gnats and turkey-gnats. About five-eighths of an
inch long when full grown, they resemble small black worms or
leeches, and live in swiftly flowing—even turbulent—water, anchored
by a circlet of minute hooks at the tail-end, sometimes to the surface
of rocks or stones, but more often to the stems or leaves of aquatic
plants. Having also a second organ of attachment—a single pro-leg
or "foot" immediately behind its rather large head—the larva can
progress by a looping motion not unlike that of a Geometrid or
"measuring" caterpillar, but normally it remains fixed in one spot,
the body stuck straight out into the current, with the conspicuous
"mouth-fans" sweeping microscopic food-particles into the gullet.
After moulting six times it spins a pouch-like cocoon of dark silk,
with its broad, open end—from which the respiratory filaments of
the pupa subsequently protrude—facing downstream. When the
adult is almost ready to emerge, air collects within the pupal skin,
which eventually splits open, so that the insect escapes and is carried
to the surface in a bubble without being wetted and instantly,
spreading its wings flies to a nearby resting-place. In some countries
the female flies of this family are notorious for their blood-sucking
habits, and have caused serious losses among farm stock. In Britain,
happily—although their bite is annoying and even painful to human
beings—they are not sufficiently numerous to be called pests.

In the above paragraphs only a few of the more typical aquatic
insects indigenous to Britain have been mentioned. A bare list of
those which have been studied more or less closely—to say nothing
of the very numerous species whose structure and habits still await
investigation—would fill many pages. Readers who are attracted
by statistics may find the following table interesting.

Plecoptera (Stone-flies) ..	Stages preceding the imago always aquatic, breathing dissolved air cutaneously or by means of gills.
Ephemeroptera (May-flies)	
Odonata (Dragon-flies) ..	
Trichoptera (Caddis-flies)	
Hemiptera (Bugs)	About one-third of the bugs (Sub-order Heteroptera), are more or less aquatic in all stages, breathing atmospheric air.

Neuroptera (Alder-flies, etc.)	In one family (*Sialidae*—alder-flies) the larvae are aquatic, breathing dissolved air by means of gills, but the pupae are terrestrial. Larvae of the genus *Sisyra* live as parasites in the cavities of freshwater sponges.
Coleoptera (Beetles) ..	Water-beetles are fairly numerous, some being aquatic in all stages of their development. Larvae and imagines usually come to the surface to breathe atmospheric air, but in some instances (e.g. larvae of *Gyrinus*—whirligig beetles) dissolved air is absorbed by means of gills. The pupal stage is nearly always terrestrial.
Diptera (Two-winged Flies)	A considerable number of two-winged flies live either in water or very wet situations during the early stages of their development, breathing atmospheric air at the surface, or (when continuously submerged) dissolved air cutaneously or by means of gills.

Besides the above, the caterpillars of several moths are aquatic, some possessing gills, while others appear to absorb their supply of oxygen through the skin. That of the brown china-mark moth is a notable example. It is often common in pools, where it feeds on the floating leaves of water-lily, pond-weed, etc., to the underside of which the female fixes her eggs. At first the larva burrows into the tissues of the leaf, but later it cuts out two oval pieces and fixes them together with silk to form a sheath or case. By some means not perfectly understood it contrives to keep the interior of this habitation dry and filled with air, so that although frequently submerged it can still breathe in the way usual with insects—i.e. through open spiracles. The caterpillar of the ringed china-mark moth of the same genus has gill-tufts along the sides of its body and lives continuously beneath the surface in a retreat formed by spinning together leaves of the water-soldier or some other aquatic plant, where it also spins its cocoon. Yet another of these unconventional moths has two kinds of females, one winged, capable of aerial excursions, the other almost wingless, spending its whole life under water, where it swims by means of its legs.

No less astonishing are the habits of certain aquatic ichneumons. One remains submerged for lengthy periods in order to lay its eggs in caddis-worms, which its larvae subsequently destroy, afterwards

spinning their cocoons in the cases of their victims. Mention should
also be made of the minute "fairy flies", several of which enter the
water to lay their eggs in those of larger aquatic insects, such as
dragon-flies and beetles. Most of these midgets employ their legs
in swimming, but one of them uses its wings as paddles. In other
words, it flies underwater!

Chapter Eighteen

INSECTS AND PLANTS

THE most obvious relation of insects to plants is that they—in common with all other forms of animal life—depend absolutely on the vegetable kingdom for the wherewithal of subsistence. Many insects, as we have seen, are predacious or feed as parasites, but upon investigation their victims will nearly always turn out to be vegetarians. Green plants, in short, are the universal providers of animate nature. By taking carbon dioxide from the atmosphere and combining it with water and salts drawn from the soil, they produce the essentials of living matter—starch, sugar, fats and proteins—not only for their own maintenance but in the last analysis for that of all animals as well. The part played by animals in what is termed the "circulation of matter" is that by living they return carbon dioxide to the atmosphere which can be used again by plants, and by their excreta and ultimate decomposition replenish the soil with the so-called organic elements of which their bodies are built up.

Many kinds of insects—notably gregarious caterpillars and leaf-eating beetles in Britain, and locusts in those countries which they ravage—cause widespread devastation among trees and crops by denuding them of their foliage. The caterpillars of the black-arched tussock moth are sometimes excessively destructive to fir forests on the Continent, stripping the trees so completely as to kill them. Those of the allied gipsy moth, accidentally introduced to America from Europe, did incalculable damage to hard-wood and fruit trees before they could be brought under control. The Colorado potato beetle, a native of South America now firmly established on this side of the Atlantic, is so serious a pest that large sums of money are expended annually in efforts to check its spread and increase.

Yet insects are by no means always inimical to plants, but sometimes serve as their unwitting helpers. A fact not generally realized is that certain ants aid the dispersal of various shrubs, herbs and grasses by carrying about their fruits and seeds. Those most eagerly pounced upon—e.g. dog-violet and gorse—have at one end a fleshy outgrowth, or caruncle, by which the ants set especial store. When engaged in transporting these to their nests they not infrequently abandon some; and it is noticeable that even when the caruncle has been completely eaten off germination occurs in due season, and the seedling is able to develop at a spot more or less remote from that occupied by the parent. Seeds of other kinds are collected for storage, and, after treatment in various ways, used as food. These "harvesting ants", as they are called, are common in southern Italy, where they were observed by J. T. Moggridge systematically to garner the seeds of speedwell, nettle, fumitary and other plants, as well as oat grains. Most of these were gathered from the ground, but some ants, more enterprising than their fellows, were seen to climb up stems and detach the seeds, which they either carried down or dropped to the ground to be retrieved later. The harvest is stored in special chambers, of which each community is said to possess about one hundred, with a total capacity of twenty ounces or more. Until they are needed for food the ants prevent the seeds from sprouting—probably by keeping them cool and dry; but when rations are needed they are encouraged to germinate, so that their stored starch is converted into sugar, which the ants consume, having first arrested further growth by nipping off the young shoots.

The harvesting ants of Texas were formerly said to practise a primitive kind of agriculture by clearing away all the vegetation in the vicinity of their nest save two species of grass, the seeds of which —known locally as "ant-rice"—are especially liked by these insects. Recent investigations have tended to discredit this specious story. Certainly these ants assiduously collect the grass seeds and maintain a clearing around the domed nest; but the latter labour seems to be undertaken with the object of securing a warmed, dry area where the larvae may be sunned and the seeds dried. The reason why the nest is surrounded by little else than these favourite grasses is that the ants habitually carry out seeds that have sprouted too far to be fit for food and dump them at the periphery of the cleared circle, where they frequently take root and grow; so that—after all—the activities of these astonishing little insects do result in the production of near-at-hand crops of the kind of seeds which they prize most!

That certain kinds of ants and white ants, or termites, cultivate fungi for food is beyond question. For the first detailed account of the habits of the tropical American saüba ants we are indebted to H. W. Bates. The workers issue from their nests in gangs, ascend trees and, by half cutting, half tearing, detach pieces of leaf, which are carried to their subterranean galleries. The insects are often so numerous and work with so much energy that trees are sometimes completely denuded of their foliage in the course of a few hours. Bates was not able to satisfy himself as to what use the ants made of their spoils, but another naturalist—Thomas Belt—discovered that the original pieces of leaf, after conveyance to the nest, were cut into tiny fragments and piled up in special chambers to form sponge-like masses, which subsequently became covered with a minute white fungus, upon which the ants appeared to feed. It remained for Fritz Müller to complete this fascinating

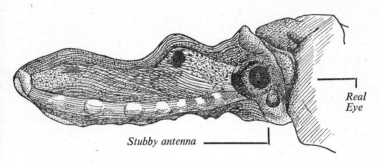

Real Eye

Stubby antenna

The extraordinary profile of the South American alligator bug. The hollow snout is marked with mock eye, nostril and teeth. The real eye is seen on the right above the stubby antenna

history. He found that the ants keep their fungus-beds clear from bacterial and other foreign intrusions and by a method known only to themselves induce the production of little white masses which form the chief food of the community. Moreover, he demonstrated by experiment that these miniature mushrooms, as they may fairly be styled, were only produced when the fungus was tended by ants.

Termites or white ants, many of whose manners and customs seem to have been imitated by the true ants, were presumably first in the field as fungus-growers, and continue to practise the art as it was performed by their remote ancestors millions of years ago. As a rule, the workers heap up chewed wood to form beds, which soon become plentifully sprinkled with small, white, fungoid growths of a peculiar kind, believed to be due to termite cultivation. When a portion of the prepared wood, or "mushroom cake" as it has been called, becomes exhausted, it is removed and replaced by a fresh supply. The fungus extracts from the wood its nitrogenous content, and the insects thus secure a supply of concentrated food, which is said to be employed chiefly for nourishing the rising generation. The workers of at least one African termite have been observed to issue from the nest at high noon to collect grass, specially cut in lengths of about two inches, which when carried home are no doubt stacked and used as mushroom-beds.

The special association of insects with flowers is a topic which must be reserved for a separate chapter: but we may note here that ants in general play no part in this symbiotic or mutual-benefit relationship. On the contrary, they are commonly treated by plants as intruders and denied access to the essential organs by sticky secretions on the flower-stalks—as in some of the catch-flies and campions—or more commonly by obstructing hairs on the calyx or in the throat of the corolla. The "honey-glands" which occur on the leaves or petioles of some plants—e.g. plum, cherry and cherry-laurel—may quite likely serve to divert the attention of ants and other wingless insects from the flowers, where they are not wanted.

Nevertheless, that ants serve as bodyguards to certain plants is a fact first brought to light by Thomas Belt in the course of his travels in the Central American Republic of Nicaragua. He noticed that the twin thorns of the bull's-horn acacias growing in this area are nearly always tenanted by ants, which "make a small hole for their entrance and exit near one of the tips and also burrow through the partition that separates the two thorns, so that one entrance serves for both". The soft young thorns are filled with a sweetish pulp, which the ants eat out, leaving the walls to harden, and afterwards using the interior as a nest in which to store their food and rear their young.

Further investigation showed that these ants protect the tree, more especially from the assaults of their leaf-cutting kindred, whose depredations have already been mentioned. If so much as a leaf of the acacia is touched or a branch shaken the defenders swarm out from their retreats by thousands, ready to attack with jaws and stings, and usually succeed in driving off marauders—even, it is said, browsing beasts—for their sting is extremely painful. In return (so to say) for their services the tree supplies the ants with food as well as shelter. Crater-like glands at the base of the petioles or leaf-stalks secrete a sugary fluid of which the ants are very fond, while many of the bipinnate leaflets are tipped with small "pseudo-fruits" known as "Belt's bodies". These latter, being rich in albumen and easily broken off, are sedulously collected as they ripen by the ants, which appear to subsist almost exclusively upon the two kinds of food provided by the tree.

Belt also found ants of other genera living habitually in the hollow swellings at the juncture of the leaf-stalks with the stems of other Nicaraguan plants related to the myrtle and eucalyptus; and, more recently, numerous examples of myrmecophyly—as this association is called—have been recorded, both in the Old and New World, a large percentage of them relating to epiphytic or "perched" plants. These latter, clinging to elevated supports, usually the branches of trees, and without contact with the soil, have a precarious water supply, and in consequence frequently develop special moisture-storing structures. An example is the cow-horn orchid of Honduras, which, at the approach of the dry season, produces "pseudo-bulbs"—really hollow resting-stems a foot or two in length—in the thick walls of which food materials and water are conserved. At the base there is always a small opening that admits ants to the interior, which they fit up with galleries and cells, converting it into a regular formicarium, or ant-city, to be defended against all comers.

Other epiphytic orchids, growing in the dripping forests of Guiana, produce special masses of fibrous roots—quite distinct from their ordinary aerial roots—among which ants make their homes, filling in the interstices with particles of soil carried up from the ground. According to James Rodway, their discoverer, the ants, being in the main carnivorous, "can do the plant no harm, but on the contrary are so useful that without them it suffers greatly from cockroaches and other pests".

In some of the islands and archipelagos of the East Indies a score or more of very remarkable ants'-nest plants grow as epiphytes in the forest areas. Their peculiarity is that the base of the stem consists of a globular mass of tissue riddled by a labyrinth of chambers and passages invariably inhabited by colonies of ants, notable for their pugnacity and the virulence of their stings. Opinion is still divided as to how the tumours of these strange plants take their origin. According to H. N. Moseley—the naturalist of the *Challenger* expedition, who studied them growing wild in Amboina —as soon as a stem develops the ants gnaw and excavate its base, and the irritation thus set up induces a swelling which may become larger than a man's head. He adds that without their insect associates these plants cannot thrive. But H. O. Forbes, who subsequently succeeded in raising specimens from seed in complete isolation from ants, found that they grew vigorously and developed tumours from the outset. Moreover, it seems certain that at first the whole mass of the swollen stem—save for a central chamber containing water—is filled with a delicate pith, and that the ants excavate this before going into residence.

The most extraordinary case of myrmecophyly on record is that of certain very abnormal East Indian epiphytes called *Dischidia*. Like other "perched plants" they have no contact with the soil, and so are mainly dependent on atmospheric moisture for their water supply. Many of their congeners collect between their closely set leaves a certain quantity of humus mixed with organic dust carried up by the wind; but *Dischidia* has gone one better than this by evolving pitcher-shaped leaves of a unique type—one pitcher inside another like the cook's double-saucepan or the carpenter's glue-pot! The inner pitcher appears to serve for catching insects of various kinds, which are subsequently digested and assimilated. but the function of the outer pitcher is quite different. Its stomata, or breathing pores, open on its inner surface, so that whatever vapour is given off in transpiration condenses, and becomes available for further use. The inner walls of this outer pitcher also secrete a sweet substance very similar to grape sugar in its chemical composition. This attracts ants, which, having entered and fed, find things so much to their liking that they start house-keeping, carrying up soil from the ground to build cells and galleries. Thus in the end the space between the two pitchers is converted into a sort of flower-pot, filled with moist earth, into which the plant sends a special root system to absorb water and chemical nutriment for its own use. Speaking in human terms, therefore, we may say that the plant bribes the ants to make their home in its pitchers and by so doing does itself a very good turn!

Mention in the preceding paragraph of "pitchers" which catch and digest insects introduces a somewhat sinister aspect of our subject. That insects should eat plants seems reasonable enough, but the reverse of this procedure strikes one at first sight as rather shocking. Yet, in fact, some 450 species of plants belonging to several distinct families are insectivorous wholly or in part, having been driven to this expedient—so it is said—by a paucity of nitrates in the soil or water where they grow. Several different methods of capturing the prey have been evolved. Among the true pitcher plants the leaf, or leaf-stalk, takes the form of a hollow vessel which may be described as a combination of lure, pitfall and stomach.

The inner walls are either intensely slippery or beset with minute, downward-pointing hairs—devices which favour the ingress of a victim but effectually prevent its escape. The lower part of this pitcher or drowning-pot is charged with liquid which may be in part rain-water, but is largely the secretion of special glands. There are two types of these pitchers, one (*Nepenthes*) pendent from a long stalk, the other (*Sarracenia* and *Darlingtonia*) rising elegant and vase-like from the soil. Both are attractively coloured, and secrete nectar from glands in the neighbourhood of the mouth. Insects are completely deceived by their resemblance to flowers and creep into the pitchers or fly to them from a distance, and after feasting on the sugary bait usually wander or slip downwards until they reach the water. Winged species often make desperate efforts to extricate themselves by flight ; but they buffet against the sides of their prison, or knock against the leaf-like lid that guards the approach to the mouth, until they are exhausted. Few succeed in making good their escape. The majority fall sooner or later into the bath, where they drown, and their soft tissues are slowly digested and absorbed by the plant.

Apart from the winged insects caught by these plants many more visit the pitchers—some, such as ants, to imbibe the sugary secretion, others to feed on the ensnared victims. For the latter purpose

The diving beetle "taking breath" with its tail-end thrust through the surface film of the water

toads, tree-frogs and lizards also frequent the immediate neighbourhood, while at least one spider normally makes its web just
below the pitcher's rim and so takes toll of the plant's lawful prey.
Still other insects—e.g. mosquitoes and small dragon-flies—pass
the early stage of their existence in the fluid content, though how they
contrive to escape being digested is an unsolved puzzle.

The true pitcher-plants belong to tropical or sub-tropical
regions; but we have in Britain an interesting water-plant, the
bladderwort, which captures its prey in a somewhat similar manner.
In this instance the traps are little bladder-like structures, the
orifices of which are closed by valves so contrived that tiny creatures
can enter the fatal door but not return. It used to be stated that they
push their way in of their own volition in order to escape pursuing
enemies. But investigations by F. E. Lloyd have shown that the
bladder does the catching by means of long, sensitive hairs which
protrude from the valve. When one of these is touched by a small
aquatic creature the valve springs open and the wall of the bladder
simultaneously expands, with the result that more water is sucked
in, together with the prey. After this the valve closes, and in a period
varying from twenty minutes to half an hour the process of digestion
is completed and the trap re-sets itself.

The butterworts and the sundews are both represented in Britain
by several species. The leaves of the former are sticky, and small
insects which settle on them are held fast as by a fly-paper. After a
capture the edges of the leaf curl slowly inwards and a peptic secretion is poured forth by which the meal is slowly digested and absorbed.

In their way, the leaves of the sundews are as highly specialized
as those of the pitcher-plants, though along very different lines.
From their upper surface radiate numerous red hairs or tentacles,
each tipped with a drop of clear mucilage—this glistening array
being very attractive to insects. When one alights upon the leaf it is
unable to escape. The tentacles bend slowly over, carrying the
victim to the centre of the leaf, where it is drenched with digestive
fluid. The sundew's leaf is an extremely sensitive organ. It will
detect and bend towards a dead fly or an atom of lean meat placed
in its near neighbourhood, and may even lay hold of the coveted
dainty if the distance to be covered does not exceed half an inch.
But if a grain of sand or a tiny pellet of blotting-paper is dropped
upon it the fraud is at once detected by the tentacles and the object
is slowly discarded. Captured insects that are too large to be

digested by the leaf are dropped to the ground, which they serve to fertilize.

The most remarkable of all insectivorous plants is the Venus's fly-trap of North America. Darwin called it "the most wonderful plant in the world", and certainly in the structure and sensitivity of its leaves it stands unique. Each leaf consists of two components, a flat stalk with foliaceous expansions on each side, and a bilobed blade bordered with long, curved spines. Three delicate, almost invisible, bristles on each lobe act, so to say, as triggers to the mechanism. Normally, the mature blade, or "trap", is spread out flat or nearly so; but if an insect ventures upon it and comes into contact, as it is almost certain to do, with one of the bristles, the two lobes come together with considerable rapidity and force, so that the intruder is imprisoned beneath the interlocking marginal spines. Then the plant pours digestive fluids upon its victim and literally makes a meal of all but its hard integuments, which are cast out when the leaf re-sets itself. Darwin found that each leaf is able to deal with at least two, sometimes three, insects in succession, after which it withers and makes way for a young successor.

A floating aquatic, a native of southern and central Europe, where it occurs in ditches and pools of clear water, has gin-like leaves similar in structure to, but much smaller than, those of the Venus's fly-trap. The swimming larvae of gnats and the like, as well as tiny crustaceans, make up the bulk of its captures; but whether these meet their fate by misadventure, or are attracted by a seductive secretion, has not been ascertained; nor do we know by what artifice the Venus's fly-trap tempts its visitors to their doom.

While ants, termites and ambrosia bark-beetles feed on moulds and fungi which they foster or actually cultivate, there are parasitic fungi that may be said to retaliate by subsisting exclusively on insects. The curiosities known as "vegetable caterpillars" are the burrowing larvae of large swift moths from Australia and New Zealand which have been done to death by a fungus that destroys the tissues of the body and eventually sends up a long fructifying shoot through the soil. Caterpillars similarly mummified by the same or an allied species of fungus are said to be esteemed as dainties by the Chinese, who sell them in bundles as we sell asparagus. In Britain the scarlet, club-shaped fructification of another caterpillar-killing fungus may frequently be seen during the autumn months raised an inch or so above the surface of the ground, and by careful digging the remains of the larva or pupa from which it originated may be found. Fungi of other genera destroy larvae, pupae and perfect insects of many kinds, one causing the disease of silkworms called "muscardines"; while in the late summer and early autumn house-flies may often be seen sticking to walls and window-panes, their bodies swollen and surrounded by a quantity of white powder. These are the victims of a fungus that attacks flies of various kinds, especially those nearly related to the house-fly. All the internal organs of the infected insect are gradually invaded and when death results the dust-like spores are ejected in all direc-tions. Grasshoppers, crickets, caterpillars and aphides are also liable to attack by specific fungoid organisms, while bacteria cause epidemic diseases among insects, the most serious from the economic standpoint being the "flacherie" of silkworms and "foul brood" of hive-bees.

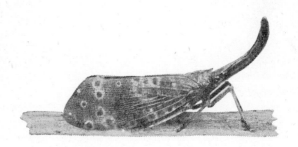

Chapter Nineteen

INSECTS AND FLOWERS

THE most astonishing relation subsisting between insects and plants is that which results in the fertilization of flowers. Exactly when and how this originated is largely conjectural, although geological evidence suggests that it may have been during the Jurassic Period of the earth's history, perhaps one hundred and forty million or more years ago. Prior to this there had been no flowers in the strict sense of the word, for the Gymnosperms, of which the conifers of today are the most familiar examples, held undisputed sway. In the heyday of these cone-bearers cross-pollination must have been effected mainly by the wind; and many of these plants were so prodigal of their pollen (as, for convenience, the microspores then in vogue may be termed) that certain deposits of coal consist of little else. Already a considerable number of insects of several different types had come into existence. Some, such as the giant dragon-flies referred to in an earlier chapter, were presumably predacious; but others which (as we must suppose) formed an important item in the dragon-flies' diet were almost certainly omnivorous, probably with a strong bias in favour of vegetarianism; and it is tempting to suppose that many of the latter were largely pollen-feeders. By taking advantage of the accumulations which at certain seasons must have drifted like snow to windward of rocks and tree-trunks, filling every chink and crevice, these insects may be assumed sooner or later to have discovered the source of this bounty, and to have learnt to visit and pillage the cones. Moreover, we may go on to surmise, without an unwarrantable stretch of imagination, that any cones which happened to be surrounded by a collar of leaves or bracts, especially if these were differently coloured from the rest of the foliage, would be more likely to attract insects than those which were devoid of such ostentation; and so we may account, at least in principle, for the evolution by natural selection of a showy perianth or floral envelope.

That the evolution and spread of what may be called modern insects—such as bees, butterflies, moths and two-winged flies—was almost certainly associated with the advent of the Angio sperms, or true-flowering plants, may be inferred from the fact that for the most part these types and the highly specialized blooms which they visit are mutually dependent, the former transporting the fructifying pollen from one blossom to another and taking a toll of nectar or some other comestible in return for their services. Numerous examples of these insects, as well as ants, wasps and other new-comers, sealed up in the fossilized resin known as amber, are so perfectly preserved that they might have been entrapped only yesterday, instead of at a time when flowering plants as we know them today were recent innovations.

The variety of floral structure is now well-nigh endless, and botanists are not agreed as to which of the simpler forms should be regarded as primitive. We shall not greatly err, however, if we take one of the meadow buttercups as approximating to an early type of hermaphrodite or bisexual flower. In the centre we find a group of carpels, containing ovules, called collectively the gynaecium or female element, surrounded by whorls of stamens constituting together the andraecium or male element. Ranged round these again are the five yellow petals—the corolla, with an outermost circle of five green sepals—the calyx. The upper extremity of each carpel is its pollen-receiving part, called the stigma, which may take the form of a sticky disk or knob mounted on a slender shaft or style. The whole organ—carpel, style and stigma—is conveniently referred to as the pistil. A stamen consists of a stalk or filament surmounted by anthers which, when ripe, set free the pollen grains. In favourable circumstances pollination—i.e. the transfer of pollen to the stigma—results in fertilization, whereby the ovules develop into seeds.

Wide-open bisexual flowers like those of the buttercup in which insects can creep about freely must frequently be self-pollinated; but since the anthers usually ripen before the stigmas become receptive cross-pollination probably occurs quite often, especially on warm, sunny days when the visitors fly quickly from one bloom to another. In fact, the differential maturing of the essential organs is very widespread among flowers and is often combined with structural peculiarities which favour cross-pollination, although if this does not occur self-pollination is usually possible as a last resort. But a certain number of flowers are unisexual, either the carpels or the stamens being abortive or suppressed, while sometimes the male and female flowers are produced by separate plants. In all such cases self-pollination is clearly out of the question.

Some flowers offer nothing but pollen to their insect visitors, examples being rose, wood anemone, poppy and St. John's-wort. As a rule the stamens in such blossoms are numerous and always the quantity of pollen produced is very great. But only a small modicum promotes the fertility of the plants. The bulk is either consumed by insects on the spot, or in the case of bees carried away as food for their grubs. It has been estimated that a strong colony of hive-bees will collect and use 120 lb. or more of pollen in the course of one season. For reasons already stated we may infer that the first entomophilous or insect-fertilized flowers were of this kind.

At the present day the majority of flowers attract insects by means of a sugary secretion called nectar exuded from glands so situated that to reach it the visitor must come into contact with the essential organs. The location of these glands, or nectaries, varies in different flowers. In buttercups, for example, there is one under a little scale at the base of each petal, whereas in some more highly specialized members of the same family (e.g. hellebore, monk's-hood) they figure as distinct organs ("honey-leaves") which may be modified stamens or petals. It seems possible that the secretion of nectar was originally induced by the irritation caused when insects bit into the soft tissues of flowers in search of nutritious juices. Be this as it may, flowers have certainly proved astonishingly responsive to the demands made upon them by insects, adapting themselves in all manner of ways to attract their attention and to reward their service. Of course the adjustments have all along been reciprocal; yet insects have always been the prime instigators, the flowers having had no option but to modify themselves in accordance with this lead. Hence we may say that insects have been the makers of flowers.

Bees, flies, moths, butterflies and beetles are the chief flower-frequenting insects, bees as a class being the most important pollinators. Not only have they feathery or plumose hairs that readily collect and hold pollen grains, but their mouth-parts are elaborately adapted in accordance with the particular flowers which are visited. Thus, there are short-tongued bees, medium-tongued bees and long-tongued bees. In many of the latter the tongue is an extremely sensitive, extensile organ with a ladle-shaped tip known as the bouton or "honey-spoon", used to extract the nectar from the innermost recess of the floral tube. Moreover, the hind-legs of the most advanced forms are provided on the inner sides of the greatly enlarged tarsal joints with "combs" or "brushes" by means of

M

which pollen is raked from the hairs and transferred, by a crossing of the legs, to the corbiculae or "little baskets" situated on the outer sides of the same joints. If we watch a hive-bee that has jus left a flower we usually see that it hovers in the air for a few seconds and those who have keen vision will notice that it makes quick passes with its legs. It is, in fact, combing the pollen from its hair and packing it into its baskets; but its movements are so rapid that their precise sequence eludes the eye. When it reaches the hive, the bee thrusts its hind-legs into a cell and scrapes off the pollen, using spurs on its middle legs for this purpose.

Certain beetles, mostly of the smaller sorts, are attracted by flowers which produce plenty of pollen or whose nectar is easily accessible,—the same kinds that are favoured by short-tongued bees. Flower-frequenting two-winged flies have relatively short trunk-like mouth-parts, more or less similar to those of the common house-fly, through which nectar as well as the smaller pollen grains can be absorbed. Most butterflies and moths have the first maxilla elongated and grooved on the inner faces so that when in contact they form a sucking-tube or proboscis through which liquids can be drawn into the mouth. This organ, which in some instances is immensely long, is rolled up spirally beneath the head when not in use. These insects consume no pollen, and moths do not usually settle upon or enter flowers, but hover over or in front of them.

That colour and odour play important parts in attracting insects to flowers is certain, although in many instances we are at a loss to prove this. The Austrian naturalist, von Frisch, demonstrated by a series of experiments that the worker hive-bee, at all events, can distinguish between colours, choosing blues and purples rather than yellows and pinks, but is blind to red. It can also appreciate the lines and patterns which have been called "honey-guides" because they appear to focus attention upon and point the way to the flower's store of nectar. Flowers especially attractive to butterflies are mostly delicately tinted—as, for example, several of our native orchids. White butterflies may often be seen high up among the topmost branches of horse-chestnuts, flying from one spike of bloom to another, the nectar of which they share with humble-bees. Flowers pollinated by night-flying moths are usually white or pale yellow and strongly scented. Compare, in this connexion, the evening campion, which opens and sheds its perfume at nightfall, with the closely related red campion—a bee-flower and much less fragrant—whose petals, fully expanded in daylight close at dusk. Dull or livid purples and various shades of brown, in conjunction with rank or foetid odours, are characteristic of flowers which cater specially for carrion-feeding flies, and to a less extent for wasps. Darwin found that the flowers of the orchids called helleborines are visited by wasps exclusively, and remarked upon the strangeness of the fact that their copious nectar should not be attractive to any kind of bees. Conceivably its sweetness is combined with a subtle savour repellent to the latter, whereas wasps are notoriously catholic in their tastes, imbibing sugary liquids and the juices of decay apparently with equal gusto. In Britain our commonest "wasp flower" is the figwort, which exhales a faint carrion-like odour, and whose corolla is exactly proportioned for one of these short-tongued clients easily to reach the nectar. On a warm summer day enormous numbers of wasps may be seen hovering about the flower-spikes of figwort plants.

Most of the more highly specialized flowers—e.g. sage, dead-nettle, toad-flax, orchis—have only a few stamens and a convenient lip or landing-stage on which insects can alight and stand in comfort, and in these instances the nectar is hidden deeply at the bottom of the tubular corolla or at the far end of a hollow spur, so that it can be reached only by long-tongued bees, butterflies and moths. While hive-bees are invaluable to the agriculturist as the chief fertilizing agents of the white or Dutch clover, they are of little service where the red clover is concerned, since the latter relies upon the various species of humble-bee with tongues sufficiently long to probe its floral tube. When red clover was first introduced into New Zealand the crops yielded little or no seed. Living humble-bees were subsequently imported into the country, where they have now established themselves, with the result that the pollination and consequent seed-setting of the red clover is duly accomplished.

Only a large and powerful bee can deal effectively with the floral mechanism of the snapdragon because the mouth of its corolla is guarded by two tightly closed lips between which small insects are quite unable to force an entrance. Weight is obviously an indispensable factor when an alighting bee forces down the united "keel" petals of the broom or gorse bloom and gets sprayed with pollen from the stamens inside. When a bee enters a sage flower it pushes against the stamens and depresses them, thus bringing the pollen-bearing anthers into contact with its back. In older flowers that have shed their pollen the style of the pistil lengthens and bends down so that the receptive stigma touches the

visitor at the exact spot where pollen was deposited by a younger
flower. The Indian nasturtium, a popular garden annual, has the
calyx produced into a long spur which holds the nectar, its mouth
guarded by a sort of *chevaux-de-frise* that is said to prevent ants—
and the like unwanted guests—from entering. The statement that
this flower can only be pollinated in Europe by the humming-bird
hawk moth is a mistake, for humble-bees frequently visit it, and
there can be no doubt that they are largely responsible for the
abundance of seeds which are produced. The germander speedwell
has a very shallow corolla tube in which the nectar can easily be
reached through the mouth; but it has no landing platform, so
that its visitors—mostly small flies—are forced to gain a footing
by grasping the bases of the stamens. In this way the anthers are
drawn together under the insect's body, dusting it with pollen
some of which is sure to be caught up by the projecting stigma
of the next flower visited. The fact that the speedwell's stamens
are reduced to two indicates that this seemingly haphazard method
is actually very successful. The stamens of some flowers (e.g. ber-
berry and kalmias) are so sensitive that if their bases are touched
by a visiting bee they spring forward so that the anthers deposit
pollen on the insect's back.

Of all flowers none are more elaborately adapted to promote
cross-pollination by insects than the orchids, the structure of which
for this very reason is exceptionally puzzling to the amateur botanist.
Its most remarkable feature is the so-called "column" crowning
the ovary or united carpels and formed by a merging of the male
and female organs—the stamens and pistil. Disregarding for the
moment the Cypripediums or "slipper orchids" (whose modification,
though very remarkable, is less extraordinary than that seen in the
other tribes or families of these plants), this column carries two
functional stigmas or pollen-receiving areas—though these may be
so completely confluent as to seem one. But its most outstanding
component is the male or fertilizing element, claimed by morpho-
logists to represent the anthers of a single stamen, the others having
been suppressed. What actually appears are two loosely compacted
masses of pollen (pollinia) connected by short, tapering stalks
(caudicles) with round, sticky disks lying in a sort of container
(the rostellum)—this last being regarded as a sterile and transformed
stigma.

The perianth of an orchid—the "flower" of popular parlance—
consists of three petals and three sepals, all of which are generally

attractively coloured. Moreover, one of the petals is very commonly projected forward, forming a lip or labellum, and is often extended backward as a hollow spur within which nectar may be stored. When an insect settles on the labellum (or, in the case of a butterfly or moth, hovers in front of the flower) and probes the spur with its proboscis, the latter—or some other part of its head—strikes against the rostellum, ruptures it, and so pulls out the pollinia by means of their adhesive disks. Then, as the insect wings its way to another bloom, the disks usually contract unequally in drying, with the result that the pollinia are bent forward and at the same time diverge slightly from one another, so that when their carrier arrives at

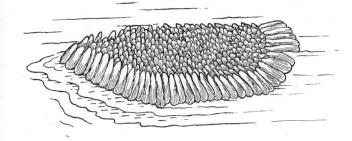

The egg-raft of the common gnat, greatly magnified

another orchid they are in exactly the right position to strike against its stigmatic areas. In the particular instance of the early purple orchis Darwin found that this movement of adjustment occupies thirty seconds on an average—time enough, as he proved, for the insect to fly to a neighbouring plant.

The above is a very generalized description of the floral mechanism characteristic of most orchids, with a hint as to the manner in which insects may act as pollen-carriers. As might be expected, details vary enormously among the 5,000-odd species that have been collected and described—most of them tropical. A Malagasy species was made famous by Darwin, who, after examining its 11-in.-long whip-like spur, confidently inferred the existence in its native island of a moth whose proboscis must be capable of extension to a length of between ten and eleven inches in order to reach the nectar which fills only an inch or so of the spur's lower extremity. For this "inspired guess" he was ridiculed by some of his contemporary critics. But when, years later, he visited the

Natural History Museum in Cromwell Road, London, armed with a permit to relax and unroll the proboscides of likely specimens, he soon found a moth from Madagascar which agreed exactly with his prediction.

In several species of *Bulbophyllum* from the tropics of the Old World the labellum is joined to the rest of the bloom by an elastic hinge and is so sensitive that when one of the flies on whose visit fertilization depends alights upon it the insect is instantly pitched between the teeth of a kind of clutch, which holds it for a few seconds struggling against the essential organs, so that the pollinia get fixed to its back. Orchids of a South American genus (*Catasetum*) shoot out their pollinia, like bullets from a gun, when certain sensitive "antennae" (modifications of the rostellum) are touched by a bee, to whose thorax the missiles become firmly attached. Bees, too, play the leading rôle in a comedy which results in the cross-pollination of another genus of orchids (*Coryanthes*), also of South America. In these an important part of the floral mechanism is a kind of "bucket", charged by the plant with a watery fluid into which bees—congregated in a quarrelsome crowd around the rim—are liable to tumble; and when this happens the victim— half drowned and unable to use its wings—extricates itself through an "overflow spout", when perforce it rubs against the flower's essential organs.

The slipper orchids referred to above are exceptional in having two sets of anthers, a third stamen being represented by a shield-like body projecting over the centrally placed stigma, while the labellum forms a pouch (the "slipper") which has a large and two small openings. Bees or flies entering by the former can only escape through one of the latter, and in so doing touch first the stigma, then one of the stamens. Our sole British representative of this family— the lady's slipper—is a great rarity, but a hardy North American species, easily grown in moist, peaty soil, is visited by some of our native bees, whose entry and exit is interesting to watch.

In the most astonishing inter-relationships which have been established between orchids and insects, scents, rather than colour and nectar, seem to operate as the determinative factor. Thus, an Australian orchid is fertilized because it smells like a female ich-neumon wasp, the male of which, in futile attempts to mate with the flowers, transfers pollen from one to the stigma of another! This discovery was made in 1927 by Mrs. Edith Coleman; and two years later Colonel Godfrey showed that our native fly-orchis is imilarly pollinated by a burrowing wasp. The males emerge from he pupae before the females, and while waiting for their advent erform the motions of copulation on the lips of any fly-orchids hat may be growing in the neighbourhood. In so doing they effect he cross-pollination of the flowers !

Like the orchids, the swallow-worts and milk-weeds have lowers marvellously adapted to secure cross-pollination by insect gency. They are chiefly tropical, but some of the latter—the 'pinch-trap flowers'' of North America—are grown in Britain as hardy perennials. Although the blooms are regular—in the botanical sense of the term—the structure and arrangement of their essential organs are too complicated to be described in detail here. Suffice it to say that when a bee or some other insect visits the flower to avail itself of the copious and easily accessible nectar its leg—or some other part of its anatomy—is liable to be gripped by one of five clips, to each of which two pollen masses, belonging to neighbouring anthers, are firmly fastened. A sufficiently strong insect subsequently tears away the whole contraption and carries it to another blossom, into whose stigmatic chamber the pollen masses get wedged. Then follows a second tussle, with the result that the insect—if lucky—breaks away with only the clip attached to its person. But weaklings may lose legs or be held captive until death puts an end to their struggles, especially when these "cruel plants", as they have been called, are grown in regions where the insects which come to them are too feeble to cope with their mechanism.

Certain moths, attracted in the first instances by the promise of nectar and having imbibed their fill, remain to oviposit either upon or close to the flowers which they visit, the caterpillars subsequently entering the capsules to feed on the seeds. The lychnis coronet and several other night-flying moths visit the white and fragrant blooms of the evening campion, carrying pollen from the anthers of one to the stigmas of another, without which assistance their fertility would be impossible, this plant being dioecious —i.e. the male and female flowers are produced by different individuals, often growing some distance apart. Since the young caterpillars are destined to consume the seeds in the production of which their parents have played an indispensable part, this arrangement seems at first sight peculiarly lopsided. In practice, however, the seeds in attacked capsules are seldom all destroyed, while the plants always bear numerous uninjured capsules which owe their fructification to the visits of male moths, or of females which have exhausted their store of eggs.

The facts relating to the fertilization of the American yuccas or "Adam's needles" by certain small, white-winged moths would seem incredible had they not been vouched for first by C. V. Riley and subsequently by other competent observers. The male moth is not specially remarkable, but the mouth-parts of the female are quite unlike those of any other members of the scaly-winged Order. Not only are her maxillary palpi well developed (the reader should be reminded that in all other moths these organs are either very small or altogether absent), but each is equipped with a unique sickle-shaped tentacle. Also, her exceptionally long, protrusible ovipositor unites the functions of awl and saw. Visiting the yucca soon after dark, she scrapes ripe pollen from the anthers of the stamens and—using her fore-legs "very much as a cat does when cleaning her mouth"—moulds it into a ball which is often thrice as large as her own head. Holding this booty firmly between her tentacles she flies to another flower, in the ovary of which she lays one or more eggs ; and immediately after climbs up its pistil, thrusts her pellet of pollen into a special hollow at the summit of the stigma, and rams it firmly home. As a result of this forceful pollination the yucca's ovules develop into seeds, some of which are consumed by the moth's larvae, but plenty are left over to perpetuate the plant.

The flowers of two unrelated groups of plants—the birthworts and the arums—are remarkable in that they entice insects into the recesses of their corollas, where they are held captive until they have applied to the stigmas the pollen which they have brought with them and have been dusted with a further supply to be carried away when they are allowed to depart. The odours exhaled by these flowers are offensive to human nostrils but attract flies and other insects with a partiality for decomposing substances. The majority of the birthworts are indigenous to tropical South America. In many instances the blooms are strangely grotesque in form and surprisingly coloured and patterned ; but in essentials the structure varies little and can be studied in the European species, which, as a garden escape, may be found growing wild in a few localities in the south and east of England. The corolla-tube is lined through part of its length with inwardly directed hairs which allow flies of suitable size to pass down into the expanded base but not, for the time being, to creep out again. They come first into contact with the receptive stigmas, and later get dusted with more pollen from the anthers, by which time the deterrent hairs in the tube through which they entered have withered, allowing them to escape.

Similar tactics for securing cross-pollination have been adopted by our native wild arum or cuckoo-pint, whose flowering spike or spadix is enveloped by a large sheathing bract, or spathe. The apex of the spadix is a conspicuous purple club: the basic part, within the bulbous swelling of the spathe, bears circular clusters of simple flowers, the upper being abortive and hair-like, the next staminate or male, the lowest pistillate or female. Insects, especially small midges attracted by the purple club and the foetid odour which it exhales, fly to and enter the spathe. They manage to creep down through the hair-like flowers but cannot return as long as these remain stiff. If they have brought pollen from another inflorescence some of this is deposited on the female flowers, which mature first. Later, the male flowers dust them with more pollen; and finally, as the hair-like flowers shrivel up and the spathe begins to wither, the insects make good their escape.

In order to appreciate the relationship existing between certain small Chalcid wasps and figs it is necessary to bear in mind that the latter, before they develop into fruits, are really hollow inflorescences—chambers bearing a multiplicity of simple flowers out of sight on their inner walls—access to which is gained through a small orifice beset with tiny scales at the point where the calyx or "eye" of an apple would be found. In the case of the common or wild fig tree of the Mediterranean region four different kinds of flowers are produced, namely (1) staminate or male flowers, each with from three to five stamens; (2) fertile, single-seeded female flowers; (3) unproductive or dummy flowers, female in origin, and (4) so-called "gall-flowers" specially adapted to meet the needs of visiting insects. The first or spring inflorescences of the season consist of male flowers massed just inside the orifice and gall-flowers further in. Female gall-wasps enter and lay their eggs in the barren carpels or seed-boxes of the latter—one in each, and in them the larvae feed, change to pupae, and eventually complete their metamorphosis. Of the resulting brood of adults the wingless males appear first, gnaw their way into the gall-flowers in which the females are still imprisoned, and there pair with them. This accomplished, they die. But a little later the females, which are winged, leave the galls and make their way out of the inflorescence. In so doing they inevitably brush against the ripe anthers of the male flowers and get well dusted with pollen before gaining the open.

All this happens towards the end of May, when the second—or summer—batch of inflorescences has started to develop; and into these the newly emerged matrons penetrate, but find only normal female flowers in which, owing to structural peculiarities, they are unable to oviposit effectively. Nevertheless, their entry is profitable to the fig tree, since they pollinate the flowers, which subsequently set seed, while the fleshy envelope swells up and ripens about the end of September—becoming, in fact, a fig within the fruiterer's meaning of the term.

Meanwhile, the third or autumn-winter batch of inflorescences have come into evidence. These contain nothing but gall-flowers and never become fruits. Apparently they exist solely to benefit the gall-wasps, for it is in them that the larvae of the second brood spend the winter and from them that the generation of adult females emerges during the following spring. By these astonishingly circuitous means the annual life cycle of this insect is accomplished and the due fructification of the fig trees ensured.

The foregoing details apply only to the wild fig. Further complications occur in the fertilization of its cultivated varieties, which are chiefly of two races, the fruit-bearer and the infertile or "goat-fig". The inflorescences of the former consist solely of female flowers (sterile in the spring crop) and normally need to be fertilized by pollen brought from those of the goat-fig, which comprise male flowers and gall-flowers only. When the first relay of gall-wasps emerges they enter the spring inflorescences of both the goat-fig and the fruit-bearing varieties. In the former they insert eggs into the gall-flowers, but in the latter do nothing but wander around and come out again, because, as we have seen, the flowers are mere dummies in these inflorescences, which usually wilt and drop off the tree, though occasionally they develop into fruits of inferior quality. But in June the next generation of gall-wasps coming from the goat-figs enter the summer inflorescences of the fruit-figs and by pollinating the fertile female flowers promote the production of the season's most important crop. The same thing happens in the case of the autumn-produced inflorescences, with the dual result that a second crop of edible figs ripens before the onset of winter, and a third generation of gall-wasps matures in the goat-figs to emerge when spring returns.

Figs have been cultivated from time immemorial, and the fact that the sterile goat-fig is an essential element in the plenteous cropping of the fruit-fig was recognized before the days of Herodotus.

Fig-growers in many districts still practise traditionally what is called "caprification"—i.e. branches of goat-fig are placed among those of the fruit-bearing trees at the season when the gall-wasps are emerging. But whereas these non-fruiting goat-figs are in general necessary for the most profitable fig cultivation, and although the Smyrna figs introduced into California did not succeed until goat-figs and gall-wasps were brought to their aid, there are in north Italy varieties which are able to dispense with this assistance; in the absence of pollen the inflorescences swell up and become edible. It is these self-fructifying varieties that are grown in Britain, where the helpful gall-wasps do not occur. But although the fruit is juicy and good to eat, no fertile seed is produced. This, however, is a minor defect from the standpoint of the horticulturist, since experience has shown that all the cultivated races of the fig, whether they produce seed or not, must be propagated by cuttings and grafting, because plants raised from seeds always revert to the wild type.

Some insects—notably humble-bees—play a scurvy trick on certain flowers whose store of nectar they cannot easily reach by cutting a hole in the corolla and so getting at the coveted dainty without touching the essential organs. The worst offenders appear to be the buff-tailed and small earth humble-bees. John Curtis, in his *Farm Insects*, referred to the harm which they do, especially to scarlet runners and broad beans. A hole is bitten through the calyx and corolla into the nectary, and in this way the fertility of the flowers is greatly reduced, in some instances only one out of a cluster of five or eight producing a pod with the full complement of seeds. With reference to the buff-tailed species, F. W. L. Sladen states that its depredations in New Zealand have "resulted in damage to the seed-vessels of certain flowers and the seed-growers there would now be glad to have this species supplanted by another". Exactly why humble-bees mutilate flowers after this fashion is not always clear. Darwin suggested that they do it simply to save themselves trouble; but in most cases it seems more likely that owing to the relatively short length of their tongues they are unable to reach the nectar through the floral tube in the legitimate manner. Lord Avebury, quoting from H. Müller, tells of a female humble-bee which, after several unsuccessful attempts to reach the nectar of a columbine, bit a hole in the corolla; and subsequently, when visiting other flowers, bit holes through them "without making any attempt to suck them first, conscious apparently that she was unable to do so".

Ants, being wingless and so incapable of rapid transit from one blossom to another, are usually unprofitable visitors from the plant's point of view, and, as we have seen, are frequently debarred by various means from access to the necaries. But according to Kerner von Marilaun these insects have been pressed into service as a bodyguard by certain knapweeds and other Compositae indigenous to south-eastern Europe whose capitula or flower-heads are especially liable to attack by chafer beetles, which bite big holes in them. The ants are attracted by a sugary liquid secreted in considerable quantities by the involucral scales of the capitulum; and when a beetle approaches they assume menacing attitudes, and squirt formic acid in the direction of the intruder.

Chapter Twenty

COURTSHIP WILES AND RITUALS

THE colours and decorative patterns displayed by insects are generally regarded as adaptations, established by natural selection, to cope with the exigencies of their daily life, and have accordingly been classified by biologists under such headings as "protective", "warning" and "mimetic"—the term "epigamic" being reserved for those types that are supposed to be especially associated with courtship and mating. The extent to which this particular assumption is justified still provokes controversy, since the evidence at present available is scanty and in some respects conflicting. The males of many insects are often more colourful and attractive than the females. This is true of most of our "blue" butterflies, while the fore-wings of the male orange-tip are adorned with glowing yellow spots which are absent from those of his mate. Among certain exotic species this "sex-dimorphism"—masculine splendour yoked with feminine dowdiness—is even more astonishing, perhaps the most striking instance of all being the bird-winged butterfly of paradise from New Guinea, the female of which is a buxom but sombre matron, the dapper male being resplendent in green and gold with a quaint little tail terminating each hind-wing.

Charles Darwin believed that the gay colours and attractive adornments exclusive to male insects have resulted from what he called "sexual selection": in other words, that the females of the species, through countless generations, have consistently chosen the most ornate from among their suitors, whose embellishments have thus been transmitted to posterity. On this view the reason why the females fail to inherit the coloration that they appreciate in the opposite sex is that their need for protection is more urgent. As a rule they are less alert than their mates, and when egg-laying are exposed to much greater risks. Thus, while in many instances the female repeats more or less closely the coloration of the male, this tendency is held rigorously in check by natural selection whenever the need for protection is paramount. The male's greater wariness and agility—qualities which are associated with his superior sense-organs and well-balanced physique—may be supposed to offset the enhanced hazards which his splendours may entail. Moreover, it is a fact that the bright colours and conspicuous patterns which are believed to play a part in courtship are usually concealed at other times. The male "blue" butterfly, when at rest with folded wings, is not less perfectly concealed than his mate, while the same is true of the orange-tip.

Because no completely convincing evidence in favour of Darwin's sexual selection theory has so far been brought forward it must for the time being be regarded as specious but unproved. Not a few competent judges prefer to ascribe the superior attractiveness of the male insect to his superabundant vitality, compared with that of the female, whose energies are for the most part employed in reproduction. This, however, by no means rules out the earlier interpretation, since the essential natures of the sexes must always obtain, and might well constitute the foundation upon which specialized characters, due either directly or indirectly to the discrimination of the female, could be based. That several of our common butterflies can distinguish differences in colour, and that the sexes discover one another by sight and the use of colour-vision, has been demonstrated by H. Eltringham and E. B. Ford, while many amateur observers have been struck by the frequent visits paid by white butterflies to pale-coloured leaves, as if mistaking them for potential mates. Nevertheless, the probabilities are that scent, rather than colour, plays the major part in the courtship and mating of most insects.

The olfactory nerve-endings are chiefly located in the antennae, and in the male these organs are often greatly amplified, as for example in the emperor moth and the cockchafer. The males of many moths are able to detect the characteristic odour of their females carried by air-currents, and by this means can readily discover the whereabouts of mates from considerable distances, perhaps as far as three miles.

We are indebted to Sir E. B. Poulton for a particularly graphic description of this "assembling" of antler moth males which converge from all points of the compass to a freshly emerged female, around which the suitors wheel in an excited crowd. Suddenly one is accepted, and all the others immediately disperse. "The males do not fight or struggle in any way, and as one watches the ceremony the wonder arises as to how the moment is determined, and why the pairing did not take place before. All the males are evidently most eager to pair, and yet when pairing takes place no opposition is offered by the other males to the successful suitor. Proximity does not decide the point, for long beforehand the males often alight close to the female and brush against her with fluttering wings. In watching this wonderful and complicated courtship one is driven to the conclusion that the female must signify her intention in some way unknown to us, and that it is a point of

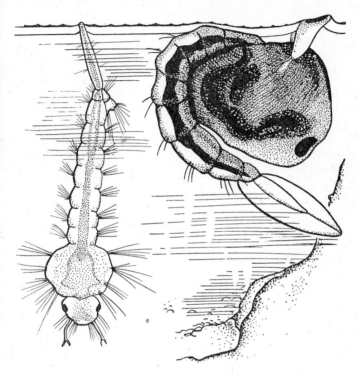

The larva of the common gnat with its breathing tube thrust through the surface film. The curiously shaped pupa (*right*) is equipped with a pair of breathing trumpets or horns

honour with the males to abide by her decision." Experiment has shown that blinding, by coating their eyes with an opaque substance, does not prevent these males from flying straight to the spot where the female is waiting.

The odours exhaled by insects may be roughly separated into two groups, namely (1) those which are repulsive or nauseous, usually common to both sexes, and often associated with peculiar or conspicuous colour schemes—in other words, with the "warning liveries" referred to in a previous chapter; (2) those which by inference are grateful and alluring, generally produced by one sex only as an attraction to the opposite sex. We have seen that many male insects track down their mates by scent, but there are others which when on courtship bent diffuse perfumes for the delectation of the females of their fancy. This discovery was made by Fritz Müller, who spent many years of his life in studying the fauna and flora of Brazil, thereby adding much to our knowledge of insect life.

The scent-producing organs of butterflies and moths have been identified in many instances with certain of the minute scales which clothe the wings. If we examine a portion of the wing's surface beneath the microscope we find that, in the male, some of the scales differ from the majority by which they are surrounded and overlapped in being attached by their stalks to peculiar glandular cells which secrete a volatile fluid that passes into the scale and is eventually given off from its surface as an odorous vapour. These "androconia", as they are called, vary considerably in shape in different species of butterflies, but usually agree in being branched or tufted at their free extremities—an arrangement which apparently facilitates the rapid diffusion of the perfume upon the air. As we have seen they are frequently scattered among and often hidden by the ordinary scales; but they are sometimes massed together in brand-like patches, or along certain prominent nervures or "veins" of the wing. In other instances they are concealed beneath a fold of the wing membrane, or within a little pocket or pouch. In many moths hair-like androconia form a thick, glistening white felt under a folded-over flap of the hind-wing's inner edge. Some butterflies have manes of these scent-distilling hairs on a restricted area of each hind-wing, while tufts of them occur on the hind-legs of certain moths—the common ghost moth being a good example. The case of this moth is especially interesting because the male's white and glistening wings almost certainly apprise the female of his exact whereabouts when in the dusk of the evening he hovers, emitting his perfume, over the grass or herbage among which she lies hidden. If these overtures are accepted she comes forth and the nuptials are celebrated. This view is supported by the fact that in Shetland, where the summer nights are very light, the male is often no longer white, but yellowish like the female.

So far as is known, none of the alluring odours of female insects are perceptible by human noses, but some of those emitted by male butterflies and moths are easily detected and often bear a recognizable resemblance to familiar essences. That of the ghost moth has been likened to pineapple, of the green-veined white butterfly to lemon verbena, of its cousin the small white to sweet-briar, of the meadow brown to sandal wood, and so forth.

Perhaps the most complicated structural features associated with scent-production are found among butterflies of the Danaine family, many species of which occur throughout tropical and subtropical regions, the best known being the "Monarch" or "milkweed" butterfly, whose range is well-nigh cosmopolitan. The males have a pair of brushes tucked away in the hinder end of the abdomen, which can be extruded by the pressure of fluid within the body. These are saturated with perfume, which is distilled from glands at the base of the hairs and escapes as a vapour through minute pores at their tips. In addition, many males of this family are equipped with a pocket or patch of scent-secreting cells on the hind-wings and use their brushes to sweep out the odoriferous material from these reservoirs and diffuse it around the females. In the case of one African genus the hairs forming the males' brushes are of two kinds. Some are stiff and durable; others are exceedingly fine and microscopically segmented, so that when the brush is used they break up into minute dust-like fragments impregnated with scent which are cast adrift upon the air. Some of these butterflies, when courting, have been seen to hover over females and sprinkle them with this perfumed powder!

While insects have no true vocal powers, many of them are capable of producing sounds of varying intensity. Probably the most noisy of all insects are the cicadas or "harvest-flies", the so-called "song" of some species having been compared to the shrill whistle of a locomotive engine. In Britain we have only one small representative of these remarkable insects; but the species are very numerous in the warmer regions of both hemispheres. The males alone are sonorous—a fact which inspired the sarcastic comment of the Greek poet Xenarchus, "Happy the cicadas live, since they all have voiceless wives"! If we examine the ventral side of a male cicada we notice two large plates which spring from the thorax and overlap the abdomen, to a greater or less extent. Beneath these "opercula" are cavities containing the twin sound-producing mechanisms, the most notable parts of which are the membranes, or drums, operated by powerful muscles. It is to the rapid vibration of the drums that the "song" is primarily due, although other

N

membranes within the cavity are also agitated, while the whole exoskeleton of the insect, including the opercula, presumably help to increase or modify the volume of sound.

Apart from the cicadas most other insects that produce sound do so by a method called stridulation. In other words, one part of the body is rubbed against another part, much as the bow is rubbed across the strings of a violin. For example, the shrilling or chirping of short-horned or meadow grasshoppers is produced by rubbing the thigh or femur of the hind-leg against the tegmen or wing-cover. On the inner side of each hind femur is a ridge surmounted by a row of tiny tubercles—really modified hairs—and these are rubbed against a prominent nervure or vein of the corresponding tegmen—left or right as the case may be.

Both the crickets and the long-horned or "tree" grasshoppers —including the katydids of the North American continent—are notoriously melodious insects, and in these families the tegmina—unassisted by the legs—are the sound-producing organs. Those of male crickets are nearly alike, the right one being usually, though not invariably, uppermost. Each tegmen has a file-like vein on its underside, and this can be rubbed across a prominent ridge of the tegmen lying below. In the long-horned grasshoppers, by contrast only the left tegmen—which is invariably uppermost when the insect is at rest—is furnished with a file-like vein. But a particularly sonorous species of this family from South Africa is an exception since it performs by scraping with its hind-legs over ridged areas on each side of the abdomen. The male, known locally as the "flying gooseberry", seems to be inordinately corpulent, yet in reality his swollen hind-body contains little but air, and serves to increase the resonance of sound which he makes. Incidentally, his mate is so extravagantly bedizened that she appears as if tricked out for a fancy-dress ball, while his colouring is unadorned green. These remarkable insects are not very uncommon, but detailed information concerning their courtship habits is lacking.

With respect to the origin of sound-producing mechanisms in male insects most naturalists agree that they are the outcome of long-continued sexual selection. It is believed that they excite amorous proclivities in members of the opposite sex. Female crickets, for example, seem to listen eagerly—one might almost say critically—to the chirping of their wooers, as if anxious to enjoy every note to the full. For the fact that many insects produce sounds indicates that they can also hear; although in some instances no specialized auditory organs, or "ears", can be demonstrated. Among cicadas—the noisiest of all insects!—anatomists have completely failed to discover any such structures. This has given rise to no little speculation, and some authorities are of the opinion that these insects do not hear at all in the usually accepted sense of the word, but "feel rhythmical vibrations"—which seems uncommonly like a distinction without a difference! Yet the nervous system of an insect includes vast numbers of minute nerve-endings which, through microscopic pores in the chitinous exoskeleton, communicate with the ganglia and brain. The precise function of these nerve-endings, even when their structure has received careful investigation, is often difficult to determine; but it seems certain that while it is often tactile or olfactory it is sometimes auditory. We are free to believe, therefore, that cicadas—and possibly insects of other kinds—are endowed with a generalized faculty for receiving sound vibrations, and that in this sense they may be said to "hear", notwithstanding their lack of organs that can properly be termed "ears".

With certain other insects—notably the grasshoppers, crickets and their allies—the case is quite different. Here we find definite ear-like structures, obviously adapted for the reception of sound-waves and their transmission to the nerve-centres. Briefly, they consist of a tympanum or "drum" with a complex arrangement of muscles, nerves and tracheal tubes. These organs are paired, but their external openings are not in the head, as in vertebrate animals. Those of a meadow grasshopper, for example, are to be found in the first abdominal segment, their openings being just above the articulation of the hind-legs. Similar auditory organs have their place in the fore-shins, or tibiae, of crickets, as well as of long-horned grasshoppers; while J. W. Folsom claims that structures, presumably analogous in function, occur on the tibiae of ants, termites and stone-flies, and on the tarsi of certain beetles. Many species of two-winged flies have organs whose general structure resembles that which has just been described. In blow-flies a circular "drum" in connexion with air spaces and nerve-endings is situated in a cavity beneath the bases of the wings, while above this, under the scutellum —the shield-shaped termination of the mesothorax—is a supra-tympanal structure like that of a long-horned grasshopper. A definite "ear" has also been found in the second antennal joint of certain mosquitoes and midges. The joint in question is much swollen and cup-shaped; and although in the females a similar structure is present, it is far less perfectly developed than in the males—the inference being that the latter rely chiefly on their sense of hearing when seeking mates. Indeed, it has been shown that the minute lateral hairs on the shafts of the male mosquito's antennae vibrate to the note produced by the movement of the female's wings in flight, and that they do so most strongly when the sound-waves strike them at right angles—that is to say, when the tips of the antennae point in the direction from which the sound comes; so that the male must be able to estimate very exactly the whereabouts of the female.

The characteristic "songs" of insects are as distinctive as those of birds, and some are more pleasing than others to human ears. W. H. Hudson remarks upon the intrinsic beauty of the sounds produced by the field cricket, contrasting them with the coarser more creaky notes of the house cricket. The chirping of the small wood cricket is, like the screeching of bats, so high-pitched that few people can hear it, while the churring of the mole cricket resembles that of the nightjar, but is less acute. In localities where it occurs the faint but penetrating *tss-tss* of the bush-cheep may be heard on fine summer evenings and far into the night. By contrast, the song of the great green grasshopper, which is loud, prolonged and somewhat harsh, is chiefly audible—according to Hudson—in the early morning between five and six o'clock, and again in the early evening, especially when the weather is fine and warm.

S. H. Scudder and other observers in America, having studied the songs of crickets and grasshoppers and recorded them in musical notation, found incidentally that a relation exists between the rapidity of the stridulation and the state of the temperature. In warm weather when the sun is shining brightly these little musicians fiddle away with all their might, whereas when it is dull and chilly their execution is slow and mournful. Thus, below 50 degrees Fahrenheit a field cricket is said to chirp 40 times per minute, and increase the rate by from 4 to 4·7 for each rise of a degree in temperature.

In his forty-sixth letter to the Hon. Daines Barrington, Gilbert White, the Selborne naturalist, writes that a male field cricket "confined in a paper cage and set in the sun, and supplied with plants moistened with water, will feed and thrive, and become so merry and loud as to be irksome in the same room where a person is sitting; if the plants are not wetted it will die". The roulades of stridulating insects, especially grasshoppers and crickets, have long been appreciated by the peoples of southern France, the countries of the Iberian Peninsula and throughout the Far East. The captives are confined in tiny ornamental cages made of wire, wood or bamboo. In some instances the crickets, which are notoriously pugnacious, are also kept for fighting contests.

Stridulatory or frictional sounds are made by many beetles in a variety of ways. In most cases one part of the body serves as a rasp, the other as a scraper; but in no instance is the mechanism as perfectly developed as among the grasshoppers and crickets. Very surprisingly the burrowing larvae of some beetles are equipped with these sound-producing organs: e.g. that of the stag beetle, which tunnels in decaying wood. Rasp-and-scraper appliances have also been found in several species of ants and a few South American butterflies, some of which emit a sharp crackling noise as they fly. The death's-head moth when alarmed or molested utters a shrill squeaking not unlike the cry of a startled mouse, but more plaintive, and the experiments of Rossi and Wagner seem to have shown that the sound is produced by the expulsion through the proboscis of air from the air-sacs of the tracheal system: in other words, that it is much nearer in origin to a vocal than an instrumental performance. The same is true of the humming of many flies and bees, which is produced by a mechanism within the spiracles. The contrivance is too complicated to describe in detail here; but it may be roughly likened to a wind instrument, such as a cornet.

Most of the so-called "death-watch" insects are beetles, one being the culprit usually responsible for the "worm-eaten" condition of our furniture and floorboards. The larger species, whose larvae originally burrowed in the dead and decaying wood of oak, willow, hawthorn and other trees, has during recent centuries done extensive damage to the timbers of ancient buildings, notably the roof of Westminster Hall. To attract one another's attention these beetles rap with their heads or jaws against the surface on which they are resting—a habit which in the past gave rise to the superstition that the sound heralded an approaching death in the house where it was heard. Another, very different, insect—known as the "book louse"—has also been credited with a capacity for these sinister rappings; but this seems doubtful, if only because the creature is very minute—just about visible to the naked eye!

Certain beetles, most of them nocturnal in their habits, emit a more or less brilliant light which used to be called phosphorescent, but is now known to be due to the oxidization of a peculiar fatty matter. In the larva and adult male of the common glow-worm beetle the "glow" proceeds from two spots—mere pin-points—on the terminal segment of the abdomen beneath, but in the female these are replaced by a broad belt of luminescence which its owner is at pains to display by twisting her body to right or left so that the ventral surface is clearly visible. Hence it is reasonable to suppose that by this means she attracts her mate—which, in fact, can easily be proved with the aid of a flash-light by anyone who has the patience to watch these "earth stars", as Wordsworth called them on an early summer evening. The same cannot be claimed, however, in the case of the "fire-flies"—also beetles—which are common throughout the warmer regions of the Eastern Hemisphere, for among them the males far outshine the females and congregate in bachelor parties on calm warm nights, gyrating madly among the foliage or resting for brief periods on twigs or leaves. According to Dr. David Sharp, who witnessed one of these gatherings, they serve either as an amusement or as incitement to rivalry among the males, which alone take part in them. From South America come reports of a "railway beetle", apparently a distant cousin of our own glow-worm, of which the female emits "a strong red light from the two extremities of the body, and a green light from numerous points along the sides"! In the New World, too, the fire-flies are replaced by a group of luminous beetles belonging to the skip-jack family. One of the most abundant and largest has on each side of the thorax a pale-coloured, polished patch which shines brightly at night. A third luminous area is situated at the base of the ventral surface of the abdomen, but this is only visible when the insect is on the wing. So brilliant is the light given off by these insects that they are used by the natives on nocturnal excursions and by women for ornaments.

That the great horns and antlers of male beetles are in some instances more ornamental than useful seems not unlikely, but frequently they are employed in amorous conflicts between rival suitors, or as implements for grasping and carrying off coy or reluctant females to some safe honeymoon retreat. Several males of the European stag beetle at times pay court to the same female and engage in conflicts for her possession, although little or no damage to the combatants results from these encounters. They simply push each other about until all but one tire of the scuffle and make off. Allied to our native species is one from Chile whose male is equipped with down-curved jaws which are rather slender but of great length their inner edges set with a continuous row of small teeth. Whether these formidable-looking weapons are used in combat when their owner is sexually excited is still a matter of conjecture. Darwin tells us that when threatened "he faces round, opens his great jaws, and at the same time stridulates freely" : but this seems to be mere bluff, since his mandibular muscles are so feeble that he causes no pain if he nips the human finger. Another beetle mentioned by Darwin dwells in pairs in burrows during the breeding season, and when a couple has once set up housekeeping, woe betide any intruder that may try to force an entrance. Not only does the occupying male attack him fiercely, but his spouse stands guard at the entrance of the burrow and encourages her lord in his defence by pushing him from behind. Wallace, again, describes a conflict between two long-beaked weevils that were paying court to the same female, "who stood close by busy with her boring. They pushed each other with their rostra (snouts), and clawed and thumped in the greatest rage. The smaller male, however, soon ran away, acknowledging himself vanquished." Darwin (in *The Descent of Man*) gives other instances, apparently well authenticated, of contests between male saw-flies, digger-wasps, bees and even butterflies for possession of a particular female. Unfortunately, such records are far less numerous than one could wish, and a wide field for discovery is open to those naturalists who, in the future, may make the courtship habits of insects their special study.

Truly spectacular is the male of the giant Hercules beetle from the West Indies and tropical America by reason of his imposing display of antlers. The crown of his head is prolonged into a great upturned beam with tooth-like knobs, while a longer and more massive forward-directed projection springs from the roof of the thorax, its lower edge being padded with a velvety pile of short, chestnut-coloured hairs. By raising his head these two prongs serve as a pair of forceps, and on more than one occasion a Hercules has been seen using this appliance for carrying about his "better half" ; and it seems highly probable that the monstrous "horns" of other beetles—e.g. the European "rhinoceros"—are employed for a like purpose ; while (according to W. P. Pycraft) the calliper-like jaws characteristic of the male North American alder-flies enable these giants of their kind to seize and hold the females during the act of mating.

Many and varied structures have been developed among insects enabling the male to capture the female and detain her during

the sexual embrace. Thus, the males of the big leader weevil fron
Assam and of the long-armed chafer from the North Pacific islan
of Amboina are furnished with immensely elongated fore-legs, whic
are very effective prehensile organs. In other instances—e.g. some c
the oil beetles—the masculine antennae have been pressed int
service, two or more of their joints being enlarged and bent, formin
pincers for gripping those of the female. Males of the diving-beetl
fraternity have wonderful sucker disks on the underside of the tars
of the fore-legs by means of which a firm hold is maintained on th
female's back, whose elytra are usually deeply grooved, wherea
those of the male are smooth and highly polished. Somewha
similar modifications of the anterior tarsi occur in the males o
certain digger-wasps.

The aerial nuptials of the larger may-flies are so tragicall
evanescent that they have been called "the dance of death". W
have already seen that the compound eyes of the male are divided
so that the insect appears to have two on each side of the head
which must considerably enhance the scope of his vision. Moreover
detailed examination of these organs points to the conclusion tha
their special function is to discern moving objects in the dusk. On i
calm, warm evening, usually towards sunset, a swarm of male
commences its ceremonial minuet, rising and falling in the still ai
as if in obedience to some mysterious signal. At intervals a fev
females flutter from neighbouring vegetation and mingle with th
throng, the act of mating being performed during flight. The actua
process, as described by J. G. Needham, occupies only a few seconds
The male flies beneath the female, using his long fore-legs to drav
her down to him, so that the genital organs of the two are brough
into contact, and fertilization takes place. The male then dies, an
the female follows suit as soon as she has dropped her eggs into th
water. Female may-flies are far less numerous than males, an
myriads of the latter perish in bachelorhood.

The mating procedure of dragon-flies is unique among insects
as also is the possession by the male of a special receptacle under th
second abdominal segment which—prior to the sexual act—h
charges with spermatozoa from the true reproductive organs that ar
situated in the ninth segment by curving his tail forward. The initia
move in the courtship ritual is made by the male. Seated con
spicuously on a leaf or stem, he signals his marital inclination t
passing spinsters by raising his long body high into the air an
spreading his wings in a seductive fashion. Should a member of th

posite sex respond to these blandishments she approaches and
vers over the expectant male, who immediately darts up and
izes her, either by the head or the neck, with his anal claspers.
hus linked, the pair may continue for hours at a stretch, skimming
ver the water, or resting on a branch or reed, always with their
dies held rigidly in the same horizontal plane—except during
tual copulation, when the female curves the tip of her body round
receive sperm from the male's "accessory genetalia" referred to
ove. When the female is ready to oviposit, the male may liberate
r; but in some species he continues to hold her in tandem forma-

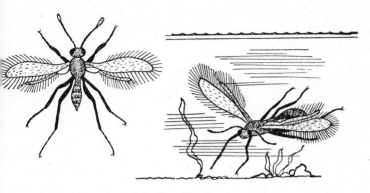

The minute fairy fly, which lays its eggs in
those of dragon-flies, for which purpose it enters the
water and uses its wings as paddles. (Magnified)

on, lowering her into the water, supporting her while she is sub-
erged, and pulling her out again when her task is completed.

Among the bark-beetles some species are monogamous, others
lygamous. After hibernation, a female of one of the former—
ch as the common elm-bark beetle—scoops out a small chamber
the bark of the chosen tree, then takes a short flight, and returns
ith a male. Pairing takes place either in, or close to, the chamber,
ter which the male takes himself off and the female sets to work
earnest, drilling a long horizontal tunnel between the bark and
e wood and depositing her eggs along it to right and left alter-
ately. When the larvae hatch each eats its way outward from the
mother gallery", first at right angles, but soon shaping a curving
urse so as not to interfere with the burrows of its brothers and
sters. In this way curious and intricate patterns are traced upon
e surface of the wood; and it has been found that the particular

angle made by the juncture of the larval burrows with the moth
gallery differs in the various species, and is thus serviceable as
ready means of identification. Pupation takes place at the end
the larval burrow, and the perfect beetle bores its way through t
bark and escapes, leaving behind a tell-tale "flight-hole".

A polygamous bark-beetle—e.g. the two-toothed species
has a different mode of procedure. The male takes the initiative
excavating a roughly circular chamber under the bark in whi
he receives from four to six females. After pairing he deserts h
harem, each member of which constructs a separate egg-tunn
radiating from the nuptial chamber; and as the grubs in their tu
burrow outwards at all angles from the burrows made· by the
mothers very complicated patterns are apt to result.

The late Lord Avebury has left us a charming description
the way in which the yellow spring-tails conduct their wooin
"It is very amusing to see these little creatures coquetting togethe
The male, which is much smaller than the female, runs round he
and they butt one another, standing face to face and moving bac
wards and forwards like two playful lambs. Then the female preten
to run away and the male runs after her. With a queer appearance
anger, he gets in front and stands facing her again; then she turi
coyly round, but he is quicker and more active, scuttles round to
and seems to whip her with his antennae; then for a bit they sta
face to face, play with their antennae and seem to be all in all to o
another."

Very different is the connubial behaviour characteristic
the mantids or rear-horses—and, indeed, of other predatory insec
in so far as details have been made available. Fabre tells us that tl
female praying mantis soon tires of her accepted suitor, ar
rushes upon him with menace. The male attempts to defend himsel
but since he is no match physically for his infuriated spouse he
quickly worsted and—shocking to relate—made a meal of by h
quondam mate. According to A. D. Imms the male of the curiot
scorpion-fly, before venturing to approach his enchantress, spi
out little globules of saliva on a leaf near where she is sitting. "SI
obligingly turns to the offering and feeds on it: the male the
seizes the end of her abdomen and mates with her. It has bee
suggested that if she is fed in this manner she will be less likely
exercise her carnivorous instincts and devour her spouse once matir
has been effected."

The same authority has written very divertingly of certain sma black Empid-flies, which he describes as of all insects "the most accomplished artists in keeping their spouse occupied during mating". A male, on courtship bent, first scours the air and captures a small insect, which he kills and offers to the female of his choice. She accepts the gift, and while she discusses it copulation takes place. The more crafty males wrap their love-tokens in a few strands of silk, the unravelling of which keeps the female busy during subsequent operations. This silk, by the way, is produced from glands situated in the tarsi of the fore-legs—not from spinnerets near the mouth, or at the tail-end, as is usual. Sometimes, when the male's hunting is unproductive, his bundle contains such inedible items as bud-scales, buttercup stamens or daisy florets. What happens if and when the female discovers the fraud is not stated!

Chapter Twenty-One

INSECTS IN WINTER

T HAT insects are "children of the summer" is a pretty fancy of the poets, for at the approach of winter in northern climes these marvellous winged beings vanish almost completely from sight. Yet the race of insects still persists. It is merely passing through a period of hibernal dormancy from which it will awaken with renewed vigour when the earth swings round once more to its vernal inclination. Indeed, this seasonal eclipse of insects as Jack Frost's fingers threaten to close upon land and water is proof in itself of their perfect adjustment to the environment in which they live. Crowds of wasps, mostly males and females of the social species, together with a varied assortment of two-winged flies, assemble in the sunshine of late autumn to quaff the easily accessible nectar of the ivy's flowers. Big humble-bees, incipient queens, and showy nymphaline butterflies visit the late-blooming starworts in our gardens, while red admirals are attracted by the over-ripe and rotting fruit lying on the turf in the orchards. But soon they disappear mysteriously, only to reassert themselves as permanent members of our British fauna with the return of spring. In short, although theoretically our English winter should prove a period of extreme hardship to organisms of such seeming frailty, each species manages to survive the inclemencies of the season with unvarying good fortune.

Insects may pass through the winter in any of the four stages of their life cycle—i.e. as eggs, larvae, pupae or imagines. Usually a species lies perdu in only one of these stages, although a few winter simultaneously in two, or even three, of them. That very many should pass the winter as eggs is not strange, when we reflect upon the obvious advantages which accrue from this procedure. In the first place the egg requires no food. Secondly, it is generally small and inconspicuous, likely to escape detection by the prying eyes of birds and other enemies, even if it is laid in an exposed position. Thirdly, as we have already seen, most insects' eggs possess wonderful powers of resistance. Without detriment to their contents they may be subjected to severities of temperature which in most instances would prove fatal to the adult, with all its faculties alert and operative. Thus, many typical forms of insect life—grasshoppers, moths, green-flies, and a host of others—complete their life cycle with the fall of the year, and lay eggs which will not hatch until the succeeding spring. But certain kinds of larvae and pupae, as well as some perfect insects, have also become cold-resistant to a remarkable degree in the course of their evolution. Ross found in the Arctic regions pupae of a clouded yellow which were hard and brittle, yet when thawed came to life and yielded butterflies. The same has been noted of certain caterpillars as well as pupae: though frozen till they tinkled against each other like broken glass, they subsequently revived completely. Gilbert White, in his account of the great frost of 1776, says that a thaw set in on the 1st of February, "and on the 3rd swarms of little insects were frisking and sporting in a court-yard . . . as if they had felt no frost. Why the juices in the small bodies and smaller limbs of such minute beings are not frozen is a matter of curious enquiry." In reference to this quotation L. C. Miall suggests that these insects were probably gnats or midges "which had escaped the extreme cold by sheltering as pupae in decaying vegetable matter, and only emerged as flies when more genial conditions had returned". Be this as it may, the fact that their vitality was unimpaired by the ordeal through which they had passed is astonishing, and speaks volumes for the amazing adaptability of living matter to the most untoward circumstances.

A considerable number of butterflies and moths pass the winter in the larval state. Some of these, such as the "surface caterpillars" which are so injurious to field crops, feed continuously, save in very hard weather, when they retire to earthen cells several inches deep in the soil, where they remain until a thaw sets in. Nearly all our native butterflies whose food-plants are grasses or low-growing herbs pass the winter in the larval state, a few of them—notably the skippers—spinning slight cocoons in which they lie up from the late autumn until the early spring. The rest creep down to the base of their food-plant and hide among dead leaves, etc., or burrow a little way into the earth, where most of them remain in a torpid condition for months on end, though they may do a certain amount of feeding during mild spells. In water meadows and low-lying districts some of these larvae, such as those of the marsh fritillary, may lie submerged for weeks without harmful results. An interesting exception is the beautiful silver-washed fritillary, whose female lays her eggs on the trunks of an oak tree during the late summer. In about a fortnight the minute larvae hatch and creep into crevices of the bark, where they remain hidden until the following spring, when they issue forth and either fall or are blown to the ground, there to seek the violet leaves on which they feed.

The larvae of our white admiral and purple emperor butterflies, which feed respectively upon the leaves of honeysuckle and sallow, construct "hibernacula" or winter sleeping-places for themselves. That made by the former has been described in Chapter Four. The purple emperor's caterpillar similarly binds the stalk of a sallow leaf to the twig by a webbing of silk and spins a pad on the upper surface of the leaf to which it holds with its pro-legs when it settles down for its winter sleep. Later on, as the leaf withers, its edges curl round, affording some protection from cold and damp. This habit, shared by a number of other caterpillars in different parts of the world, of preventing the fall of the leaf on which they pass the winter, or in which they spin their cocoons, is a very remarkable instance of what is usually called "prospective adaptation", though "instinctive foresight" would be just as suitable a term, since our knowledge of the psychical reactions of insects is extremely meagre.

Mention has already been made of the communal sleeping-tents constructed by certain social caterpillars. These would seem to provide the acme of safety and comfort during the winter months; yet only a few species have evolved the habit of weaving them. The majority of caterpillars that survive this inclement season are solitary by nature, and seek shelter in dry soil, under débris or in the crevices of rough bark. Often, as in the case of the lappet moth, their coloration promotes their concealment. Other species, such as those of the common swallow-tail moth, adopt no special precautions but simply press closely against a branch, or take hold of a twig with their anal pro-legs and stand out stiff and motionless, relying upon their deceptive likeness to sticks for protection from the assaults of insectivorous birds. The hardihood of such caterpillars is manifest when we reflect that they are exposed to the full severity of frosts and bitter winds; yet we find them busily devouring the young lilac and other leaves during the early days of spring.

Many insects, including eleven British butterflies and a much larger number of our native moths, change to pupae during the autumn and do not appear as imagines until the risk of frost and snow has abated. One need only turn over a spadeful or two of soil in the garden to disclose some of the reddish-brown, mummy-

ce packets from which with the return of mild weather soft-winged
moths will emerge. Astonishing numbers of pupae are often dug
up when a herbaceous border is being replanted. In plots where
potatoes have been grown the bulky pupa—not far short of three
inches from top to tail—of the famous death's-head moth may
occasionally be brought to light, while a rarer find is that of the
convolvulus hawk moth, easily recognized by its long, back-curved
beak, enclosing the trunk or proboscis of the perfect insect.

While the majority of caterpillars pupate in or near the surface
of the soil a considerable number construct cocoons for their protection during the quiescent stage of their development. Those made
by the emperor and puss moths, which have already been described,
are typical examples of this instinctive craft at its best. But the
pupae or chrysalides of all the more highly specialized butterflies
are "naked" and usually attached to a leaf or stem of the food-
plant, or perhaps to a wall, a fence or a rock. In the Fen districts of
East Anglia the expert searcher sometimes comes across those of
the handsome swallow-tail fixed to reeds, beyond the reach of
flood-water. The caterpillar, like those of the cabbage butterflies
and their relations, is not satisfied merely to make fast its tail, but
girdles its body with a belt of silk, so that it is held in a more or less
upright position. Thus secured, the pupa weathers successfully
the worst gales of winter. One British butterfly—the speckled wood,
whose food-plants are grasses of several kinds—passes the winter
in either of two stages—the larva or pupa.

Seven of our native butterflies, all—except the brimstone—
members of the Vanessid family, hibernate as adults and do not
mate until the following spring. But although the painted ladies
that emerge from chrysalides at the end of the summer—the offspring of immigrant parents which arrived in this country during
June—go duly into hiding in the autumn, they seldom if ever survive
the winter. The red admirals, apparently more hardy, fairly often
make their appearance in small numbers in the spring; yet neither
of these butterflies is able to maintain itself with us without annual
reinforcements from abroad. The two tortoiseshells and the peacock lie up in hollow trees, wood-piles, out-houses and so forth,
where also that rare visitor from Scandinavia—the Camberwell
beauty—is occasionally found. The comma comes to rest on a
branch among dead leaves, or it may take shelter under a bracket
fungus growing out of the trunk of a tree, while the brimstone creeps
into the fastness of an evergreen, usually holly or ivy. Several of

these species are from time to time seen in flight on exceptional
mild days during the winter months, when their appearance
hailed as phenomenally early by writers to the Press, wherea
in fact they are survivors of a departed summer, and often, i
tarnished and tattered wings, bear the marks of protracted activit

In barns and sheds herald moths may often be found sittin
motionless upon the beams. Each took up its position in the la
autumn and will not stir again until the advent of spring, whe
—true to its popular name—it will herald the opening buds an
flowers by once more spreading its wings in flight. This is one o
the relatively few moths that pass the winter as adults in this countr
the majority doing so either as larvae or pupae. Some of the wood
feeding kinds spend several years in the caterpillar state—the goa
moth usually three, during which period it is said to increase 72,00
times in weight. When fully fed it makes a cocoon in the autumn, i
which it lies up for the winter, and a second one early in the spring i
which to pupate. By contrast, the stag beetle's larva, which als
feeds for three years before its growth is complete, has only a ver
short pupal period, enacted in the autumn, the perfect inse
remaining passively in its cocoon throughout the winter and sprin
not seeing the light of day until the following June. Many kinds o
beetles, bugs and a varied assortment of other insects seek refug
from the inclemencies of wintry weather in cracks and crevices i
masonry and fences, or under the loose bark of trees. A number o
two-winged flies find shelter among the rafters of barns and ou
houses, in attics and church towers, or in the interstices of th
thatch of ricks and cottages. Indeed, there is hardly a moderatel
dry nook or corner which will not be found to harbour insects o
one sort or another during the dead season of the year. Strangel
enough, however, the manner in which the common house-fl
bridges the gap between one summer season and the next sti
awaits a completely satisfying answer. By October, the majorit
of the adults have already died of old age or disease, but in building
where the temperature is kept fairly high, and where food is obtain
able, a few house-flies may be found all the year round, and i
exceptionally favourable circumstances have been known to bree
during the winter months. But it is questionable whether a sufficien
number is maintained in these ways to account for the rapid mult
plication which marks the return of summer; and all the availabl
evidence goes to show that—in Britain, at all events—adult house
flies do not become dormant in cold weather. On the other hand,

suggestion that our house-fly population may be regularly aug-
mented by immigrants from the Continent has been turned down by
the experts. In short, this problem still awaits solution.

Biologists nowadays make a distinction between the hibernation
of certain mammals, such as the hedgehog, dormouse and bat, and
the state of suspended animation into which snails, frogs, insects
and so forth pass during the winter months. The difference is
between an all-but-complete cessation, and a mere slowing down,
of the life processes. In the hedgehog or dormouse digestion and
excretion are in abeyance, while the heart-beat and breathing
movements are scarcely perceptible. Wintering insects become far
less comatose. Although they hide away and cease from all ordinary
activities they still breathe, feed on food reserves stored in their
tissues, and are fairly easily resuscitated. According to Sir J. Arthur
Thomson they may be likened to watches that have slowed down,
not stopped working. But (he adds), "we linger over the puzzle, for
it is one of the wonders of life that it can come so near to death
and yet evade it after all".

It is an interesting fact that during the dry season in tropical
and sub-tropical countries some insects, including many butterflies,
have formed the habit of "aestivating". They seek a spot sheltered
from the scorching heat of the sun and remain quiescent until,
with the advent of the rains, vegetation breaks again into vigorous
growth.

Among the social bees and wasps in temperate regions the
winter is survived only by the fecund females of the race. Queen
wasps sleep throughout the cold months in any sheltered crevices
that they can find, and often congregate in great numbers in lofts
or under the eaves of old buildings. Others lie up in the deserted
nests when these are situated in holes or under cover. Queen humble-
bees are more often found in holes in banks, under dry moss, or it
may be in a hollow tree-trunk. They seldom if ever enter houses.

The population of an ants' nest does not die off at the approach
of autumn, but goes deep into the ground—sometimes three or
more feet below the surface—and there forms a closely packed
congeries, as if for warmth. Hive-bees, on the contrary, feed all
through the cold months upon their store of honey—or, if this
should fail, upon the syrup supplied to them by the apiarist. They
congregate in a dense cluster at the heart of the hive with the queen
in their midst, the drones having been exterminated at the close of the
summer. In his book *The Lore of the Honey-bee* Tickner Edwardes

gives us a vivid word-picture of the manner in which these insects live during their long seasonal seclusion. "The bees . . . nearest to the combs broach the full cells beneath them, and the honey is passed through the crowd, each bee getting her scanty dole. No one knows when a fresh supply may be available, although no chance will be lost to replenish the larder at the first sign of returning warmth. But now the barest minimum of food is taken, and as the nearest cells become emptied of their contents the cluster moves a step upward. Thus there is a system of slow browsing over the combs, until the dense flock of bees has reached the highest limit of the hive, when new grazing grounds must be taken. But the movement of the cluster is exceedingly slow—perhaps the slowest thing in the animate world. All recognize that existence depends on the stores being eked out to their uttermost . . . so that the largest possible army of nurse-bees and foragers may be at hand in the springtime to raise the young bees that are to represent the future colony."

In this rigorous economy we recognize again that "instinctive foresight" to which the reader's attention was directed in an earlier paragraph. Indeed, the whole phenomenon of hibernation and winter sleep bears eloquent testimony to the existence of this mysterious prescience of impending circumstances. A close study of the question points to the conclusion that it is not reaction to cold that drives insects to seek shelter, since the urge manifests itself long before the advent of bleak winds and keen frosts. Certain butterflies—e.g. the tortoiseshells and the brimstones—go regularly into hiding in early August, or even late July, though others postpone their retirement until October. Each species would seem to have its own calendar, to which it adheres strictly.

One of the few insects to be abroad and active during the cold weather from December onwards is the curiously ant-like creature which, in effect, is the mother of the oak-apple galls, or King Charles's apples. Owing to their diminutive size these venturesome matrons are not easily detected even when diligently searched for ; yet they climb in numbers up the trunks of oak trees every winter season, careless of biting winds and driving sleet. Each with her long ovipositor lays her eggs at the very heart of leaf buds, and when these hatch in the springtime the gnawing of the tiny grubs determines the growth of the well-known galls. What happens afterwards has already been told in Chapter Six.

A small number of moths are out and about during the winter

onths. The so-called winter moth is one of several common
geometers with flightless females which brave the coldest weather.
The males may often be seen on the wing in the chilly dusk of an
evening from late October until Christmas, while during November
and December the females creep up the boles of trees to lay their
eggs in clusters, usually at the base of buds, or on the pruned surfaces of twigs. No hardwood tree is safe from attack, and in some
seasons fruit trees—especially plums and damsons—suffer grievously,

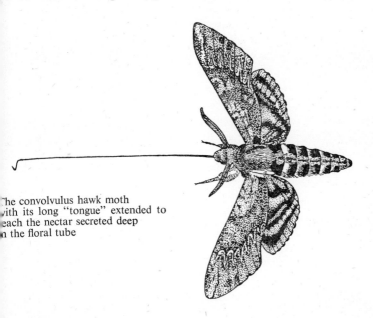

The convolvulus hawk moth
with its long "tongue" extended to
reach the nectar secreted deep
in the floral tube

the caterpillars not only devouring the young leaves and blossoms
but also gnawing the newly formed fruit. The mottled umber moth,
which also appears in October, is another of these orchard pests,
half as large again as the foregoing. The wings of the females are
rudimentary, so small as to be almost invisible, but those of the
males are fully developed and extraordinarily variable in coloration
—though why this should be in the case of a night-flying insect
which hides away during the hours of daylight nobody seems to
know. The ravages of these pests may be largely obviated by spreading a sticky compound on bands of grease-proof paper tied tightly
round the trunks of the trees. This prevents the females, bent on
egg-laying, from ascending.

The December moth, a member of the "eggar" family, is attracted to street lamps in suburban areas—often in considerable number —during the last six months of the year. Its caterpillar feeds on th leaves of various forest trees, and in the autumn spins its ver compact, egg-shaped cocoon under scales of loose bark or amon; dead leaves and grass at the base of the trunks. Edward Newma tells us that the perfect insect "sometimes comes out in the nex November or December, but if the weather at this time prove. unfavourable it remains in the cocoon one, two, three, four or ever five years". Assuming this statement to be correct—and Newma is regarded as a careful and trustworthy observer—we have a ver; remarkable instance of arrested development, apparently con sequent upon external conditions. Metamorphosis is normally continuous process, but the duration of the individual's life spa is variable. Some species accomplish it several or even many time: in the twelve months. Others, owing to scarcity of food or uncon genial climatic conditions, take two or more years for its completion Probably the longest-lived insect is the North American cicada o harvest-fly, known colloquially as the "seventeen-year locust" whose larva or nymph remains underground, feeding on roots, fo from thirteen to seventeen years before coming to the surface to assume the adult state, which may last for a month or more Compare this with the tenure of a typical may-fly—say, two o three years in the water and a day or less as a denizen of the air when pairing and egg-laying take place; or with that of the smal copper butterfly, which, weather permitting, is triple-brooded— i.e. three generations succeed one another in the course of the year the caterpillars of the third passing the winter in that stage.

Some adult aphides hide away in cracks and crevices during th cold weather, but the majority of these insects winter as eggs laic in the autumn. The spring brood of larvae rapidly complete thei metamorphosis and become viviparous females capable of virgir reproduction. Successive generations of these self-sufficient females appear throughout the summer, some of them wingless, others winged and able to fly to distant plants, which soon become infested with their progeny. The final generation of the season consists o both males and oviparous females, the latter laying the eggs which are destined to start the next year's cycle. This is the normal round of happenings; but the complete life history of certain species is much more complicated, extending over several years, and involving periodic migrations between two distinct kinds of plants. Foi example, the notorious "black-fly" goes in autumn to euonymous—

s primary or winter "host"—where the eggs are laid, but returns
ɔ the broad beans after they have started growth in the spring.

The winter months afford an opportunity for studying the
ɔale insects, one of the commonest being the mussel scale, regarded
s highly injurious to the apple, but found also on a number of other
lants, notably the hawthorn, to which it seems to do little harm.
'he details of its life history are well known and probably differ
ttle from those of related species. If, with a needle, we carefully
ft up one of the larger scales in winter and examine it under the
nicroscope, we shall find that it covers from fifty to one hundred
rilliantly white eggs, while at its narrower end the shrivelled
emains of the mother's body are apparent. The eggs hatch during
he spring, and the minute, six-legged larvae creep from under
heir shelter and roam over the twigs and branches, to settle down
ventually at spots where the cuticle is tender. Here each inserts
s haustellum or sucking-proboscis and begins to feed. The amount
f sap extracted by the individual larva is infinitesimal; but when
hey are present in millions the loss to the tree may be serious. Once
nchored, the larva remains completely sedentary. The female larva
hanges at the conclusion of its metamorphosis into an inert,
rub-like creature which never leaves its scale, but dies under it
fter depositing her eggs. The final moult of the male larva, however,
; preceded by a kind of pupal stage, after which the adult vacates
:s scale in the guise of a diminutive "fly" with long antennae and
ell-developed wings, although—since its mouth-parts are abortive
—it cannot feed. But males of the mussel scale are far from numerous,
nd in their absence the females, like those of many aphides, can
eproduce asexually.

An easily recognized scale insect is the felted beech coccus.
)wing to the whiteness of the flocculent covering secreted by the
emales, and its exposed position on the boles and main branches
f beech trees, the species is most conspicuous. At a distance the
runks look as if frozen sleet had drifted against them in a gale.
'he insects themselves are very small—almost microscopic—but
heir delicate, hair-like proboscides are long and strong enough to
ierce through the bark to the zone where the sap is flowing. Time
vas when foresters attached little importance to this infestation;
ut the insect is now recognized as a serious menace, capable, if
ot dealt with, of working destruction in beech-woods, especially
mong the younger trees.

Another scale insect likely to attract notice is found on the

smooth bark of ash, willow, etc., especially saplings. In th
instance the male form, which is much smaller than the female,
frequently the more abundant, and although the sexes may occur i
close proximity, they are more usually isolated on separate stem
Strangely enough, the eggs of this species are bright red in colou
and if during the winter a number of the female scales are crushe
the fingers are stained as if with blood.

Owing to their sap-sucking proclivity and capacity for rapi
multiplication, scale insects—like aphides—mostly figure as "pests
in relation to mankind, but a few species secrete substances whic
are useful in industry. With these matters we shall deal brief
in our final chapter. We may add here that while the majority o
scale insects are pygmies the family includes at least one giant,
native of South Africa, which clings to the bark of certain trees lik
limpets on a rock. But whereas the female is often over an inch i
diameter, the male by comparison is a mere speck. From Sout
Africa, too, and from the island of St. Vincent, come those curiositie
called margarodes or ground pearls, believed locally to be ant;
eggs. Actually they may be described as the shelly cocoons o
certain scale insects whose lives are passed underground, suckin
the roots of plants. Not unlike small amber beads in appearance
they have a small commercial value, and are systematically collecte
to be strung together as necklaces and sold to tourists.

Some of the tiny wingless spring-tails occasionally defy th
rigours of winter and are seen sporting themselves on snow-field
and glaciers in such prodigious numbers as to cause black, gre
or reddish patches visible from a considerable distance. These ar
the so-called "snow-fleas" or "snow-worms", which in the region
where they occur are regarded with alarm by the superstitiou
inhabitants, who believe their appearance foretokens impendin
calamity. In point of fact the insects, anticipating the coming o
the spring thaw, are probably trekking from their winter quarter
among the moss and lichens that cover the rocks in search of ope
water, upon or near which they spend the summer.

Thanks to the movement of the current, aquatic insects dwellin
in streams and rivers are secure against extreme cold, and nee
not adopt special precautions in times of frost. Those which ar
found in ponds and pools also benefit from the tendency of freezin
water to rise to the surface, there to form a protecting blanket o
ice, so that an equable temperature is maintained at and near th
bottom, and gill-breathing organisms—such as the larvae of may

flies, alder-flies, caddis-flies and whirligig beetles—can safely move about and continue their feeding. But most of the air-breathers, which must come periodically to the surface to take breath, bury themselves in mud or burrow into the banks, where they remain during the winter in a more or less comatose state, although some may take advantage of mild intervals to resume their activities. According to L. C. Miall, most fully armoured aquatic insects, such as beetles and bugs, pass the winter in the winged state and go into hiding only during unusually severe weather; but if they delay too long they risk suffocation when the ice-blanket forms. All but two of our dragon-flies and a high percentage of our aquatic Diptera pass the winter as larvae. Exceptions are the small metallic green de-moiselles, and several gnats or mosquitoes, which hide away as adults—the former in the cover of reed beds or waterside vegetation, the females of the latter in hollow trees, out-buildings, cellars, etc., the males dying off in the autumn. Of the common brown mosquito without spots on the wings S. P. James tells us that "adults of both sexes die off completely in the late autumn, and so far as we know at present the winter is passed only in the larval stage, the larvae being able to stand freezing".

Chapter Twenty-Two

OUR INSECT FRIENDS AND FOES

DURING the early years of the present century the round of the Press was made by a paragraph to the effect that the complete extinction of all insects—the hive-bee alone excepted—could result only in benefit to mankind. This remarkable pronouncement was supposed to emanate from "a well-known authority"; but we may safely disregard this time-honoured *cliché*, since on the face of it the notion is ridiculous. Consider, for example, our indebtedness to the activities of insects as scavengers—a work in which many species commonly regarded as unmitigated nuisances play an honourable part. Not only do they rapidly dispose of filth and rottenness, but in tropical countries the termites, longhorn beetles and other wood-feeders reduce the trunks and branches of dead trees to pulp or powder, which serves to replenish the soil. Nor is this process of natural fertilization the only end gained. So great is the excess of growth over dissolution in these regions that, but for the intervention of insects, the forests would gradually become blocked with dead timber, to their own destruction.

In temperate climes insects are constantly rendering an equally important if less obvious service, since vegetable refuse offers a stubborn resistance to the processes of decay. The chief agents of chemical dissolution are the extremely minute forms of life known as "microbes" or "bacteria", and so far as can be ascertained their absence would involve stagnation in the circulation of organic matter. The dead bodies of plants and animals would remain unchanged upon the face of the earth, and eventually life would completely disappear, all the available matter for its physical manifestation having been used up and locked up. Thanks to the ubiquity of certain bacteria and their almost incredibly rapid increase in favourable circumstances a catastrophe such as this is impossible. Yet it may be questioned whether bacteria, alone and unaided, could cope with the enormous masses of refractory material which the dead tissues of plants represent, and it is in this relation that the nibbling millions of the insect world probably perform their most important service—not only by reducing dead vegetation a condition in which it can be dealt with by bacteria, but also by checking a too luxuriant leafage during the period of growth.

If plants were completely exempt from the attacks of insects too many leaves might be produced, resulting in an excessive accumulation of effete vegetable matter, with ultimate disaster to the entire scheme of things. For in the last resort plants are just as dependent on animals as animals are on plants. They get their carbon for the building up of their bodies from the carbon dioxide in the atmosphere, and the supply of this gas would soon be exhausted but for its continual renewal by members of the animal kingdom, since these take in oxygen and give out carbon dioxide, which to all intents and purposes is the reverse of the process carried on by plants in sunlight.

In view of this fundamental interdependence the world of animate matter may be likened to a vast co-operative mechanism delicately adjusted to perform a special kind of work in a definite way. If any part should fail to act, either as a result of internal disorder or of a check in the flow of raw material, the hurt must be speedily remedied or the whole machine will be brought to a standstill. This is the guiding principle that underlies all the ceaseless adjustments and readjustments which in ordinary circumstances serve to maintain what we call "the balance of Nature". But agriculture produces artificial conditions which upset this balance, enabling certain species to increase and multiply as they could never have done normally. Hence, otherwise inoffensive animals and plants become pests and weeds, and mankind is compelled to devise means for their control, which may involve the use of chemical sprays, washes and fumigants, but depend ultimately for their efficacy upon the science known as ecology—i.e. a study of the relationship of organisms and their environment, animate as well as inanimate. In regard to insects, the first naturalist to recognize this was Gilbert White of Selborne who, in a letter written to his correspondent Thomas Pennant more than two centuries ago, opined that "A full history of noxious insects hurtful in the field, garden and house, suggesting all the known and likely means of destroying them would be allowed by the public to be a most useful and important work. What knowledge there is of this sort lies scattered, and wants to be collected : great improvements would soon follow of course. A knowledge of the properties, economy, propagation, and in short of the life and conversation of these animals, is a

P

necessary step to lead us to some method of preventing their depreda
tions."

That this step was eventually taken in this country durin
the second half of last century was due, in the main, to the zea
of two individuals—John Curtis and his worthy successor Elennc
A. Ormerod. The former, working under the auspices of the Roya
Agricultural Society of England in 1859, pointed out that "if insec
ravages could be brought under control, by lessening the number c
these destructives whenever they appear in excess, the benefi
would exceed anything of which at present we have any conception'
Reiteration of such "appeals to the pocket" served slowly to rall
the support of public opinion, and nowadays huge sums of mone
are expended annually in the warfare against pests of all kind
throughout the civilized world. At home, the Ministry of Agricultur
and Fisheries, through its various departments and publications
ensures the effective working of the necessary legislation, whil
circulating information and advice. The Commonwealth Institut
of Entomology has its headquarters at the British Museum (Natura
History), and facilities for the training of experts and for researc
are provided by most of our universities, as also by the variou
Stations and agricultural Colleges which the widespread deman
for education in these matters has called into existence.

Locust control constitutes a perennial problem of internationa
importance with which the Anti-Locust Research Centre, a smal
organization also housed in the British Museum (Natural History)
is concerned. Although a British institution, it serves as a centr
of information available to the whole world, and is frequentl
called upon for advice by foreign governments.

Locusts breed in circumscribed areas, by no means all of whicl
have so far been located, and in favourable circumstances—o
which, probably, a particularly genial temperature and rainfa
with suitable vegetation are the most important—sally forth i
immense numbers in search of food. On these occasions instinct
which have been in abeyance, perhaps for a decade, resume thei
sway, and the swarms set out in the same directions that have bee
followed by their ancestors from time immemorial. In some specie
the migratory urge asserts itself in the young before the wing
have developed, and long journeys are accomplished afoot by thes
"hoppers" or "voetgangers" as they are called in South Africa
They cross wide rivers by plunging impetuously into the water an
grasping each other or any floating objects, and in this way forn

eventually a kind of bridge, over which fresh relays continually pass to the other side. Comparatively few are destroyed, because the same individuals are seldom submerged for more than a short period : and locusts are exceedingly tenacious of life, the apparently drowned soon reviving when exposed to the warmth of the sun's rays.

According to Dr. D. L. Gunn, Principal Scientific Officer of the Anti-Locust Research Centre, locusts consume about ten times their final weight while growing up, so that a 1,000-ton swarm has probably eaten about 10,000 tons of vegetation : and it has been calculated that a migrating swarm of this size will need as many calories of energy per day as 100,000 men, and requires to eat its own weight of vegetation daily.

The most effective method of destroying hopper locusts is the scattering of poisoned baits, benzene hexachloride being usually employed, since this substance, while peculiarly effective against locusts, is harmless to stock. Where adult swarms on the wing are concerned spraying and dusting from aeroplanes with approved insecticides is the most promising method of attack. This technique, based on experiments designed by the Anti-Locust Research Centre and carried out in the first instance at the Experimental Station of the Ministry of Supply at Porton near Salisbury, has recently proved very promising in field operations in Tanganyika territory and elsewhere.

Insects as a class being omnivorous in the most comprehensive sense of the word, it is not very surprising that certain species, in addition to their depredations in fields and gardens, levy annually a considerable tax upon stored goods of every kind, in cellars, warehouses, shops, and even in domestic wardrobes and larders ; and it is this imposition that most often rouses the rancour of the general public. Clothes-moths and furniture-beetles must have made their appearance at one time or another in most houses throughout the land, the caterpillars of the former destroying woollen and other fabrics, as well as furs and feathers, the grubs of the latter tunnelling into chairs, tables, shelving, piano-casings, and occasionally floor-boards. Then there are the larvae of the brown house-moth, which have been described as the most destructive insects imaginable, nothing in the smallest degree edible coming amiss to them. The present writer once found a thriving family in a hay-box (used for cooking) that had lain idle for several months. They appeared to be feeding both on the hay and the thick

felt lining, to say nothing of the paper that had been used fo
padding, while the very wood of the box itself had evidently bee
rasped away in places.

Insects of many kinds take their toll of nearly all the ingredient
needed for the manufacture of cakes, biscuits and confectionery
The caterpillars of the Mediterranean flour-moth—a widely dis
persed species first recorded in Britain in 1886—are a veritabl
scourge if they establish themselves in a corn mill. Not only d
they devour the fine flour and siftings, but frequently clog th
machinery with the copious silk webbing which they spin. Those o
several other small moths do mischief in mills and granaries, whil
the grubs of a variety of beetles have similar feeding habits, an
are even more destructive when they gain the ascendancy. The so
called mealworms—the larvae of beetles—are probably the bes
known on account of their relatively large size, and the fact tha
they are in constant demand by anglers and for the feeding o
captive beasts, birds, reptiles and other insectivores. Where store
cereals are concerned the worst offenders are the grain- and rice
weevils. After long voyages, and in default of adequate preventiv
measures, cargoes have arrived at their destinations swarming wit
these pests. The female lays one egg in each grain on the content
of which the resulting grub feeds, eventually changing to the pup
within the eaten-out husk. In the early years of this century th
bionomics of these weevils were exhaustively investigated by F. J
Cole, whose recommendations, put into practice, soon reduced th
losses to a fraction of what they had been in the immediate past.

The weevilly biscuits which frequently formed a large part o
the rations of long-suffering mariners in bygone years were usuall
infested by the grubs of the bread- or paste-beetle, which is probabl
more catholic in its tastes than any other insect, being able to thriv
on almost any organic substance that may be available, from dr
wood to capsicum, cayenne pepper and root ginger, although it
special preference is for commodities in which flour and water ar
the chief ingredients. It figured prominently in the Army Biscui
Enquiry of 1912-13, is a perennial cause of loss in stores, as well a
in the shops of grocers and druggists, and not infrequently gains
footing in the larders and cupboards of private houses. Furthermore
it is probably the worst offender among the enemies of books. I
neglected libraries the grubs have been known to gnaw the edge
of the pages and drill tunnels from cover to cover. In one wel
authenticated instance twenty-seven folio volumes standing sid

y side were perforated in a straight line by a single grub, the
urrow being so perfectly excavated that it was possible to pass a
tring from end to end of it and so raise the entire set of volumes
t once. These grubs have also been known to bore through sheet-
ad when this has come in their way—a fact which bears eloquent
stimony to the hardness of their heads and the strength of their
w muscles.

Neither tobacco nor wine is immune from spoliation by insects,

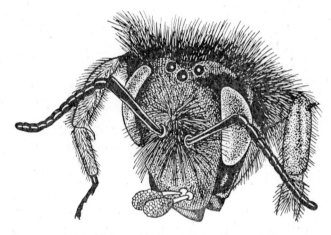

A humble-bee with the pollinia of an orchid
attached to its "face" just above the jaws

lthough the latter suffers only indirectly. The tiny wine-cork moth
held in dread by wine-merchants and cellarers in many parts of
he world. It haunts the gloom of subterranean vaults and lays
s eggs on or close to the corks of wine bottles. When the caterpillars
atch they burrow into the substance of the cork—just as those of
e big goat moth burrow into the wood of an oak or an apple
ee. The presence of the pest is first evidenced by an accumulation
f dust and excrement (technically "frass") round the exposed portion
f the cork; and eventually, if several caterpillars are at work, the
hole cork is so much tunnelled that leakage may occur—this being
he so-called "ullage of wine". Sherry, madeira and champagne
orks are attacked indiscriminately, and even when the damage is
ot sufficiently serious to cause ullage, the wine is usually tainted,
nd so rendered valueless.

New corks in store are sometimes eaten into by the caterpillar of another small moth, though in this case the taste appears to be a recently acquired one, the species in question—the fig-moth—being one of a group whose members attack dried fruit in general, and occasionally cocoa beans and chocolate. So prevalent are these pests that they may almost be described as common objects of the dessert table, for unwrapped figs and dates (save those very recently imported) are seldom free from the small, white caterpillars, or the signs left behind them when they creep away to spin their cocoons in convenient cracks and crevices.

Tobacco merchants and manufacturers are sorely tried at times by the activities of a beetle which has acquired the habit of feeding upon stored tobacco of all kinds, especially in the form of cigars and cigarettes. The caterpillar of the tobacco-moth also attacks cigars and cheroots, although its more usual food-stuffs are chocolates, biscuits and dried fruits. Yet another beetle damages nutmegs and spices, but its special preference is for dried coffee berries, in which the grubs burrow and feed. Their attacks, however, do not destroy the whole berry, nor is the quality and aroma of the coffee affected. Hence, when buying old coffee one is likely to purchase also a quantity of ground-up beetles into the bargain !

The only ant in this country that does serious mischief to stored goods is the cosmopolitan Pharaoh's ant. Its place of origin is unknown, but—like the common cockroach and the cricket of the hearth—it craves warmth and shelter and cannot tolerate an open air life in our climate. The workers, which make up the bulk of a community, are very small, 17,000 being needed to weigh down one gramme ; but in warehouses and factories, where insufficient attention is paid to cleanliness, they often accumulate in and on provisions in prodigious numbers. Sugar, spices and ground almonds are among the special favourites of this ant, but it can and does subsist on many less delectable dainties. Tradition credits it with one dietetic virtue namely that despite its diminutive size it will mob and massacre bed-bugs if the chance arises—completely clearing a house of these objectionable lodgers in a few days' time. The Argentine ant is another troublesome species which is carried about by shipping. When once established in a new locality it soon becomes a serious pest. Happily, it has not so far gained a footing in the British Islands, although its presence has been reported from two or three widely separated places.

Besides ravaging our crops in field and garden, and despoiling our stored goods, certain insects are agents in the dissemination of zymotic diseases. Since the discovery that many diseases are caused by micro-organisms, and that these may be carried from one host-individual to another by blood-sucking creatures, including insects, signal successes in the campaign against these evils have been achieved. One of the most spectacular was the virtual extermination of the mosquito-carrier of the deadly yellow fever, or "Black Jack", in the Canal Zone of Panama. When in 1879 the French essayed to construct a canal across the Isthmus the scheme had to be abandoned, chiefly because of the appalling mortality among the labourers due to fever. But from 1904 onward the Americans were able to carry the enterprise to a conclusion by adopting the methods of control worked out by Ross, Mason, Grassi and others for dealing with the malarial mosquito menace, the most important being the destruction of their aquatic larvae by draining swamps and filling in pools, or—when this is impracticable —covering the surface of the water with a film of oil to prevent them from breathing. Towards the end of 1912 a journalist, J. F. Fraser, wrote: "Before the Americans came the Isthmus was one of earth's pestiferous spots. . . . In the immediate Canal region it is no longer a country dangerous to health. The Americans have laid by the heels the mosquitoes which carried the disease. All likely breeding grounds or swamps are saturated with kerosene. . . . Nearly every ditch is smeared with it. Where pools accumulate in the vicinity of the workings, niggers with copper cans on their backs saunter about and spray freely."

The control of the African tse-tse flies, which harbour and transmit the minute trypanosome parasites that cause sleeping sickness in mankind and other fell diseases in domestic cattle and horses, is beset with special difficulties, since these insects are viviparous, the new-born larvae pupating soon after they leave the parent's body. For this reason they cannot be exterminated whole-sale. On the other hand, the adult flies are relatively slow to multiply, and may be caught in large numbers in specially designed traps, where they soon die of hunger and exposure. Attempts have been made to restrict their range by clearing vegetation from wide belts of land, thus forming barriers in which they cannot breed. The suggested total destruction of antelopes and other wild animals believed to be "reservoir hosts" of the trypanosomes scarcely falls within the sphere of practical politics. But unremitting energy and vast sums of money have already been expended in the war against these pests, and although the final battle has yet to be fought and won, much has been done to mitigate the plague.

The louse is another potential disseminator of disease, especially in times of war among front-line troops when personal cleanliness is difficult or impossible to maintain. It transmits the germs of typhus, endemic in eastern Europe, from one person to another, and in bygone days was responsible for the terrible prevalence of "gaol fever" in prisons and penitentiaries, as also for the notorious "black assizes", when many of those attending the court were—as it then seemed—mysteriously smitten with the pestilence. Fleas, too, are carriers of infection, especially the bacilli causing bubonic plague, a fatal disease of rats, proved by the Indian Plague Commission to be transmitted from the dead bodies of these animals to human beings by the Asiatic rat-flea. Other fleas, including the species specially associated with mankind, have been shown experimentally to be capable of transmitting plague, but whether this has ever occurred under natural conditions is uncertain. Writing in 1932 of that other undesirable lodger the bed-bug, the late B. F. Cummins stated that although it has long been under suspicion as the carrier of certain human diseases, recent investigations tend rather to acquit it of responsibility in this respect.

Among disease-carrying insects which do not suck blood, eminent hygienists have indicted the house-fly as enemy number one—this ban, of course, including several other equally common species with similar habits. During the Boer War, it was estimated that 30 per cent of the deaths on the British side were caused by typhoid fever, all precautions by the Army Medical Corps to check the spread of the epidemic having been frustrated by the enormous numbers of flies which swarmed in and about the latrines and mess-tents.

The peculiar deadliness of house-flies and their congeners consists in the dual activities of the individual insect and its consequent change of habit in the course of its metamorphosis. The larvae or maggots feed on moist refuse of many kinds, particularly stercoraceous matter. Hence the adult females constantly resort to such places as manure-heaps and middens in order to lay their eggs, and from them often fly straight to our dairies, food-shops and larders, carrying among the hairs of their legs and bodies germs of many kinds. Let a fly walk over a specially prepared and sterilized plate of gelatine such as is used in laboratories for the experimental culture of bacteria and moulds. In twenty-four hours every footstep of the insect on the gelatine will be plainly indicated by a large and varied crop of microbes. But this mechanical transport is only one (some say the least effective) of the ways in which flies spread diseases. They greedily suck up all sorts of liquid, and in this way their excreta—the familiar "fly-blows" or "fly-spots"— are often rendered infective. Moreover, the food absorbed passes first into a kind of reservoir or crop (comparable to the paunch or storage-stomach of a ruminant animal), from which it is subsequently regurgitated and eaten again before finally entering the alimentary canal for digestion. These "vomit spots" may easily contaminate the vessels destined to contain our food and drink.

The house-fly is probably far less numerous in Britain nowadays than it was even two decades ago. Its favourite breeding-places were heaps of stable manure, and with the decline of horse traffic, consequent upon the multiplication of motor-cars and tractors, these have largely disappeared ; while the rigorous enforcement of sanitary measures in all urban and most rural areas has contributed to the same desirable end. Nevertheless, since the total elimination of house-frequenting flies is impracticable—and because even a few of these insects constitute a menace to health—the public cannot be too often warned against leaving milk and other comestibles uncovered during the summer months, or neglecting precautions to exclude flies as far as possible from factories, larders, restaurants and living-rooms. The new D.D.T. insecticide in its various forms, though not perhaps the complete panacea that had been hoped, is undoubtedly a valuable deterrent, especially when sprinkled on window-ledges. As a poisonous bait for flies which have already invaded a building, sweetened milk laced with formalin in the proportion of one teaspoonful to the half-pint is recommended. The concoction should be left exposed overnight, all other liquids having been removed or well covered. The old-fashioned sticky fly-paper, though unsightly, is not to be despised.

A very important indirect service rendered by insects to mankind arises from their activities as flower visitors, which have already been described in Chapter Nineteen. In this respect hive-bees are pre-eminent. Recent observations in a clover field indicated that they accomplish 75 per cent of the cross-pollinating, while it has been estimated that the worth of their services in our orchards averages £4,000,000 annually—a sum much greater than the value of the honey which they produce during the season.

Erasmus Darwin, the grandfather of Charles Darwin, was

apparently the first Englishman to realize the usefulness of pre-dacious and parasitic insects in checking the increase of pests. In his *Phytologia, or the Philosophy of Agriculture and Gardening*, published in 1800, he suggested that the onslaughts of aphides might be countered by encouraging their enemies—the larvae of hover-flies. From this beginning has grown up the modern practice of "biological control", one of the earliest examples of which was enacted in the citrus-fruit orchards of California when in 1880, by an unlucky accident, a species of scale insect was introduced from Australia. So devastating were its ravages that in a single year the orange crop was reduced from 8,000 to 600 car-loads. All attempts to stamp out the invader by the use of chemical applications proved unavailing, and eventually the situation became so critical that the citrus-growing industry seemed doomed. In these circumstances the United States Department of Agriculture despatched an expert entomologist to Australia, where a brilliant red ladybird was found preying upon the scale insect. Large numbers of these "natural enemies", skilfully packed, were sent across the ocean and liberated in the Californian orchards, where they increased and multiplied, and have held the pest in subjection ever since.

The success of this experiment encouraged other countries to adopt a system of fostering, breeding and distributing beneficial insects. In 1927 a special parasite-breeding laboratory was established at Farnham Royal in Buckinghamshire under the Commonwealth Institute of Entomology, from which, during the first nine years of its existence, more than 630 consignments—comprising in all over 11,000,000 separate individuals—were sent out to various parts of the world. But the problems presented to the economic entomologist for solution are often complicated. He has, for example, to bear in mind that some parasites and insects of prey may themselves be inimical to the interests of mankind because they attack species that are serviceable. A little Chalcid wasp that lays its eggs in the aphid-feeding grub of a hover-fly obviously does the gardener a bad turn. So, too, when the parasite of a destructive pest becomes the victim of a secondary parasite (a not infrequent occurrence), the pest—not the agriculturist—reaps advantage : nor does this phenomenon of hyperparasitism, as it is called, end here ; for some secondary parasites are attacked by tertiary parasites, while it seems probable that a certain amount of quaternary parasitism exists among insects !

Broadly speaking, beneficial insects may be separated into

two main groups, namely the parasites and the predators; and these again may be subdivided in accordance with the partiality or impartiality of their members: that is to say, some species in both groups restrict themselves quite rigidly to a special kind of prey or victim, while others attack almost any insect of convenient size that they chance to encounter. The latter are exemplified by the dragon-flies and the robber flies, also by the carnivorous ground beetles. The devil's coach-horse—our largest "cocktail"—likewise plays a beneficial rôle, being very abundant and a voracious slayer of soil pests.

Of the partial predators the most important are the ladybirds, hover-flies and lacewings, whose aid in our perennial campaign against aphides and scale insects is invaluable. Most of the capsid bugs, of which there are nearly 190 British species, are economically injurious—some, apparently, spreading virus diseases from unhealthy to healthy plants; but two or three have taken to sucking the juices of other insects, and to this extent are serviceable. The same is true of several of the larger shield-bugs, the red-legged species being common in late summer and autumn on trees and shrubs. Another group of insects not usually credited with carnivorous proclivities is that of the long-horned grasshoppers, of which we have nine indigenous species, not to be confused with the short-horned or "meadow" grasshoppers, whose tastes—like those of their giant kindred the migratory locusts—are strictly vegetarian. The long-horns, on the contrary, destroy many caterpillars and other insects—although, living as they mostly do on trees or among undergrowth, they probably nibble leaves when their favourite food is in short supply.

The snake flies and the scorpion flies—two families of insects with net-veined wings, represented in Britain by three or four species each—also call for mention. The latter get their popular name from a curious masculine appendage not unlike the sting of a scorpion in appearance: it is not, however, a weapon but an elaboration of the male genital apparatus. Both sexes have prettily mottled wings and quaint horse-shaped heads. The caterpillar-like larvae burrow in the soil, especially round tree-stumps, and are believed to feed on dead animal matter; but the adults capture living insects.

Scorpion flies are often very numerous during the summer months, especially in woodland districts, whereas snake flies are much more retiring in their habits and are seldom seen unless searched for. They are black insects with transparent wings and may be easily recognized by the curious elongation of the head and prothorax, which is suggestive of a snake. The active, six-legged larvae are found under bark, where they hunt their prey—small insects and the like that frequent similar situations.

The manners and customs of Hymenopterous ichneumons and of the Tachinid flies have already been dealt with in Chapter Sixteen, but it is impossible to over-estimate the importance of the services rendered to mankind by these two groups of insects. With regard to the earwigs, the wasps and the ants, opinion is divided. The common earwig—the only species that need be reckoned with in this country—is often very numerous; nor can it be doubted that it is responsible for much damage, particularly in orchards and gardens. But should earwigs be stigmatized as out-and-out pests? Probably most people would answer unhesitatingly in the affirmative; yet these insects undoubtedly destroy considerable numbers of small caterpillars, pupae, slugs, etc.; and it seems likely that when their numbers are not excessive in a district the mischief done is fully compensated by benefits conferred.

Every year brings its autumnal swarms of wasps, while in seasons especially favourable to their increase these insects become a veritable but short-lived plague. There is, however, another side to the picture. Adult wasps are certainly greedy for sweet juices, but they feed their grubs largely on insect fare. Thus, to quote O. H. Latter, "It is only when fruit is ripe that they do serious damage—granted that in a 'wasp year' the loss inflicted is very great; nevertheless in the earlier part of the season they are good friends to the gardener and fruit-grower, for they destroy enormous numbers of caterpillars, of green-fly and black-fly, and other harmful insects." To which may be added the assurance that wasps are by no means the aggressive monsters of popular imagination. Left to themselves, they may be trusted to pass peacefully to and fro on their lawful occasions, never using their stings if unmolested.

Most British ants are very fond of nectar, sap—indeed, of every sort of sweet substance; but they also kill and eat many caterpillars and other pests, and act as scavengers by cleaning up such dead animal matter as they may find in the course of their wanderings. True, they may often be seen running in large numbers over vegetation, although in this country they are innocent of any direct injury to plants. All things considered, little hesitation would be felt in recommending the ant to the goodwill of the husbandman were it not for its habit of fostering aphides on account of their sugary secretions. As we have seen, they guard these protégés with the utmost diligence, fight for them if need be, and in certain instances actually store up their eggs during the winter, bringing them out into the open again when the mild days of spring come round. Now aphides are by nature a peculiarly feeble folk—soft, succulent, sedentary and—in many cases—entirely defenceless. They live openly on the plants which they infest, exposed to the attacks of every passing enemy. Yet they have survived from very early times, and there is geological evidence to prove that their honey-dew was appreciated by ants in the mid-tertiary period of the earth's history—which points to the conclusion that ant-patronage has been an important factor—if not, indeed, the dominant factor— in saving aphides from extinction. Could this be proved, we should be bound to admit that the prehistoric ants, by gratifying their tastes for honey-dew and adopting very cute measures to secure a regular supply of this dainty, did our modern agriculturists a very bad turn.

Insects have been employed to check the growth and spread of noxious weeds, the outstanding example being the successful control of certain kinds of cactus known as "prickly pears" which were introduced into Australia in 1787 by some person or persons unknown. Two species in particular increased and multiplied to such an extent that by 1925—which marked the peak of the invasion—60,000,000 acres in Queensland and New South Wales were computed to have been overrun by them. Not only was much of the native flora crowded out, but grazing lands were invaded, while in many areas the cultivation of crops became impossible. Every effort to combat the scourge proved unavailing, until a small moth was brought from the Argentine, which speedily solved the problem. Its caterpillars feed gregariously, burrowing into the juicy stems of the cacti, and—with the help of disease organisms which subsequently gain access to the tissues—soon reduce the attacked plants to rotting masses of pulp. In another instance, where the European gorse was encroaching upon agricultural land in New Zealand, its spread was effectively checked by the introduction of a small weevil from England. The grubs feed in the pods of the plant and destroy large numbers of the seeds—sometimes as many as 90 per cent.

Certain insects are directly serviceable to mankind, by furnishing him with silk, honey, wax and other substances of commercial importance. Most of our silk is derived from the caterpillars or "silkworms" of the moth which is extensively cultivated in southern

Europe and the East. In 1934, at Lullingstone in Kent, Lady Hart Dyke instituted a silk farm which, despite early vicissitudes, has achieved notable success, raw silk having been supplied for the manufacture of royal dresses and robes. Coarser kinds of silk are obtained from the cocoons of several species of larger moths of the Far East and North America, the most important being the tusser moth, whose silk has been utilized in India and China from very early times.

Three centuries ago honey was the only sweetening agent in common use. Today its place in this respect is taken by cane, beet and maple sugars. Yet the incomparable virtues of honey are well known, and its annual consumption in all civilized countries is still very considerable. Pure beeswax is less in demand than heretofore. chiefly because many of the uses to which it was once put are now served by waxes of different kinds obtained from other sources. At the present day, the largest demand for pure beeswax is for the manufacture of candles employed in religious ceremonial. But beeswax retains its ductility and tenacity under greater ranges of temperature than any of its competitors, and thus, for certain purposes, remains indispensable. A white wax imported from China is secreted by the pe-la scale insect found upon the native ash tree. It was formerly greatly prized, but its use is now largely superseded by petroleum products. In India a similar wax is secreted by another scale insect, while the wax produced by several more Asiatic species of the same genus have been used by mankind for various purposes.

Strangely enough, the family of the scale insects, which—as we have seen—includes many destructive pests, also comprises a number of economically useful species. Besides those mentioned above, one indigenous to Mexico yields a fatty substance from which a peculiar acid—axinic acid—is derived. This is used as a varnish which dries and hardens rapidly on exposure to the air, also as an external medical application in various ailments. A scale insect which infests the leaves of tamarisk in the Mediterranean region causes an exudation of a sweet gummy substance which is collected and eaten by the Arabs, who call it "man", and regard it as the "manna" endowed by the wandering Israelites with a miraculous origin—although, in fact, this is more likely to have been an edible lichen. But the most important products of scale insects are lac and cochineal. The former is secreted in large quantities by the lac insect upon the twigs of its food-plants—species of fig, buckthorn and other trees—where it hardens to form an incrustation.

This is the "crude lac" imported from India which, after treatment, is used in the manufacture of varnish, French polish and other preparations, as well as in the making of gramophone records. The bodies of the female lac insects also yield the crimson pigment known as "lake"; but the chief dye-producing coccid is the cochineal insect. A native of Mexico, it was long ago carried by man to the Eastern Hemisphere, and became thoroughly acclimatized in the Canary Islands, where its cultivation is still an important industry.

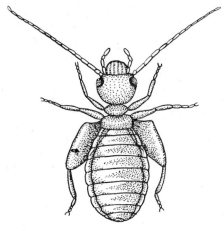

The so-called "book-louse": a tiny but often destructive domestic pest

The cochineal of commerce consists of the dried bodies of the female insects ground to a powder, from which a distillation may be made; but its use has been largely superseded by aniline dyes. It is still employed for colouring sweetmeats and confectionery, and in pharmacy as a specific in whooping-cough.

Several kinds of soft-skinned beetles whose blood contains a large admixture of cantharidine are used in allopathic medicine— the European blister beetle, or "Spanish fly", being the most important. The pharmacopoeia of the homeopaths includes a number of insects (e.g. the hive-bee, the cockroach, the ladybird and even the Colorado beetle), all of which, so the writer is credibly informed, have proved useful in alleviating some of the ills to which human flesh is heir.

Certain species of insects are important food items among savage and semi-civilized races, locusts probably being the chief

among them. They have been treated as luxuries from the earlies
times of which any records remain to us. In the British Museum a
Nineveh sculpture is exhibited showing men carrying differen
kinds of meat to a festival, and among them are some with long rod
to which locusts are attached. In Athens of old locusts were sold ir
the markets and are said to have been preferred as dainties to the
most succulent quails or the best figs. Whether the locusts eater
with wild honey by John the Baptist were really insects or the bean
like fruits of the locust or carob tree is debatable; but in the law o
Moses, as set forth in the Book of Leviticus, locusts are permitted
as food for the Jews; and today, throughout the Middle East and
in most parts of Africa, they are regarded with favour as a comestible
In some instances they are eaten raw. More often they are cooked
in various ways and perhaps served with a condiment; or they
may be ground into a kind of flour and made into cakes. According
to P. L. Simmonds, who made an extensive study of strange kind
of animal food, the flavour of locusts when skilfully prepared is fa
from disagreeable. A broth made by boiling a quantity for a couple
of hours in water with pepper and salt added of which he and
several of his friends partook experimentally was scarcely to be
distinguished from beef-tea! From the same authority we learn
that locusts, fried in their own fat and seasoned with salt, have a nutty
flavour and are by no means unpalatable. That a judicious course o
locust fare is wholesome and nourishing cannot be doubted, since
locust-eating tribes are said invariably to put on flesh when this
addition to their diet is plentiful.

One can appreciate to some extent the relish for honey-po
ants evinced by the natives of those countries where these living
sweetmeats are available. They are not unlike small, amber-coloured
sultanas in size and shape, and can be bought by the gallon ir
Mexican markets. All that the buyer need do to convert them into
mead is to pound them in a mortar, after which the fluid is strained
off through muslin and then allowed to stand until it ferments
A more potent liquid, comparable to whiskey or arrack, is distilled
from a concoction of boiled beetles! In Mexico, too, a kind o
caviare is made by compressing into cakes the eggs of certain large
aquatic bugs allied to our water-boatmen. Savoury rissoles are—
or, at any rate, were—compounded by the aborigines of New
South Wales from the crushed bodies of strong-smelling butterflie
which, at certain seasons of the year, are found in vast number
upon the slopes of the Bugong Mountains. The "black fellows"

ght great fires beneath the trees on the branches of which the
utterflies settle for the night, thus suffocating them and bringing
hem to earth. When a sufficient quantity has been collected, the
shes are swept away and the insects spread out on the heated ground
nd ranked about until their wings, legs and antennae are singed
ff; after which the bodies are pounded in a wooden vessel and
ressed together. When eaten they at first produce nausea; but these
ymptoms pass off in a few days, and the diet is said to be fattening.

The epicures of ancient Rome delighted in a dish consisting of
large, corpulent grub which they called "cossus". The identity
f this insect is uncertain. Some authorities think that it was the
aterpillar of the goat moth; others that the larva of the stag beetle
s indicated; while still others insist that the true "cossus" of the
Romans was none other than the grub of the Prionus long-horn
eetle. Be this as it may, none of these insects is eaten today—so far,
t least, as the present writer is aware. Towards the end of last
entury, however, an attempt was made to popularize cockchafer
rubs as a dainty. A banquet was given at the Café Custoza, in
Paris, for the express purpose of demonstrating their nutritious
nd palatable qualities; and it was noteworthy that of the fifty
uests present the majority called for a second helping. The insects
vere fried in a paste of flour, milk and eggs to a golden-brown
olour, and when so prepared are said to emit a very attractive
dour "which disposes one favourably to taste the delicacy, which
vill be found more appetizing than snails, and will be declared
ne of the finest delicacies ever tasted". Equally laudatory reports
re current respecting the large grubs of a West-Indian weevil—
he famous gru-grus—which burrow in and feed on the pith of
alm trees. These are roasted on tiny spits after being highly spiced,
nd are said to surpass all other animal food in flavour.

We have it on the authority of A. R. Wallace that in the Malay
Archipelago dragon-flies are extensively eaten. "Every day" (he
vrote) "boys were to be seen walking along the roads and by the
edges and ditches, catching dragon-flies with bird-lime. They
arry a slender stick with a few twigs at the end well anointed,
o that the least touch captures the insect, whose wings are pulled
ff before it is consigned to a small basket. The dragon-flies are so
bundant at the time of the rice-flowering that thousands are caught
n this way. The bodies are fried in oil with onions and preserved
hrimps, or sometimes alone, and are considered a great delicacy."

In conclusion, something may be said concerning the use of

Q

insects as ornaments and for decoration. Most notable, perhap
is the so-called "Brazilian beetle", a distant cousin of our tortois
beetle, which feeds on the coffee plant, but on account of it
metallic splendour is in considerable demand for mounting a
brooches, tie-pins, sleeve-links, etc. The "gold bug" of Poe's tal
of that name was probably the Southern and Central America
gold chafer, almost every part of which seems as if made of th
precious metal. Needless to say, this insect commands a high price
but its rare silver-hued variety is even more valuable. The beautife
African emerald beetle is also worthy of special note. Specimens ar
collected in Togoland from flowering shrubs during the rain
season, and are mounted as centrepieces of brooches and othe
jewelry by native goldsmiths. Nearer home we have the little cerulea
chafer, a native of southern France, where its collection by wome
and children for decorative purposes is quite a lucrative industr}
The colour of the wing-cases is exquisite sky-blue, with an indes
cribable lustre, and it was formerly much used by milliners fc
embellishing feminine headdresses. Great care is taken not t
capture or destroy the females, which are much less resplender
than the far more numerous males.

Many of the tropical Buprestids—a family allied to the "skip
jacks", but represented in Britain by only a few insignificant ex
amples—are remarkable for the magnificence of their iridescer
green, red or gold colouring, which is often of the greatest brilliance
The shards or elytra of a very large South American species ar
highly prized by the Indians of the western coastal areas, who sev
them on cloth from which they make dazzling cuirasses and othe
articles of attire; while the natives of Ecuador employ them in th
manufacture of necklaces and ear-ornaments. In India and Ceylo
the wing-cases of other species are used to decorate embroidere
table-cloths, bed-covers and the like, as well as for the adornmer
of ladies' dresses.

In some parts of the world living insects serve as ornaments c
charms. A South American beetle is worn by native girls as a
amulet suspended by a band and fine chain of gold from the necl
It is cherished with great care, since its wonderful metallic lust
—doubtless also its reputed efficacy as a safeguard against mi
fortune—vanish with death. In Brazil the "cucujo" or native "fir
fly"—already referred to in Chapter Twenty—is lured and caught a
night by the aid of a glowing coal waved in the air. These beetle
are kept till needed in small wire cages, fed with pieces of sugar can

nd supplied with moisture twice daily so that their luminescence
nay not deteriorate. The combined light emitted by several is
ufficient for the reading of small print. When enclosed in a gauze
ontainer and worn in the hair or attached conspicuously to the
pparel of a dancer the effect is spectacular.

Towards the end of last century certain craftsmen hit upon
he device of mounting fragments of butterflies' wings under glass
1 brooches, pendants and other trinkets. Those usually chosen
re species of the South American genus *Morpho*, renowned for
heir exquisite colouring, which ranges from deep purple-blue to a
ale tint suggestive of mother-o'-pearl—like the nacreous lining
if a sea-shell. Some of the more resplendent moths are pressed into
ervice for a like purpose, notably a magnificent species from
Madagascar with bands of burnished green and patches of brilliant
:oppery-red on a background of black.

GLOSSARY

List of English names of insects mentioned in this book
with Latin names appended.

cacia-thorn Ant (*Pseudomyrma bicolor*).
frican Mimetic Swallow-tail Butterfly (*Papilio cenea*).
grippa Moth (*Thysania agrippa*).
lder-fly—Common (*Siatis lutaria*).
lder-fly—Giant (*Corydalis cornuta*).
leppo Gall-wasp (*Cynips tinctoria*).
lligator Bug (*Lanternia lucifera*).
mazon Ant—European (*Polyergus rufescens*).
merican Blight (*Eriosoma lanigera*).
mulet Beetle (*Zopherus bremei*).
ntler Moth (*Cerapteryx graminis*).
nt-lion (*Myrmelion formicarius*).
nt-mimicking Bug (*Nabis lativentris*).
nts'-nest Fly (*Microdon mutabilis*).
nts'-nest Moth (*Myrmeconella ochracella*).
pantelles Ichneumon (*Apantelles glomeratus*).
phid-Lion (*Hemerobius sp.*).
quatic Fairy Fly (*Cataphractus cinctus*).
quatic Ichneumon (*Agrityphus armatus*).
ru Island Mimetic Moth (*Alcidis aruus*).
sh Scale Insect (*Chionaspis salicis*).
tlas Moths (*Attacus spp.*).
ustralian Orchid-visiting Ichneumon (*Lissopimpla leptochile*).
xinus Scale Insect (*Llaveia axinus*).

ack-swimmer (*Notonecta glauca*).
acon Beetle (*Dermestes lardarius*).
ark-Beetles (*Scolytidae*).
at-flies (*Nycteribia spp.*).
attledore-wing Fly (*Mymar pulchella*).
ean Aphis (*Aphis fabae*).
ean-gall Saw-fly (*Pontania proxima*).
ed-Bug (*Cimex lectularius*).
edeguar Gall-wasp (*Rhodites rosae*).
ee Beetle (*Trichius fasciatus*).
ee-flies (*Bombylius spp.*).
ee Louse (*Braula coeca*).
embex Wasps (*Bembex spp.*).
irch Leaf-rolling Weevil (*Rhynchites betulae*).
ird Flies (*Ornithomyia spp.*).
ird-winged Butterflies (*Ornithoptera spp.*).

Bird-winged Butterfly of Paradise (*Ornithoptera paradisea*).
Black-arched Tussock Moth (*Lymantria monacha*).
Black Borer Wasp (*Trypoxylon figulus*).
Black Flies (*Simulium spp.*).
Black-fly, *see* Bean Aphis.
Black Muslin Sweep Moth (*Pachythelia villosella*).
Blackthorn Pigmy Moth (*Nepticula plagicolella*).
Blister Beetle (*Lytta vesicatoria*).
Blood-red Ant (*Formica sanguinea*).
Blood-worm Larva (*Chironomus plumosus*).
Bloody-nose Beetle (*Timarcha tenebricosa*).
Blue-bottle Flies (*Calliphora spp.*).
Bombardier Beetle (*Brachinus crepitans*).
Book Louse (*Liposcelis divinatorius*).
Bramble Leaf-miner (*Nepticula aurella*).
Brazilian Beetle (*Desmonata variolus*).
Bread Beetle (*Sitodrepa paniceum*).
Brimstone Butterfly (*Gonepteryx rhamni*).
Broad-bordered Bee-hawk Moth (*Hemaris fuciformis*).
Brown China-mark Moth (*Nymphula nymphaeata*).
Brown House Moth (*Borkhausenia pseudospretella*).
Brown Mosquito (*Anopheles bifurcatus*).
Brown-tail Moth (*Euproctis chrysorrhoea*).
Brussels-lace Moth (*Cleora lichenaria*).
Buff-tailed Humble-bee (*Bombus terrestris*).
Buff-tip Moth (*Phalera bucephala*).
Burying Beetles (*Necrophorus spp.*).
Bush Cheep (*Pholidoptera cinerea*).

Cactus Moth (*Catoblastis cactorum*).
Caddis-flies (*Trichoptera*).
Camberwell Beauty Butterfly (*Nymphalis antiopa*).
Capsid Bugs (*Capsidae*).
Carder-bee Fly (*Criorhiza floccosa*).
Carpet Moths (*Geometridae*).
Celery Leaf-mining Fly (*Philophylla heraclei*).
Cellar or Churchyard Beetle (*Blaps lethifera*).
Cerulean Chafer (*Hoplia caerulea*).
Cheese Fly (*Piophila casei*).
Chilian Stag Beetle (*Chiasognathus grantii*).
Chrysanthemum Leaf-mining Fly (*Phytomyza atricornis*).
Cicada—British (*Cicadetta montana*).
Cinnabar Moth (*Callimorpha jacobaeae*).
Cistus Scale Insect (*Icerya purchasi*).
Clay-coloured Weevil (*Otiorrhynchus picipes*).
Cleg (*Haematopota pluvialis*).
Clothes Moth (*Tinea pellionella*).
Clouded Yellow Butterflies (*Colias spp.*).
Cochineal Insect (*Coccus cacti*).

Cockchafer (*Melolontha melolontha*).
Cockroach—Common (*Blatta orientalis*).
Cocktail Beetles (*Staphylinidae*).
Codlin Moth (*Laspeyresia pomonella*).
Coffee Beetle (*Araeocerus fasiculatus*).
Colorado Beetle (*Leptinotarsa decemlineata*).
Comma Butterfly (*Polygona c-album*).
Common Wasp (*Vespa vulgaris*).
Convolvulus Hawk Moth (*Herse convolvuli*).
Copper Butterfly, *see* Small Copper Butterfly.
Cottony Cushion Scales (*Pulvinaria spp.*).
Crane-fly (*Tipula oleracea*).
Cuckoo Humble-bees (*Psithyrus spp.*).
Cuckoo-spit Insect (*Philaenus spumarius*).
Cuckoo Wasp (*Vespa austriaca*).
Cucujo Firefly Beetle (*Pyrophorus noctiluca*).
Currant-blister Aphis (*Capitophorus ribis*).
Cynthia Moth (*Philosamia cynthia*).

Daddy-longlegs, *see* Crane-fly.
Death's-head Moth (*Acherontia atropos*).
Death-watch Beetle (*Xestobium rufovillosum*).
December Moth (*Poecilocampa populi*).
Deer Bot-fly (*Cephenomyia rufibarbis*).
Devil-hoppers (*Membracidae*).
Devil's Coach-horse (*Staphylinus olens*).
Diabolical Spectre Mantis (*Idolium diabolicum*).
Diamond-back Moth (*Plutella maculipennis*).
Digger-Wasps (*Pompilidae* and *Sphegidae*).
Dingar (*Apis indica*).
Dingy Blow-fly (*Protocalliphora azurea*).
Dipterous Ichneumons (*Tachinidae*).
Diving Beetle (*Dytiscus marginalis*).
Dog Louse (*Trichodectes latus*).
Dot Moth (*Melanchra persicariae*).
Double-tailed Weevil (*Diurus furcillatus*).
Drilus Snail-eating Beetle (*Drilus flaviscens*).
Drone-Fly (*Eristalis tenax*).
Drummer Cockroaches (*Blabera spp.*).
Dung Beetles—Smaller (*Onthophagus spp.* and *Aphodius spp.*).

Earwig—Common (*Forficula auricularia*).
Electric-light Bugs (*Belostoma spp.*).
Elephant Beetles (*Megasoma spp.*).
Elephant Hawk Moth (*Deilephila elpenor*).
Elm-Bark Beetle (*Scolytus destructor*).
Emerald Beetle (*Smaragdesthes africana*).
Emperor Dragon-fly (*Anax imperator*).
Emperor Moth (*Saturnia pavonia*).

Empid-flies (*Hilara spp.*).
Ermine Moths (*Hypenomeuta spp.*).
Eyed Hawk Moth (*Smerinthus ocellatus*).

Fairy Flies (*Mymaridae*).
False Cone Aphides (*Adelges spp.*).
Felted Beech Coccus (*Cryptococcus fagi*).
Fiddler Beetle (*Mormolyce phyllodes*).
Field Cricket (*Gryllus campestris*).
Fig Insect (*Blastophaga grossorum*).
Fig Moth (*Ephestia cantella*).
Figwort Weevils (*Cionus spp.*).
Filbert Weevil (*Balaninus nucum*).
Fire-flies (*Luciola spp.*).
Fish Insect (*Lepisma saccharina*).
Flag-legged Bugs (*Diactor spp.*).
Flea—Chigger (*Sarcopsylla penetrans*).
Flea—Human (*Pulex irritans*).
Flea—Mole (*Histrichopsylla talpae*).
Flea—Rat (*Xenopsylla cheopis*).
Flower Bees (*Anthophora spp.*).
Flying Gooseberry (*Pneumora scutellaris*).
Forest Butterflies of South America (*Ageronia spp.*).
Four-spotted Clythra Beetle (*Clythra quadrimaculata*).
Four-spotted Darter Dragon-fly (*Libellula quadrimaculata*).
Fungus-gnats (*Mycetophilidae*).
Furniture Beetle (*Anobium striatum*).

Gad-flies (*Tabanidae*).
Gall-Wasps (*Cynipidae*).
Ghost Swift Moth (*Hepialus humuli*).
Giant Alder-flies (*Corydalis spp.*).
Giant Scale (*Lophococcus maximus*).
Giant Wingless Grasshoppers (*Callimenus spp.*).
Gipsy Moth (*Lymantria dispar*).
Giraffe Weevil (*Apoderus giraffa*).
Glow-worm Beetle (*Lampyrus noctiluca*).
Gnat—Common (*Culex pipiens*).
Gnats (*Culicidae*).
Goat Moth (*Cossus cossus*).
Gold Chafer (*Plusiotis resplendens*).
Goliath Beetles (*Goliathus spp.*).
Gorse Weevil (*Apion ulicis*).
Grain Weevil (*Calandra granaria*).
Grayling Butterfly (*Eumenis semele*).
Great Green Grasshopper (*Tettigonia viridissima*).
Great Ox Gad-fly (*Tabanus bovinus*).
Great Water Beetle (*Hydrous piceus*).
Green-bottle Flies (*Lucilia spp.*).

Green Demoiselle Dragon-fly (*Lestes sponsa*).
Green Hairstreak Butterfly (*Callophrys rubi*).
Green-shaded Honey Moth (*Aphomia sociella*).
Green Tortrix Moth (*Tortrix viridana*).
Green-veined White Butterfly (*Pieris napi*).
Grey Flesh Flies (*Sarcophaga spp.*).
Ground Beetle—Strawberry-eating (*Harpalus ruficornis*).
Ground Beetles (*Carabidae*).
Ground Pearls (*Margarodes trimeni*).

Harlequin Beetle (*Macropos longimanus*).
Harvest-fly of America (*Tibicina septemdecim*).
Harvesting Ants—of Europe (*Aphaenogaster spp.*).
Harvesting Ants—of Texas (*Pogonomyrmex spp.*).
Hawk Moths (*Sphingidae*).
Hazel-blotch Moth (*Lithocolletis coryli*).
Hazel Leaf-rolling Weevil (*Apoderus coryli*).
Heath Potter Wasp (*Eumenes coarctata*).
Herald Moth (*Scoliopteryx libatrix*).
Hercules Beetle (*Dynastes hercules*).
Hive Bee (*Apis mellifica*).
Holy Leaf-miner Fly (*Phytomyza ilicis*).
Honey Ants (*Myrmecocystus spp.*).
Honeycomb Moth (*Galleria mellonella*).
Hopper Beetles (*Orchestes spp.*).
Hornet (*Vespa crabro*).
Hornet-Clearwing Moth of Osier (*Sphecia bembeciformis*).
Hornet Clearwing of Poplar (*Sesia apiformis*).
Hornets'-nest Beetle (*Emus hirtus*).
Horntails (*Sirex spp.*).
Horse Ant (*Formica rufa*).
Horse Bot-fly (*Gastrophilus intestinalis*).
House Cricket (*Gryllulus domesticus*).
House-fly (*Musca domestica*).
Hover-flies (*Syrphidae*).
Humble-bee Fly (*Volucella bombylans*).
Humming-bird Hawk Moth (*Macroglossum stellatarum*).

Ichneumons—Ant-like (*Pezomachus spp.*).
Ichneumon of Wood-wasps (*Rhyssa persuasoria*).
Indian Mimetic Butterfly (*Hypolimnas misippus*).
Indian Wax-producing Scale Insect (*Ceroplastes seriferus*).

Jerking-disc Saw-fly (*Phyllotoma aceris*).
Jumping-Bean Moth (*Carpocapsa saltitans*).

Kauchong Mantis (*Hymenopus bicornis*).
Ked of Sheep (*Melophagus ovinus*).
Kentish Glory Moth (*Endromis versicolora*).

Lac Insects (*Carteria spp.*).
Lacewings—Brown (*Hemerobiidae*).
Lacewings—Green (*Chrysopidae*).
Lackey Moth (*Malacosoma neustria*).
Ladybirds (*Coccinellidae*).
Lantern-flies (*Fulgoridae*).
Lappet Moth (*Gastropacha quercifolia*).
Large Blue Butterfly (*Maculinea arion*).
Large White Butterfly (*Pieris brassicae*).
Lawn Bee (*Andrena fulva*).
Leader Weevil (*Cyrtotrachelus dux*).
Leaf-butterfly—Indian (*Kallima inachis*).
Leaf-cutting Bees (*Megachile spp.*).
Leaf-insects—Green (*Phyllium spp.*).
Lesser Honeycomb Moth (*Achroia grisella*).
Lice—Bird or Biting (*Mallophaga*).
Lice—Sucking (*Anoplura*).
Lilac Leaf-miner Moth (*Gracilaria syringella*).
Lime-blossom Gall-midge (*Contarinia tiliarum*).
Lobster Moth (*Stauropus fagi*).
Long-armed Chafer (*Euchirus longimanus*).
Long-horned Beetles (*Longicornia*).
Long-horned Grasshoppers (*Tettigoniidae*).
Long-necked Ant-Lion (*Necrophilus arenarius*).
Long-nosed Weevils (*Brenthus spp.*).
Louse—Human (*Pediculus humanus*).
Luminous Skip-jack Beetle, *see* Cucujo.
Luna Dung-beetle (*Copris lunaris*).
Lychnis Coronet Moth (*Hadena bicruris*).

Magpie Moth (*Abraxas grossulariata*).
Malagasy Orchid-visiting Moth (*Macrosilius cruentius*).
Malagasy Lichen-like Weevil (*Lithinus nigrocristatus*).
Manna Insect (*Gossyparia mannifera*).
Mantis Flies (*Mantispidae*).
Marble Gall-wasp (*Cynips kollari*).
Margarodes, *see* Ground Pearls.
Marine Skater Bugs (*Halobates spp.*).
Marsh Fritillary Butterfly (*Euphydryas aurinia*).
Marvel-du-jour Moth (*Griposia aprilina*).
Masked Bug (*Reduvius personatus*).
Mason Bee—British (*Osmia rufa*).
Mason Bee—European (*Chalicodoma muraria*).
May-bug, *see* Cockchafer.
May-flies (*Ephemeroptera*).
Meadow Brown Butterfly (*Maniola jurtina*).
Mealworm Beetles (*Tenebrio molitor* and *T. obscurus*).
Mediterranean Flour Moth (*Ephestia sericarium*).
Mexican Cockchafer (*Polyphylla petiti*).

Midge—Arum (*Psychoda phalaenoides*).
Midges—Blood-sucking (*Ceratopogon spp.*).
Mining Bees (*Andrena spp.* and *Halictus spp.*).
Mole Cricket (*Gryllotalpa gryllotalpa*).
Mole-like Beetle (*Hypocephalus armatus*).
Monarch Butterfly (*Danaus plexippus*).
Mosquito Bees (*Melipona spp.*).
Mosquitoes (*Culicidae*).
Mosquitoes—Spotted-winged (*Anopheles spp.*).
Moth-like Swallow-tail Butterfly (*Papilio laglaizei*).
Mottled Umber Moth (*Erannis defoliaria*).
Mourning Cloak Butterfly, *see* Camberwell Beauty Butterfly.
Mullein Shark Moth (*Cuculla verbasci*).
Musk Beetle (*Aromia moschata*).
Mussel Scale (*Lepidosaphes ulmi*).

Narcissus-Fly (*Merodon equestris*).
Narrow-bordered Bee Hawk Moth (*Hemaris tityus*).
Naucoris Bug (*Naucoris cimicoides*).
Negro Ant (*Formica fusca*).
New Forest Fly (*Hippobosca equina*).
Nightmare Insects, *see* Devil-hoppers.
Norwegian Wasp (*Vespa norvegica*).

Oak-apple Gall-wasp, winged form (*Biorhiza pallida : terminalis*).
Oak-apple Gall-wasp, wingless form (*Biorhiza pallida : aptera*).
Oak Leaf-rolling Weevil (*Attelabus nitens*).
Oil Beetle (*Meloë proscarabaeus*).
Orange-tip Butterfly (*Euchloë cardamines*).
Orchid-visiting Burrowing Wasp (*Gorytes mystaceus*).
Owl Butterflies (*Caligo spp.*).
Oyster Scale (*Aspidiotus oestraeformis*).

Painted Lady Butterfly (*Vanessa cardui*).
Palm Weevil (*Rhyncophorus palmarum*).
Parasite Flies (*Tachinidae*).
Paste Beetle, *see* Bread Beetle.
Pea-and-Bean Beetles (*Laria spp.*).
Peacock Butterfly (*Nymphalis io*).
Pea Gall-wasp of Rose (*Rhodites eglanteriae*).
Pear Gall-midge (*Contarinia pyrivora*).
Pear Saw-fly (*Eriocampa limacina*).
Pebble Prominent Moth (*Notodonta ziczac*).
Pe-la Scale Insect (*Ericerus pe-la*).
Pellucid Drone-fly (*Volucella pellucens*).
Peppered Moth (*Biston betularia*).
Phantom Larva of Gnat (*Chaoborus plumicornis*).
Pharaoh's Ant (*Monomorium pharaonis*).
Pill Beetles (*Byrrus spp.*).

Pimpla Ichneumon (*Pimpla instigator*).
Pine Beauty Moth (*Panolis flammea*).
Pineapple Gall Aphides (*Adelges spp.*).
Poplar Hawk Moth (*Laothoe populi*).
Powdered Dagger Moth (*Simyra albovenosa*).
Praying Mantis (*Mantis religiosa*).
Prickly Stick-insect (*Eurycanthus horrida*).
Prionus Long-horn Beetle (*Prionus coriarius*).
Privet Hawk Moth (*Sphinx ligustri*).
Processionary Caterpillars (*Cnethocampa processionea* and *C. pithyo-campa*).
Pteromalus Ichneumon (*Pteromalus puparum*).
Pug Moths (*Eupitheciinae*).
Purple Emperor Butterfly (*Apatura iris*).
Purse-galls of Poplar (*Pamphigus bursarius*).
Puss Moth (*Cerura vinula*).

Railway Beetle (*Phengodes hieronymi*).
Rain Breeze-fly, *see* Cleg.
Rat-tailed Larvae of Crane-flies (*Ptychoptera spp.*).
Rat-tailed Larvae of Drone-fly (*Eristalis tenax*).
Red Admiral Butterfly (*Vanessa antalanta*).
Red Ant, *see* Horse Ant.
Red Ladybird of Australia (*Vedalia cardinalis*).
Red-tailed Humble-bee (*Bombus lapidarius*).
Red Underwing Moth (*Catocala nupta*).
Resin Gall Moth (*Evetria resinella*).
Rhinoceros Beetle (*Oryctes nasicornis*).
Rice Weevil (*Calandra oryzae*).
Ringed China-mark Moth (*Nymphula stratiotata*).
Ringlet Butterflies (*Satyridae*).
Riverside Beetles (*Donacia spp.*).
Robber Ants (*Solenopsis fugax*).
Robber Flies (*Asilidae*).
Robber Hornet Fly (*Asilius crabroniformis*).
Rose-Beetle (*Cetonia aurata*).
Rose-leaf Mantis (*Gongylus gongyloides*).
Rosette-causing Gall-midge of Hawthorn (*Perrisia crataegi*).
Rosette-causing Gall-midge of Willow (*Rhadophaga rosaria*).
Rove Beetles, *see* Cocktail Beetles.

Sand-flies, *see* Black Flies.
Sand-wasps (*Sphex=Ammophila spp.*).
Saüba Ants (*Atta spp.*).
Saw-flies (*Tenthredinidae*).
Sawyer Beetle, *see* Prionus Long-horn Beetle.
Scalloped Hazel Moth (*Gonodontis bidentata*).
Scar Large Case Moth (*Coleophora vibicella*).
Scoliad Wasps (*Scoliidae*).

Scorpion-flies (*Mecaptera = Panorpidae*).
Seroot-flies (*Pangonia spp.*).
Seventeen-Year Locust, *see* Harvest-fly of America.
Sexton Beetles, *see* Burying Beetles.
Sheep Nostril Fly (*Œstrus ovis*).
Shield-Bug—Red-legged (*Tropicoris rufipes*).
Short-horned Grasshoppers (*Acrididae*).
Silkworm Moth (*Bombyx mori*).
Silver-bellied Water Beetle, *see* Great Water Beetle.
Silver Lady, *see* Fish Insect.
Silver-washed Fritillary Butterfly (*Argynnis paphia*).
Silver-Y Moth (*Plusia gamma*).
Skater Bug—Common (*Gerris thoracica*).
Skip-Jack Beetles (*Elateridae*).
Skipper Butterflies (*Hesperidae*).
Slave-making Ant, *see* Blood-red Ant.
Slave-making Ants' Nest Beetle (*Lomechusa strumosa*).
Slugworm of Rose Saw-fly (*Eriocampa rosae*).
Slugworm of Pear Saw-fly (*Eriocampa limacina*).
Small Copper Butterfly (*Lycaena phlaeas*).
Small Elephant Hawk Moth (*Deilephila porcellus*).
Small Heath Butterfly (*Coenonympha pamphilus*).
Small Poplar Gall-causing Long-horn Beetle (*Saperda populnea*).
Small White Butterfly (*Pieris rapae*).
Snail-eating Beetle (*Cychrus rostratus*).
Snake-flies (*Rhaphididae*).
Snow Fleas and Snow Worms (*Podura spp.*).
Soldier-fly (*Stratiomys chamaeleon*).
Spanish Fly, *see* Blister Beetle.
Speckled Wood Butterfly (*Paraga aegeria*).
Spectre or Stick Insects (*Phasmidae*).
Spider-Flies (*Hippoboscidae*).
Spiked Pea Gall-wasp of Rose (*Rhodites nervosus*).
Sponge-fly (*Sisyra fuscata*).
Spotted-winged Gnats or Mosquitoes (*Anopheles spp.*).
Spring-tails (*Poduridae*).
Stable-fly (*Stomoxys calcitrans*).
Stag Beetle (*Lucanus cervus*).
Stag-horned Flies (*Elaphomyia spp.*).
Stalk-eyed Flies (*Diopsis spp.*).
Stick Insect—Palaearctic (*Dixippus morosus*).
Stoat-fly, *see* Rain Breeze-fly.
Stone-flies (*Perlidae*).
Swallow-tail Butterfly (*Papilio machaon*).
Swallow-tail Moth (*Ourapteryx sambucaria*).
Swift Moth—Common (*Hepialus lupulinus*).

Thorn Bug (*Umbonia spinosa*).
Tiger-Beetles (*Cicindela spp.*).

Timberman Beetle (*Acanthocinus aedilis*).
Tobacco Beetle (*Lasioderma serricorne*).
Tobacco Moth (*Ephestia elutella*).
Tortoise Beetles (*Cassida spp.*).
Trident-bearer (*Ceratophyus typhaeus*).
Tse-tse Flies (*Glossina spp.*).
Turf Ant (*Tetramorium caespitum*).
Turnip Gall-weevil (*Ceutorrhynchus pleurostigma*).
Tusser Moth (*Antherea mylitta*).
Two-toothed Bark-beetle (*Pityogenes bidentatus*).

Umber Moth, *see* Mottled Umber Moth.

Velvet Ants (*Mutilla spp.*).
Viceroy Butterfly (*Limenitis disippus*).

Warble-Flies (*Hypoderma spp.*).
Warrior Termite (*Termes bellicosus*).
Wasp Beetle (*Clytus arietis*).
Wasps' Nest Beetle (*Metoecus paradoxus*).
Wasps' Nest Fly, *see* Pellucid Drone-fly.
Water-Boatman, *see* Back-swimmer.
Water-Boatman—Sponge-dwelling (*Sigara minutissima*).
Water-Boatmen—Lesser (*Corixa spp.*).
Water-Gnat or Water Measurer (*Hydrometra stagnorum*).
Water-Scorpion (*Nepa cinerea*).
Water Stick-Insect (*Ranatra linearis*).
Webbing Clothes-Moth (*Tineola biselliella*).
Whirligig Beetles (*Gyrinus spp.*).
White Admiral Butterfly (*Liminetis camilla*).
Willow Gall-midges (*Rhabdophaga spp.*).
Willow Scale, *see* Ash Scale.
Willughby's Leaf-cutter Bee (*Megachile willughbiella*).
Wine-cork Moth (*Oinophila v-flava*).
Winter Moth (*Operophtera brumata*).
Wood-Ant, *see* Horse Ant.
Wood-Cricket (*Nemobius sylvestris*).
Wood Leopard Moth (*Zeuzera pyrina*).
Wood-wasps, *see* Horntails.
Wood White Butterfly (*Leptidea sinapis*).
Wool-carder Bee (*Anthidium manicatum*).
Woolly Aphis, *see* American Blight.

Yellow Ants' Nest Beetle (*Claviger testaceus*).
Yellow-faced Bees (*Prosopis spp.*).
Yellow-fever Mosquito (*Stegomyia calopus*).
Yellow Spring-tail (*Smynthurus luteus*).
Yew Gall-causing Midge (*Oligotrophus taxi*).
Yucca Moths (*Pronuba spp.*).

INDEX